# KINGS IN CONFLICT

## IRELAND IN THE 1690s

PUBLISHED BY

## THE ULSTER MUSEUM

COMPILED AND EDITED BY

EILEEN BLACK

EXHIBITION RESEARCHED AND ORGANISED BY W.A. MAGUIRE
EXHIBITION DESIGNED BY ROY SERVICE
CATALOGUE DESIGNED BY JAMES HANNA

Published on the occasion of an exhibition
in the Ulster Museum, Botanic Gardens, Belfast
11 April-2 September 1990

The Ulster Museum gratefully acknowledges
the generous financial assistance of Belfast City Council
towards the publication of this catalogue

ISBN 0-900761-24-5

Kings in Conflict
Ireland in the 1690s

ULSTER MUSEUM PUBLICATION No.265

COVER:
Portrait of William III by permission of the National Portrait Gallery
Portrait of James II by permission of Manchester City Art Gallery
Portrait of Louis XIV by permission of the Château de Versailles

Printed in Northern Ireland by W & G Baird Ltd
at the Greystone Press, Antrim

# Contents

## Lenders to the Exhibition

Duke of Abercorn
Aberdeen Art Gallery & Museums
Atlas Van Stolk, Rotterdam
Belfast City Council
British Library, London
Trustees of the British Museum, London
Professor R.S.J. Clarke
Alec Cobbe, Esq.
Duke of Devonshire
Drogheda Corporation
Dublin City Council
Viscount Dunluce
J.A. Gamble, Esq.
Duke of Hamilton
Hunterian Museum, Glasgow
Earl of Jersey
Kilkenny Castle
Lady King
Manchester City Art Gallery
Musée National du Château de Versailles
National Army Museum, London
National Gallery of Ireland, Dublin
National Library of Ireland, Dublin
National Maritime Museum, London
National Museum of Ireland, Dublin
National Portrait Gallery, London
National Trust
Lord O'Neill
First Presbyterian Church, Belfast
Public Record Office of Northern Ireland
Queen's University, Belfast
Earl of Roden
Earl of Rosebery
Trustees of the Royal Armouries, London
Royal Hospital, Dublin
Royal Museum of Scotland, Edinburgh
Ulster Museum, Belfast
Union Theological College, Belfast
N.A. Whittley, Esq.
Dr M. Wynne
and other lenders who prefer to remain anonymous

# Preface

With the approach of the tercentenary of the battle of the Boyne, the Board of Trustees decided in 1985 to mark the anniversary by devising an exhibition to deal with the war between Jacobites and Williamites in Ireland in the years 1689 to 1691. The events of the war were of major importance for the history of Ireland at the time. Their importance in that sense, however, has been overtaken by their use as political symbols during the three centuries since. Inevitably, continuing political significance combined with distance in time has created myths around these events and historical fact has become obscured.

Folk memory has emphasised the conflict as one between two rival kings, William III and James II, in contention for the throne of England. Gaelic Ireland referred to it as Cogadh an Dá Rí - the War of the Two Kings - reflecting a somewhat insular view of an event of major importance in European history. Myth has largely obscured the fact that behind James II stood Louis XIV of France, while the Holy Roman Emperor and the Catholic King of Spain supported William, whose ambitions for a time even enjoyed papal endorsement. These historical realities are reflected in the exhibition's title, 'Kings in Conflict', while its Irish content and scope are indicated by the sub-title, 'Ireland in the 1690s'.

The exhibition has as its main objective a review of events in Ireland in the late seventeenth century in the light of recent historical research, illustrated by paintings, prints, drawings and objects of contemporary relevance assembled from institutional and private collections throughout the British Isles and from various parts of Europe.

The Board of Trustees records its thanks to the lenders for their generous support of our efforts. The exhibition has been made possible by major financial support from the Department of Education for Northern Ireland within its programme for cultural heritage initiatives, for which our thanks are due to the Parliamentary Under-Secretary of State, Dr Brian Mawhinney MP. A generous grant from Belfast City Council has ensured the production of this splendid illustrated catalogue, which will be an historical record of the exhibition, and we thank The Right Honourable The Lord Mayor, the Aldermen and Councillors for this very valuable support.

A catalogue of this quality and an exhibition of this scale required a great deal of co-ordinated teamwork by Museum staff. Our best thanks are due to Dr Bill Maguire, Keeper of Local History, who researched and organised the exhibition; Ms Eileen Black, Department of Art, who compiled and edited the catalogue; Mr Roy Service, Keeper of Design and Exhibition Services, who designed the exhibition; Mr James Hanna, who designed the catalogue, and all those staff who have also helped to bring this project to reality. It is part of the statutory remit of the Museum to acquire and disseminate knowledge relative to its collections for the public understanding of our common heritage. It is our hope that the exhibition and catalogue will also serve that purpose.

J.C. NOLAN
Director
April 1990

# Acknowledgements

Most of the catalogue entries were written by Ulster Museum staff, but a substantial number were kindly provided by experts from other institutions. It is a pleasure to record our thanks to Peter Barber (British Library), David Blackmore (Royal Armouries), Dr David Caldwell (Royal Museum of Scotland), John Edwards (Aberdeen Art Gallery and Museums), Dr Eric Kentley (National Maritime Museum), Thom Richardson (Royal Armouries), John Teahan (National Museum of Ireland) and Gordon Wheeler (Queen's University Library).

The preparation of the catalogue was very much a co-operative effort by the staff of the Ulster Museum. Eileen Black (Art) collated and edited the text as well as writing substantial portions of it; it is no exaggeration to say that it could scarcely have been done without her dedication and efficiency. In the preparation of the material for the printers, Angela Watson (Geology) deserves our special thanks for collating the entire text as well as typing sections of it. The remainder of the typing was done by Pauline Dickson (Local History), with some assistance from Lesley McGloin and Edith Gailey (Art) and Jackie Hagan (Antiquities). Richard Warner (Antiquities) gave timely help with technological problems in this area. To James Hanna (Design and Exhibition Services) goes the credit for designing the entire catalogue, a formidable task achieved under great pressure of time; his colleagues Bill Anderson-Porter, Bryan Rutledge and Michael McKeown were reponsible for most of the photographic work and Heather White for the maps.

The exhibition itself was brought into being by the co-operative efforts of Museum staff and many other people. Its design was the work of Roy Service, Keeper of Design and Exhibition Services. Construction work, painting and much of the electrical work were carried out by the Museum's joiners, painters and electricians to the high standards evident in all their work. Brian Scott, Keeper of Conservation, and his staff performed the vital work of preparing items for exhibition, receiving loans and placing them in the display. The Registrar, John Wilson, dealt efficiently with all the loan agreements and co-ordinated transport arrangements with our carriers (Wingate & Johnston and S. Slevin). Sheela Speers organised the educational side of things and gave valuable advice based on her experience as co-ordinator of the Armada exhibition in 1988. Moira Concannon supervised the audio-visual effects. Exhibition publicity was organised by Sandra Neill, assisted by Angela Reid. The vital, sometimes worrying matter of finance for the exhibition was dealt with efficiently by Marshall McKee, Acting Keeper of Museum Services, and his staff. To all of these, and to all who contributed in other useful ways to the production of the largest exhibition it has initiated for many years, the Ulster Museum owes its thanks. The roll would not be complete without the name of the Director, Mr J.C. Nolan, who chaired the meetings of the steering committee, energised its members and supported the project wholeheartedly from the beginning.

The exhibition was planned all along in close consultation with the National Museum of Ireland, as an event that could be seen and enjoyed by Irish people north and south. We owe particular thanks to the Director of the National Museum and to the Keeper of its Art and Industrial Division, John Teahan, who could not have been more helpful.

Similar remarks apply to the National Gallery of Ireland and Dr Michael Wynne, and to the National Library of Ireland and Brian McKenna. Among many others, thanks are also due to Caroline Agar, Dr Donal Bateson, Susan Beale, the Hon. Bryan Bellew, the Earl of Belmore, M. Yves Bottineau (Versailles), Mary Clark, Professor Richard Clarke, Peter Day, Patricia Friel, J.A. Gamble, Rev. Principal R.F. Holmes, B.P. Hoey, Sylvia Hopkins, Michael Kenny, Margaret Kilbride, John Killen, M. Thierry Lefrançois (La Rochelle), Dr Gerard Lemmens (Nijmegen), Dr Anthony Malcomson, Peter Marlow, Dr Klaus Merten (Stuttgart), Stanley McDowell, Carl Nix (Atlas van Stolk, Rotterdam), Fr Christy O'Dwyer, Trevor Parkhill, J.P. Pupye (Delft), Janice Reading, the Countess of Rosebery, John Rowlands and Cecil Ward. Lastly, I am grateful to Professor David Harkness, Dr James McGuire and Dr Harman Murtagh for agreeing to act as historical advisers, but hasten to add that they bear no responsibility for any mistakes we may have committed.


W.A. MAGUIRE
Exhibition Organiser

# Contributors to Catalogue
(Numbers refer to catalogue entries)

| | |
|---|---|
| Peter Barber | 79, 212, 213 |
| Eileen Black | 1, 6, 26-30, 35, 37, 48, 56, 57, 64-67, 80, 81, 85, 90, 91, 143, 154, 157, 159, 166-175, 217, 219, 223, 233, 235, 259, 261-265, 289, 291, 295-303, 307, 310, 311, 313, 326, 328, 332, 335, 336, 337 |
| David Blackmore | 39-42, 58, 59, 187-195, 197, 198, 202-206 |
| David Caldwell | 201 |
| John Edwards | 258 |
| Robert Heslip | 2, 14, 31-34, 43, 50, 51, 60-62, 95, 119-121, 127-141, 158, 161, 162,178-182, 237-244, 267, 268, 273, 283, 284 |
| Eric Kentley | 257, 286, 287 |
| William Maguire | 3, 4, 5, 7, 21-25, 38, 44-47, 49, 52, 53, 63, 69, 72, 76, 82-84, 89, 93, 94, 96, 100-112, 115, 122-126, 142, 145-147, 152, 153, 155, 156, 160, 163-165, 176, 177, 183-186, 199, 200, 207, 209-211, 214-216, 218, 220, 222, 224, 226, 227, 230, 232, 260, 266, 282, 288, 290, 293, 304, 305, 308, 309, 314, 315, 317, 318, 321-323, 327, 329-331, 338 and historical introductions |
| Noel Nesbitt | 247-256 |
| Thom Richardson | 36, 196 |
| Michael Robinson | 116-118, 319, 333 |
| Anne Millar Stewart | 97, 279, 280, 312 |
| John Teahan | 68, 98, 99, 234, 270-272, 278, 281, 306, 320, 334 |
| Gordon Wheeler | 54, 55, 70, 71, 73-75, 77, 78, 86-88, 92, 113, 114, 150, 151, 236, 245, 246, 285, 292, 294, 316 |

## A Note on Dates

Until 1752 England followed the Julian calendar, which in the seventeenth century was ten days behind the present Gregorian calendar used on the Continent (eleven days after 1700). Thus in 1690 the battle of the Boyne was reckoned to have been fought on 1 July (Old Style) or 11 July (New Style); when England adopted the New Style 1 July became 12 July. Furthermore, the Julian year dated from 25 March instead of 1 January: the reign of William and Mary officially began on 13 February 1688 (OS) according to the English, 23 February 1689 according to their Dutch allies. At the time, people seem to have switched easily from one calendar to the other, sometimes dating their letters both ways - 13/23 February - in order to avoid confusion. In this catalogue dates are given according to the New Style, except when quoting sources using Old Style.

## Abbreviations

DNB      Dictionary of National Biography

NGI      National Gallery of Ireland

NMI      National Museum of Ireland

NMM      National Maritime Museum

NPG      National Portrait Gallery

PRONI   Public Record Office of Northern Ireland

SNPG    Scottish National Portrait Gallery

UM       Ulster Museum

## Bibliographical Note
(General sources used in the preparation of this catalogue. Specific sources are cited with individual catalogue entries).

Bénézit, *Dictionnaire des Peintres, Sculpteurs, Dessinateurs et Graveurs* (Paris, 1976).

A. Blunt, *Art and Architecture in France 1500-1700* (Harmondsworth, 1953).

A. Crookshank and The Knight of Glin, *Irish Portraits 1660-1860*, exhibition catalogue, NGI August-October 1969; NPG October 1969-January 1970; UM January-March 1970.

A. Crookshank and the Knight of Glin, *The Painters of Ireland* (London, 1978).

Thieme-Becker, *Künstler-Lexikon* (Leipzig, 1907).

E. K. Waterhouse, *Painting in Britain 1530-1690* (Harmondsworth, 1953).

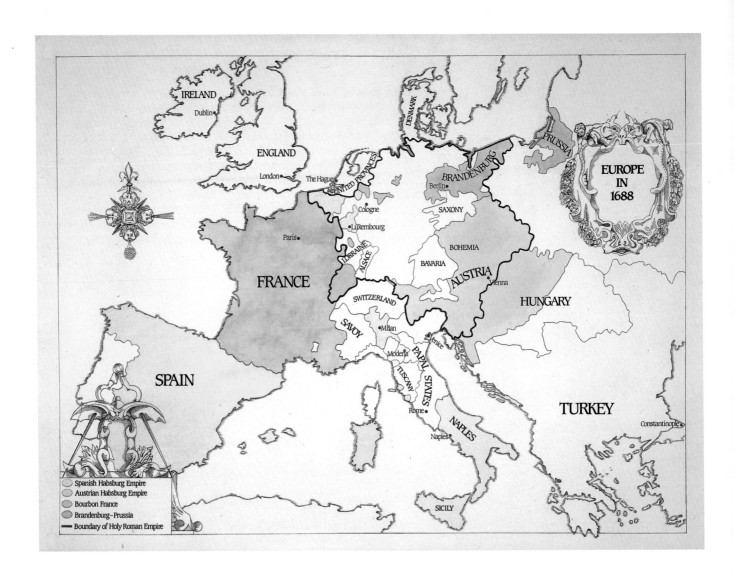

IRELAND
Dublin

ENGLAND
London

The Hague
UNITED PROVINCES

Cologne

Luxembourg

Paris

FRANCE

LORRAINE
ALSACE

SWITZERLAND

SAVOY

Milan

SPAIN

Modena
TUSCANY

PAPAL STATES

Rome

NAPLES

Naples

SICILY

DENMARK

BRANDENBURG
Berlin

SAXONY

BOHEMIA

BAVARIA

AUSTRIA
Vienna

PRUSSIA

EUROPE
IN
1688

HUNGARY

Venice

TURKEY

Constantinople

Spanish Habsburg Empire
Austrian Habsburg Empire
Bourbon France
Brandenburg–Prussia
Boundary of Holy Roman Empire

# 1 Louis XIV and William of Orange

The later seventeenth century in Europe was dominated - in diplomacy and the arts no less than in war - by France. Louis XIV, Bourbon king of France 1643-1715, was determined to make France secure against the Habsburg rulers of Germany and Spain, whose territories almost surrounded his own, and to make himself the greatest ruler in Europe. From his palace at Versailles, built to reflect his glory, the Sun King ruled over a nation of nearly twenty million people (Great Britain had about seven million, the Dutch Republic two). His main rival, the Habsburg emperor Leopold I (1658-1705),was preoccupied for many years by wars against the Ottoman Turks,who in 1683 even besieged his capital Vienna.

In the 1660s Louis made considerable gains at the expense of Spain in the Spanish Netherlands. For most of that period he was on friendly terms with the United Provinces (the Dutch Republic). In 1672, however, he invaded the United Provinces. To save themselves from complete disaster the Dutch had to open the dikes and flood the country. In that 'year of calamity', as it is called in Dutch history, the Dutch appointed as Stadtholder (president) and commander-in-chief William of Orange, then aged twenty-two.The remaining thirty years of William's life were to be largely devoted to thwarting the ambitions of Louis XIV.

The war that began in 1672 ended with the peace of Nijmegen in 1678. By that time Louis's foreign policy was regarded as aggressive and dangerous by many of his neighbours. In the early 1680s, however, it was his brutal treatment of his own Protestant subjects, the Huguenots, that brought international condemnation (among others from Pope Innocent XI, who objected to forced conversions). The persecution, culminating in the revocation of the Edict of Nantes in 1685, particularly alarmed and disgusted the Protestant states of Europe - including England - and enhanced the popularity of William of Orange as Protestant champion.

In 1686 the king of Spain, the emperor and some of the German princes formed the League of Augsburg to guard against any further expansion by France. In the following year tension between France and the papacy became so great that Louis occupied the papal territory of Avignon. In 1688, when he tried to install his own candidate as prince archbishop of the strategic state of Cologne, instead of the emperor's nominee, war became almost inevitable.

When that war came, the leading figure in the anti-French alliance was William of Orange, now king of England as well as Stadtholder. His family - rich in estates and in political ability - had long occupied a special place in the Dutch Republic. Originally counts of Nassau in the Empire, they became princes of Orange in the sixteenth century through marriage. Orange was a very small principality, entirely surrounded by the lands of the king of France and in Louis XIV's time occupied for long periods by French troops. The fact that he was its sovereign prince, however, gave William the status to negotiate directly with other rulers. Louis XIV's harsh treatment of both Orange and the Dutch Republic made William his enemy for life.

# 1 *Louis XIV (1638-1715) (1701)*

BY HYACINTHE RIGAUD (1659-1743)
MUSÉE NATIONAL DU CHÂTEAU DE VERSAILLES

Oil on canvas 130 x 97 cms.
Exh:    *Glorious Revolution. The World of William and Mary*, Nieuwe Kerk,
Amsterdam, June - September 1988 (10), repr. pl. 39.

Louis XIV was the son of Louis XIII and his Spanish queen, Anne of Austria. He succeeded his father on 14 May 1643, when only four years and eight months old. Though in theory not only the master but the owner of nineteen million subjects and their property, he was a neglected child, brought up by servants (he nearly drowned in a pond because no one was watching him at the time). His mother ruled as regent, guided by her chief minister Cardinal Mazarin with whom her relationship was so intimate that a secret marriage was suspected. Louis's minority was marked by civil wars known as the Frondes, in which the Paris Parlement (a powerful law court), leading nobles and royal princes rebelled against Mazarin's rule. Louis and his mother had to flee from Paris in 1649, and the young king suffered poverty, fear, humiliation, cold and hunger before Mazarin triumphed in 1653. Louis was never to forgive Paris, the nobles or the common people, and his experiences shaped his character and future conduct.

Louis was crowned on 7 June 1654 at Reims. So long as Mazarin lived, however, the king was content to let him continue to rule the country, learning from the cardinal how power was exercised and also acquiring his appreciation of the arts and love of display. In 1658 he fell in love with Mazarin's niece Marie Mancini, whom he gave up in 1660 only after a great emotional struggle in order to do his dynastic duty by marrying his Habsburg cousin Marie-Thérèse, daughter of the king of Spain, thus ratifying peace between their two countries. Marie-Thérèse renounced her claim to the Spanish throne at the time of her marriage, but since her dowry was never paid Louis later proclaimed the right to compensate himself with territory at Spain's expense. The marriage produced five children, only one of whom - the dauphin - lived to maturity. Louis also had a succession of mistresses, by whom he had a number of illegitimate children whom he acknowledged.

The day after Mazarin's death, to everyone's astonishment, the young king announced that from henceforth there would be no first minister, no minister-favourite; he alone would govern. He adhered to this resolution for the next fifty-four years of his reign, spending long hours at his desk each day making decisions, directing diplomacy and the army and planning reforms. Even when deeply engaged in affairs of the heart (and they were numerous), he remained a tireless servant of the state. By concentrating everything upon himself he became the sole head of state; his family, great nobles and church dignitaries were all removed from government.

One of his chief preoccupations was war; when close to death, he is said to have commented that he had been too fond of it. During the years of his personal government, namely from 1661, France was involved in five wars: the war of Devolution (1667-68) when his opponent was Spain; the Dutch war of 1672-79; war with Spain again, 1683-84; the war of the Grand Alliance (1688-97) and the war of the Spanish Succession (1701-1714). Part of his reason for war-mongering was to keep his nobles happy; removed from the provinces, they had little opportunity to plot against him. Behind his foreign policy was fear of encirclement by the Habsburgs and his desire to claim the Spanish throne for his family. By the late 1670s his aggression and greed had become a menace to the stability of Europe and gained him many enemies, chief among whom was the Prince of Orange.

His invasion of Holland in 1672 was an attempt to make the Dutch pay for having meddled in his claim to the Spanish Netherlands. However, he had not reckoned on the tenacity of the Dutch people - nor on the fact that the ice did not freeze around Amsterdam that winter to form a land mass for his troops to seize the city. As Europe began flocking to William's aid, Louis commented with wry insight into the episode which had entirely altered his apparent victory (the opening of the dikes, to flood the country): 'The resolution to put the entire country under the water was a bit violent; but what will one not do to prevent the domination of a foreigner? I cannot help admiring and praising the zeal and fortitude of those who broke off the negotiations [to accept his terms] ... even

1

though their advice, so salutary for their fatherland, brought great prejudice to my service' (Wolf, *Louis XIV*, p. 226).

His persecution of his Huguenot subjects made him worthy of the name of tyrant: the 'dragonnades' (so called because dragoons were sent to Protestant areas to force conversions by brutal means) and other harsh measures against them outraged public opinion in Protestant Europe and earned him the condemnation of the Pope, who regarded his actions as un-Christian. The revocation of the Edict of Nantes in 1685 helped unite those opposed to his policies and damaged France materially, for thousands of Huguenot refugees took their skills and capital to Holland, England, Brandenburg and America. An additional offshoot of Huguenot emigration was the spread of anti-French feeling, which coalesced in the formation of the Grand Alliance of 1688 between England, Holland and Leopold of Austria, a pact designed to curb French expansion.

Louis's intervention in Irish affairs in 1689 drew Ireland within the orbit of a European war. His support of James was partly personal and partly political. He believed in the divine right of kings and felt he should support a beleaguered brother monarch; at the same time James's restoration would be in the French interest, for William's seizure of power had been a strong blow to Louis's ambitions. When James fled England and arrived at St Germains in December 1688, Louis received him with kindness and gave him a good income. William's comment on Louis's benevolence to his father-in-law was acid: 'When he has dragged that corpse around for three or four years, he will be as much embarrassed by him as I have been' (van der Zee, p. 306).

In the event, Louis's help was not enough to save James; he returned to France after his defeat at the Boyne a broken man and French troops withdrew from Ireland a few months later. Thereafter, French help was too little or too late to keep the war going in Ireland beyond the autumn of 1691. Louis, however, still hoped to see James restored and made another attempt in May 1692, but the French fleet was soundly beaten at Barfleur and La Hogue; the projected invasion of England thus failed to take place and with that ended James's hopes. After the defeat he wrote sadly to Louis: 'My unlucky star has made its influence felt over the arms of Your Majesty, always victorious until they battled for me. I beg you not to take any more interest in a prince so unhappy ...' (van der Zee, p. 362). Not until the peace of Rijkswijk in 1697 did Louis - with great reluctance - recognise William as king, to James's mortification. On the latter's deathbed in 1701, however, Louis felt obliged to proclaim James's son, the Prince of Wales, the rightful king of England. That his lifelong enemy should meddle in the English succession enraged William beyond bounds and was renewed proof that the French were not to be trusted. One of William's last acts was to sign the Abjuration Bill excluding the Prince of Wales from the succession - a final thrust, one might say, at the French king.

Louis died on 31 August 1715 and was succeeded by his great-grandson. His parting advice to the young child was pious and full of a wisdom he himself had never shown: 'Try and remain at peace with your neighbours. I loved war too much. Do not follow me in that or in overspending ...' (Wolf, *Louis XIV*, p. 618). He was buried at Saint-Denis.

The French portrait painter Rigaud settled in Paris in 1681 and devoted himself to painting portraits of the bourgeoisie. He came to prominence in 1688 when he was commissioned to paint Monsieur, the brother of Louis XIV. Thereafter he became almost exclusively a court painter; among his sitters were members of the royal family, princes, diplomats and generals. This portrait, a copy by Rigaud of the great portrait of 1701, now in the Louvre, is full of baroque elements such as the column and draperies in the background, the swagger and contraposto of the figure and the flowing curves of the ermine cloak.

Sources:    V. Cronin, *Louis XIV*, (London, 1964); J.B. Wolf, *Louis XIV* (London, 1968); J.G. Simms, *Jacobite Ireland 1685-91* (London, 1969); R. Mousnier, *Louis XIV* (The Historical Association, 1973); H. and B. van der Zee, *William and Mary* (London, 1973).

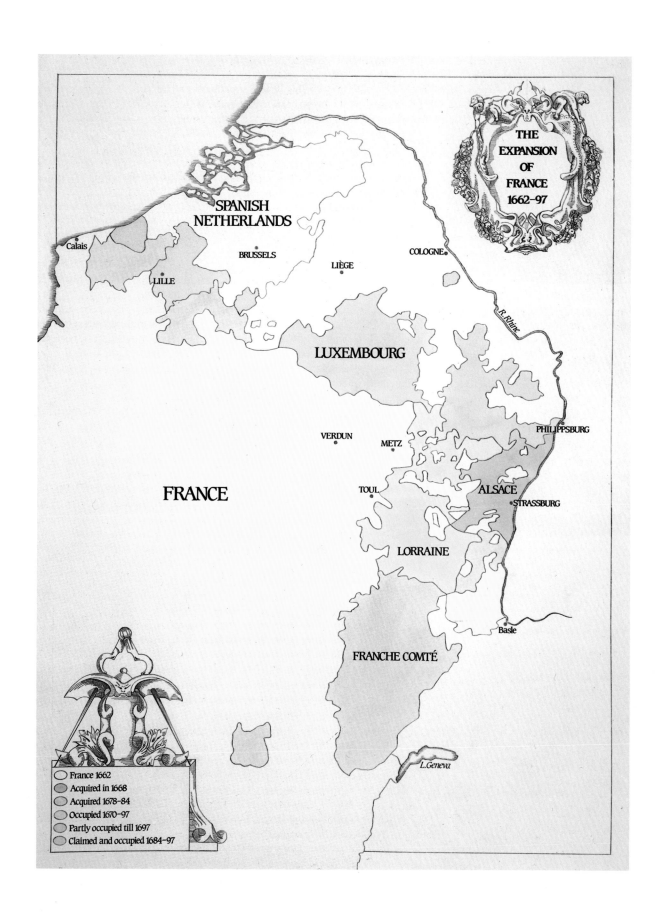

THE
EXPANSION
OF
FRANCE
1662–97

SPANISH
NETHERLANDS

Calais

BRUSSELS

LILLE

LIÈGE

COLOGNE

R. Rhine

LUXEMBOURG

FRANCE

VERDUN

METZ

PHILIPPSBURG

TOUL

ALSACE

STRASSBURG

LORRAINE

Basle

FRANCHE COMTÉ

L.Geneva

France 1662
Acquired in 1668
Acquired 1678–84
Occupied 1670–97
Partly occupied till 1697
Claimed and occupied 1684–97

2 obv.

2 rev.

## 2 *Louis XIV as peacemaker, the peace of Nijmegen, 1678*

MEDAL BY R. ARONDEAUX (FL.1680-1710 )
ULSTER MUSEUM, BELFAST

Silver, 72 mm.

Description:   obv.  bust of Louis XIV, draped and in armour, wearing a laurel wreath over a light helmet.
legend: LVDOVICVS MAGNVS ORBIS PACIFICATOR  [.the Great, peacemaker of the world].

            rev.  female representing ? Peace, draped in such a way as to leave breasts bare, standing facing on top of the world, with cornucopia in left hand and olive branch in right; swirling clouds to left and right; above, the sun with human face casts down rays.
legend: SOLVS HAEC OTIA FACIT [the Sun makes this Peace].

The medal is signed on the truncation of the bust but the lettering has been tooled away on this specimen.

Louis is shown as youthful and serene, deliberately impassive to emphasise his near-divine status. On the reverse the clouds of war are dispersed by the sun, with which he was closely identified. Technically the medal is impressive, both in terms of diameter combined with relief and as a rare example of successful full-face depiction in medallic form. This is the larger of the two sizes used for the medallic histories of the reign.

The Peace of Nijmegen was signed on 10 August 1678 (see no. 21). Arondeaux worked for d'Avaux, the French ambassador to the Netherlands.

## 3 *Toilet service, 1670*

BY PIERRE PRÉVOST, PARIS
THE DUKE OF DEVONSHIRE AND THE TRUSTEES OF THE CHATSWORTH SETTLEMENT

Silver gilt, twenty-three pieces: mirror 61.6 x 54.6 cms; pair of candlesticks, height 17.8 cms, base 12.7 cms square; pair of powder flasks, height 14.6 cms, 6.4 cms square; ewer, height 21.6 cms; basin 46.4 x 34.3 cms; pair of caskets, height 7 cms, length 22.9 cms, width 18.4 cms; small bowl with cover, diameter 10.1 cms, total height 7 cms; mug-shaped vessel, height 13.3 cms; pair of oval salvers 28.6 x 23.7 cms, height 5.7 cms; circular salver, diameter 19.7, height 7.6 cms; jewel casket 17.5 x 10.8 cms, height 10.8 cms; pair of circular boxes, diameter 6.7 cms, height 2.8 cms; pair of octagonal boxes, diameter 12 cms, height 5.7 cms; two small oval boxes, each 7.6 x 5.7 cms, height 2.8 cms; snuffer tray and snuffers.

Exh:     *Treasures from Chatsworth*, 1979-80.
       Paleis Het Loo, 1988.

Lit:      *Treasures from Chatsworth* catalogue (1979), p. 76, no. 149.
       G. Evans, 'Saved from the melting pot,' *Country Life*, vol. CLXXXIII, no. 10, 9 March, 1989.

Regarded as the finest surviving toilet service in western Europe, the Chatsworth service was either purchased by Princess Mary of Orange or given to her, probably at the time of her marriage with William in 1677. The richly decorated and embossed pieces are embellished with their applied arms and monogram. This service is one of the few major examples of Louis XIV silver still in existence, most having been melted down in 1689 or 1709 when the Sun King's wars created desperate financial crises for France and many courtiers felt obliged to follow the royal example by sacrificing their treasures. Only those exported from France shortly after being made have survived. Others include the Lennoxlove service in the Royal Museum of Scotland, one in Copenhagen and one in Toledo, Ohio - none of them as fine as this example.

Pierre Prévost was born in 1640 and became a master goldsmith in 1672. He worked in Paris till 1716, in 1689 at the Rue de la Haute Vannerie and from 1694 at the Quai des Orfèvres. One of the octagonal boxes in the Chatsworth service, presumably a replacement for one that had been damaged or lost at an early stage, bears the mark of Hans Brechtel, a German who worked at The Hague from 1640 until his death in 1675.

3

4

## 4 *Louis XIV crossing the Rhine to invade the Dutch Republic, June 1692*

BY ADAM FRANS VAN DER MEULEN (1632-90)
RIJKSMUSEUM, AMSTERDAM
REPRODUCTION

The invasion of the Dutch Republic in June 1672 by French armies, led by Louis XIV in person, was the climax of a series of moves by the French king to punish the Dutch for having thwarted his earlier attempts to seize most of the Spanish Netherlands. In 1668 the Dutch had joined with the English and Swedes to force him to accept the compromise Peace of Aix-la-Chapelle. Having bought England's help against the Dutch by the treaty of Dover (1670) and secured the neutrality of Sweden, Louis declared war in 1672 and invaded the Republic in overwhelming force, overrunning much of the country within a fortnight. He underestimated both the toughness of the Dutch and the effect of his success on other powers, however. The Dutch gave control of their destiny to William of Orange and opened the dikes to prevent any further advance; and the Emperor and the Elector of Brandenburg quickly sent armies to support them. So the initial brilliant success of the French became a prolonged war, from which England soon withdrew. The war ended in 1678 with the Peace of Nijmegen.

Van der Meulen was a Flemish painter who worked in France from the 1660s. His pictures of the French campaigns in Flanders in 1667 so impressed Louis XIV that thereafter he accompanied the king on all his campaigns. He also made cartoons for Gobelins tapestries depicting Louis's military career.

5

## 5 *Spiegel der France Tirannye Gepleecht opde Hollantsche Dorpen*
### *(Mirror of French cruelties in Dutch villages) (1673)*

BY ROMEYN DE HOOGHE (1645-1708)
ATLAS VAN STOLK, ROTTERDAM

Etching, hand-coloured 50 x 70 cms.

Romeyn de Hooghe was born in 1645 at The Hague and died at Haarlem in 1708. The family surname was spelled in a variety of ways: de Hooch was the form used by his uncle Pieter, the noted painter. De Hooghe was well versed not only in art, particularly etching and engraving in which he excelled, but also in politics, the law and mineralogy. Little is known about his early life and artistic training, but by 1662 he was in Paris at the invitation of the Dutch painter A.F. van der Meulen, who was patronised by Louis XIV (see no. 4). De Hooghe's earliest documentary prints illustrate the Anglo-Dutch wars of the 1660s, such as the destruction of the English fleet at Chatham. With the French invasion of the Dutch Republic in 1672 he became a firm supporter of the Prince of Orange, subsequently illustrating most of the memorable events in William's life and rendering him an immense service as a propagandist.

The cruelties committed by French troops in December 1672 during the invasion of Holland are illustrated in this generalised picture of murder and rapine. Louis XIV achieved an unsavoury reputation for deliberately using such methods in the Netherlands and the Rhineland, in order to cow his weaker opponents into submission quickly.

6

7

## 6 William, Prince of Orange, afterwards William III, as a boy, c. 1657

AFTER CORNELIUS JOHNSON (1593-1664)
DUKE OF ABERCORN

Oil on panel 38.1 x 25.4 cms

William, Prince of Orange was born on 14 November 1650, eight days after the death of his father William II of Orange, Stadtholder of the Netherlands (a position roughly equivalent to that of viceroy or lord lieutenant of Ireland). The young child's earliest days resounded with public mourning for the death of his father (even the cradle was draped in black) and rejoicing at the birth of a male heir for the house of Orange. Although the Stadtholder's office was not hereditary, the house of Orange had held the position for generations. The infant prince's grandfather Frederick Henry (1584-1647) had had monarchical aspirations which were encouraged by the French, who elevated his status and gave him a princely coronet. The marriage of Frederick Henry's son William Henry (later William II) to Mary Stuart, daughter of Charles I, further increased the alarm of Dutch republicans, who feared a monarchy was imminent. In the midst of the mourning at William II's untimely death, therefore, there was jubilation among those who were opposed to Orange aspirations.

From the child's birth there was strife between his mother, Mary Stuart, and his grandmother, Amalia von Solms. Mary wished to call her son Charles after her late father; Amalia insisted on his being christened William Henry, a combination of the names of her husband Frederick Henry and her son William. The baby's christening on 15 January 1651 assumed the character of farce as the assembled guests waited for two hours while mother and grandmother argued over the names. In the end Amalia had her way and Mary refused to attend. To make matters worse, Mary created something of a scandal by having the child christened in robes lined with royal ermine. There was further tension between the two women over the infant's guardianship; Mary demanded sole custody on the basis of an unsigned and undated will of her husband. After protracted wrangling a compromise was reached and guardianship was given to Mary, Amalia and her son-in-law Frederick William, Elector of Brandenburg.

The family's aspirations for the child received a setback when he was four years old, when the States-General decided to dispense with the stadtholdership; this effectively ended the role of the house of Orange in the Republic. By the Act of Exclusion, the States of Holland declared they would never again elect the Prince of Orange or any of his descendants to the stadtholdership or to any other high public office. This was not merely their wish but Oliver Cromwell's, who in peace negotiations at the end of the first Anglo-Dutch war (1652-54) made it a stipulation that young Prince William was to be barred from office. (Having ended Stuart rule in England, Cromwell was fearful of the consequences if Charles's grandson became powerful in the Netherlands).

The young boy was raised on strict lines laid down by Constantyn Huygens, his counsellor and treasurer. Simple diet, exercise and plenty of fresh air were essential, as was training in rigid self-control. His schooling began at the age of six with study of the Dutch Reformed faith. Also at this time he was allowed his first pocket money, 50 fl. a month. A travelling preacher who saw him at this age described him as '... a handsome young gentleman, very lively' (van der Zee, p.17) but was amazed to see that he was still being carried about in the arms of his nurse. Most people who saw him in public were struck by his reserve and self-control. A delicate and asthmatic child, he grew into a thin pale boy with a visibly humped back.

This half-length portrait, which shows him aged about seven, is after a painting by Cornelius Johnson. There are several versions of the Johnson portrait: a half-length at Knole, a full-length at Windsor Castle and copies of various lengths in the NPG, NGI and Ashmolean among others. He is shown wearing the pale blue ribbon of the Order of the Garter over his left shoulder; an oval jewelled George hangs from the end of the ribbon. His small peaked face, large dark eyes and wistful expression hint at his delicate health and general lack of robustness.

Sources:    D. Piper, *Catalogue of the Seventeenth Century Portraits in the National Portrait Gallery* (Cambridge,1963);S.B.Baxter,*William III* (London, 1966); H.and B.van der Zee,*William and Mary* (London, 1973);R. Bastiaanse/ H.Bots, *Glorious Revolution. The World of William and Mary* ('S Gravenhage, 1988).

## 7 *The people of Orange pledging loyalty to the Prince of Orange on 7 May 1665*

BY AN UNKNOWN ARTIST
ATLAS VAN STOLK, ROTTERDAM

Print with contemporary colouring 70 x 50 cms.

Previous to the event depicted, Louis XIV had occupied Orange for some years. The Dutch negotiated its restoration to William, but he was obliged to appoint a Catholic governor acceptable to France. Orange was subsequently reoccupied by Louis XIV. After William's death, in 1713, it finally became part of France.

The wall in the background is that of the great Roman amphitheatre at Orange.

*Reproductions of six engravings by Romeyn de Hooghe illustrating the early life of William of Orange, viz.*

**8** *Death of William II of Orange, 7 November 1650*
**9** *Birth of William III, 14 November 1650*
**10** *William's education*
**11** *William received as a ward of state, 1666*
**12** *William appointed Stadtholder, 1672*
**13** *William welcomed by the Dutch army, 1672*

ULSTER MUSEUM, BELFAST

## 14 *William III, Prince of Orange, promoted to Stadtholder, Captain and Admiral-General of the provinces of Holland and Zeeland, 1672*

MEDAL BY ANON
PHOTOGRAPH
Silver, 38 mm.

**14** obv.

**14** rev.

| | |
|---|---|
| Lit: | E. Hawkins, A. Franks and H. Gruber, *Medallic Illustrations of the History of Great Britain and Ireland to the Death of George III* (London, 1885), 552, no. 211. |
| Description: | obv. William, wearing armour and holding up a baton, with a flying sash, sheathed sword and pistol in holster, sits on a horse prancing to the left. |
| | legend: WILHELMVS III:D:G: PRINC:AVR:C:NAS. [William III, by grace of God Prince of Orange and Count of Nassau]. |
| | rev. crowned shield with William's arms surrounded by a heraldic garter. |
| | legend: (on garter) HONI SOIT QVI MAL Y PENSE ['Evil be who evil thinks']. |

This is a Dutch medal in a slightly naive style, but of great interest. The portrayal of a ruler on a prancing horse goes back to classical archetypes, reinforced by an extensive use from the fifteenth century onwards of the portrayal of leaders in suitably heroic circumstances. The raised baton (which also has Roman antecedents) symbolises military leadership. The famous statue of William which used to stand outside Trinity College, Dublin showed him in this pose. The manner in which the horse is depicted emphasises the power and control of the rider, as in the famous Van Dyck equestrian portrait of Charles I. Allowing the baton to break through the legend increases the dominance of the slightly awkward portrait.

The engraver is happier in his rendition of the reverse, which in reality amounts to a heraldic badge, the absence of a legend beyond the garter increasing the impact.

In 1667 an optimistically-titled 'Perpetual Edict' had been passed by the Dutch States-General prohibiting a person from being Stadtholder in more than one province. Charles II of England, at the peace negotiations earlier in 1672, had stipulated that William be promoted to these positions, which gave him a power and influence that were probably unassailable.

William had been nominated as a Knight of the Garter in 1653, when he was only three, and installed in 1661. The Garter is the premier British order of knighthood.

WILLEM DE II PRINCE van ORANGIE
Vader vanden Tegenwoordigen
WILLEM HENDRICK DE III PRINCE van ORAN
overleden den 7. November Anno 1650. savontswei
hier Vertoont op een truer bet van Parade

8

WILLEM HENDRICK DE III PRINCE van ORANGI
Wert Geboren
den 14. van November Anno 1650.
Acht Dagen nat overleden Vanden PRINCE
Zyn Vader Hooghloffelycke Memori

9

ZYN HOOGHEYTS IONCKHEYT
door Gebracht in Allerhande
Oeffeningen van Talen Konften Wetenfchappen
Vorftelycke en Christelycke Deuchden

10

fyn HOOGHEYT wert by die van Hollandt voor 't
alder eerft aangenomen met gemene ftemmen
als een Kind van Staat

11

fyn HOOGHEYT wert Aangeftelt tot Erf
ftadhouder van Holland Zeeland & en herftelt in alle
Waardigheden van fyne Voorvaderen

12

fyn HOOGHEYT wert verkooren tot Cappiteyn
en Admiraal Generaal van de Melitie
van den Staat en treckt te Velde

13

13

**15**

**16**

**17**

**18**

**19**

**20**

*Reproductions of six watercolours illustrating uniforms of Dutch troops in 1672, viz.*

**15** *Pikeman in a Zeeland regiment*
**16** *Pikeman in a Gelderland regiment*
**17** *Pikeman and Sergeant in a Gelderland regiment*
**18** *Sergeant in a Utrecht regiment*
**19** *Sergeant in a Holland regiment*
**20** *Musketeer in a Holland regiment*

ROYAL DUTCH ARMY MUSEUM, DELFT

The original seventeen watercolours depicting Dutch and German soldiers of the Dutch Republic in 1672 are in the Bibliothèque Nationale in Paris. Copies made in the 1920s by General F.G.J ten Raa are in the Royal Dutch Army Museum.

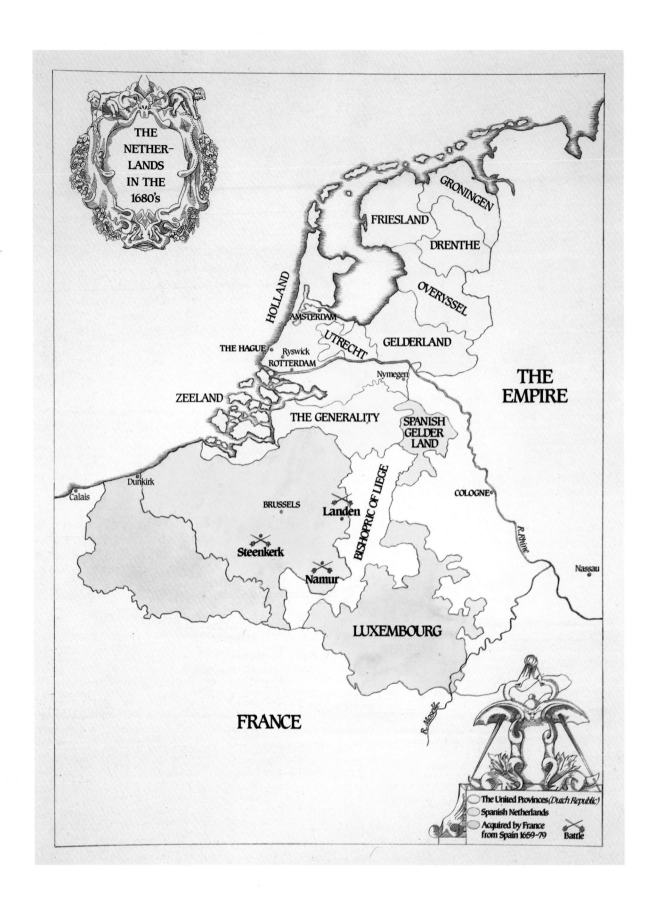

THE
NETHER-
LANDS
IN THE
1680's

GRONINGEN

FRIESLAND

DRENTHE

OVERYSSEL

HOLLAND

AMSTERDAM

UTRECHT

GELDERLAND

THE HAGUE    Ryswick

ROTTERDAM

Nymegen

THE
EMPIRE

ZEELAND

THE GENERALITY

SPANISH
GELDER
LAND

Dunkirk

BISHOPRIC OF LIEGE

COLOGNE

Calais

BRUSSELS    ⚔ Landen

R. Rhine

Steenkerk ⚔

Nassau

⚔ Namur

LUXEMBOURG

R. Moselle

FRANCE

○ The United Provinces (Dutch Republic)
○ Spanish Netherlands
○ Acquired by France
  from Spain 1659-79      ⚔ Battle

16

21

## 21 *The Peace of Nijmegen (1679)*

By Henri Gascard (1635-1701)
Commanderie van St Jan, Nijmegen
Reproduction

The war that began with Louis XIV's triumphant invasion of the Dutch Republic dragged on for several years. By 1676 most of the parties involved were ready to discuss peace terms and met for that purpose in the Dutch city of Nijmegen, which the French had captured in 1672. Negotiations were complicated and long drawn out, and there was further fighting before agreement was finally reached. The picture shows the formal signing of the peace on 10 August 1678, by the representatives of France (seated to left) Spain (seated to right) and the Dutch Republic (seated at either end of the table). A secretary is handing a pen to the head of the French delegation, Marshal d'Estrades. Seated next to him are Colbert and d'Avaux; the latter was to be Louis XIV's ambassador to James II in Ireland in 1689. The Emperor Leopold did not agree to the terms of the Peace until 5 February 1679.

Henri Gascard or Gascar, a French portrait painter who had worked previously in Italy and England, was sent to Nijmegen by Louis XIV to record the occasion.The French envoy d'Estrades described him at the time as one of the best painters in France. He died at Rome in 1701.

22

### 22 *William on a staghunt*

BY DIRCK MAAS (1659-1717)
HISTORISCHE VERZAMELINGEN VAN HET HUIS ORANJE-NASSAU, PALEIS HET LOO,
APELDOORN
REPRODUCTION

William's favourite leisure pursuit was hunting, for which he had an absolute
passion from boyhood until the day he died. Despite his physical infirmities he
was as fearless in the chase as he was in battle, and frequently spent long hours
in the saddle. In Holland, when not taken up with warfare and affairs of state he
spent as much time as possible at one or other of his hunting lodges, especially
Dieren in Gelderland. Even between campaigns he always found time to hunt.
This picture shows him animated at the conclusion of a staghunt.

Dirck or Theodor Maas or Maes was a Dutch painter of battle scenes and
horses, best known in the British Isles for his painting of the battle of the Boyne.

### 23 *Bird's-eye view of Het Loo Palace, c.1700*

BY PIETER SCHENK (1660-1718)
KONINKLIJK HUISARCHIEF, PALEIS HET LOO, APELDOORN
REPRODUCTION

In 1684 William purchased the old manor house of Het Loo, near his hunting
lodge at Dieren. Both he and Mary were interested in domestic architecture,
interior decoration and gardens. The great new palace at Het Loo was started in
1685 and took nine years to complete.The house itself was designed by the
architect Jacob Romans, while the magnificent formal gardens were laid out by
the Huguenot Daniel Marot in the French style made fashionable by André Le
Nôtre's work at Versailles.

Pieter Schenk or Schenck was an engraver of German origin who came to
Holland as a young man and studied engraving at Amsterdam. Augustus of
Saxony, king of Poland, made him his court engraver. More than six hundred
examples of his work survive.

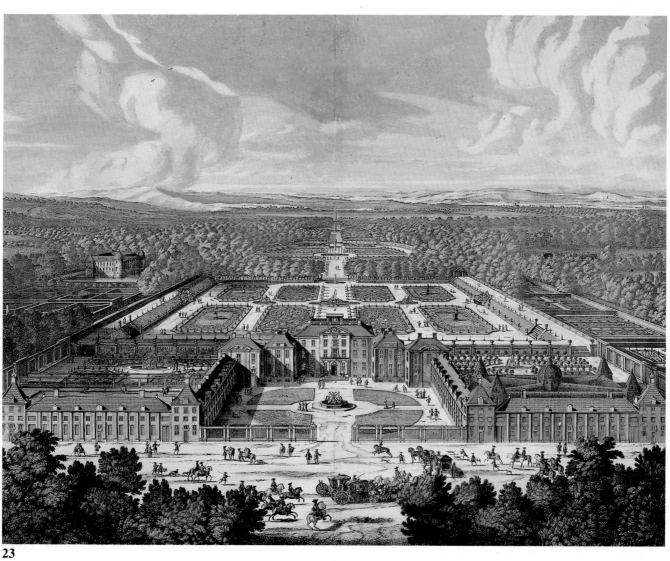

**23**

24

## 24 *Tirannien Tegen De Gereformeerden In Vrankryk (Tyrannies towards the Protestants in France)*

BY OR IN THE STYLE OF ROMEYN DE HOOGHE
ATLAS VAN STOLK, ROTTERDAM

Engraving with contemporary colouring  78 x 60 cms.

Louis XIV's persecution of his Huguenot subjects culminated in 1685, when he formally revoked the Edict of Nantes which had protected them. Despite ferocious penalties, thousands of them fled from France rather than change their religion.  Many of the refugees settled in the Dutch Republic, where they added to the existing hatred of the French king.  Dutch merchants living in France who had become French citizens were similarly persecuted.

## 25 *Portrait bust of William III in 1691*

BY J.H. BRANDON (D.1716), FROM *KOMSTE VAN ZYNE MAJESTEIT WILLEM III ... IN HOLLAND* (THE HAGUE, 1691)
ULSTER MUSEUM, BELFAST

Engraving 33.5 x 22 cms.

This fine engraving is the frontispiece to a volume published to record William's triumphal return to Holland in 1691. All the illustrations in the book, apart from this one plate, are the work of Romeyn de Hooghe.

GUILELMUS. III.
D.G. ANGLIÆ. SCOTIÆ. FRANCIÆ
ET. HYBERNIÆ. REX.

Ioh. Brandon delineavit.        Arn. Leers exc. cum Privilegio.        P.'a Gunst sculp.

**25**

26

27

## 26 *Leopold I, Holy Roman Emperor (1640-1705) (1672)*

BY BENJAMIN VON BLOCK (1631-90)
MUSEUM OF THE HISTORY OF ART, VIENNA
REPRODUCTION

Leopold I, second son of Ferdinard III, was intended for the Church but became his father's heir in 1654, on the death of his elder brother Ferdinard IV. In 1658 he was elected Emperor of the Holy Roman Empire. His long reign of forty-seven years was mainly spent opposing Louis XIV and his territorial and dynastic ambitions. Although a peace-loving monarch (he never led his troops in person), he spent most of his reign planning and directing wars, first against Charles X of Sweden, then against the Turks and then against France (three times in this case).

Louis XIV's aggressive policy towards Holland aroused considerable suspicion throughout Europe, and although Leopold was on friendly terms with Louis (to whom he was related), he felt compelled to take action against the French king in 1673. He accordingly entered into an alliance with the Prince of Orange, undertaking to supply 30,000 men to fight France in return for large subsidies; the Dutch themselves guaranteed 20,000. This league later collapsed because of the defection of the Elector of Brandenburg. A subsequent alliance for the same purpose, between Leopold, William, the king of Spain and a number of German princes lasted until the end of 1678, when peace was concluded by the treaty of Nijmegen.

Shortly afterwards, however, Louis resumed his aggressive tactics on the German frontier. Leopold, who was engaged in fighting the Turks, did not resume his struggle against France until 1682; this time hostilities lasted for two years. In 1689 he joined with William, the kings of Denmark and Spain, the Elector of Brandenburg and others in a grand alliance against Louis. The resultant struggle lasted for eight years and engulfed almost the whole of western Europe. In September 1697 England, the Dutch Republic and France, financially hard-pressed and war-weary, concluded peace at Rijswijk. Leopold refused to be a party to it, feeling that his allies had let him down, but agreed to the treaty the following month.

Following the breakdown of attempts to divide the possessions of the childless king of Spain by agreement, William III formed another grand alliance against France. Leopold, whose son Charles's claim to the throne of Spain was supported by the allies, played a prominent part in the resulting war of the Spanish Succession until his death on 5 May 1705.

Industrious and well-educated, Leopold regarded himself as an absolute sovereign and was intent on maintaining his power. A difficult and temperamental ally, he was highly intolerant in religious matters and was greatly under the influence of the Jesuits. He married three times; both of his sons became emperors.

Benjamin von Block, an Austrian portrait painter and engraver, worked in Italy for a time before settling in Regensburg. His portrait of the emperor was probably painted in 1672. Leopold wears a large, extremely expansive black wig and the new mode of collar designed to be worn with it. His full and pendulous lower lip is a Habsburg characteristic.

Sources:     *Encyclopaedia Britannica* (eleventh edition); S.B. Baxter, *William III*
                 (London, 1966); H. and B. van der Zee, *William and Mary* (London, 1973).

## 27 *Maximilian II Emmanuel, Elector of Bavaria (1662-1726)*

By Joseph Vivien (1657-1734)
Residence Museum, Munich
Reproduction

Maximilian II Emmanuel, Elector of Bavaria from 1679, was the son-in-law of Leopold I through his marriage to Leopold's daughter, Maria Antonia, and brother-in-law of the dauphin. He supported the Habsburgs during Leopold's war with the Turks. During the war of the Grand Alliance (1689-97), Leopold secured his loyalty by giving him command of the imperial forces and promised to help him attain the governorship of the Spanish Netherlands, in a treaty of May 1689. He secured this appointment in 1692 - an important point for the Dutch, who wanted to keep a 'friend' in the Spanish Netherlands as a barrier between themselves and the French. An able and dynamic soldier,he was held in high regard by William, who considered him a valuable ally.

Maximilian, however, subsequently supported France during the war of the Spanish Succession (1701-13), in the hope that his family would be able to supplant the Habsburgs on the imperial throne. His choice of ally this time was to have disastrous consequences in the short term. After the defeat of the French and Bavarians at Blenheim in 1704, his territories were divided between Leopold and the Elector Palatine. In 1706, after the French were beaten at Ramillies, he also lost the Netherlands and had to take refuge at the French court. In 1713, however, his Bavarian lands were restored to him under the treaty of Utrecht; two years later he returned to Munich. His dynastic dream came true sixteen years after his death, when his eldest son, Charles Albert, became Holy Roman emperor.

Joseph Vivien, a French portrait painter who painted in oil and pastel, studied in Paris and worked in Munich in 1706, 1710 and 1716. This portrait of the elector is a fine example of his skill in pastel.

Sources:     S.B. Baxter, *William III* (London, 1966); *The New Encyclopaedia Britannica*
                 (fifteenth edition).

## 28 *Frederick III, Elector of Brandenburg (Afterwards King of Prussia) (1657-1713) (1688)*

By Gedeon Romandon (1667-97)
Sanssouci Palace, Potsdam
Reproduction

Frederick III was the second son of the Elector Frederick William, uncle and former guardian of William III. Born at Königsberg on 11 July 1657, on the death of his elder brother in 1674 he became heir to the throne of Brandenburg, which his father had made into one of the most powerful states in Germany. He succeeded his father on 9 May 1688. As William's cousin and a possible heir to his estates (a carrot which William dangled tantalizingly under his nose for years), it was in his interest to support William in his plans for the invasion of England. William was keenly anxious that the German princes should join forces with him in an alliance during the summer of 1688. When the Electors of Saxony and Hanover would not commit themselves, Bentinck persuaded Frederick to guard the Dutch frontier against France with a thousand men (at a price). Before finally committing himself, however, he insisted on a secret meeting with William.

The meeting took place in September and was highly fruitful. Not only did Frederick agree to provide 12,000 men, but William achieved his desired alliance of the leading German princes. After France invaded the Palatinate on 27 September, a number of other German princes also joined forces with William. Frederick remained William's ally in his war against France until its culmination in 1697. In 1702 he joined forces with the Emperor Leopold in his struggle against France, after Leopold had recognised his right to declare himself king in Prussia. Ever one for pomp and ceremony, and a great admirer of the court of Louis XIV, he crowned himself king at Königsberg on 18 January 1701. His forces served with distinction during the war of the Spanish Succession and rendered great assistance to the allies.

Although extravagant in the extreme (he reduced Prussia's finances to chaos), Frederick did much to advance his country on the road to its future greatness. He founded Halle University and the Berlin Academy of Science, spent considerable sums on the erection of public buildings and gave protection to many Protestants fleeing from France. In 1696 there were hopes that his daughter Louise Dorothea Sophia would become William's second wife (he was being urged to marry again); however, her lack of personal attractions - Matthew Prior described her as 'not ugly but disagreeable, a tall miss at a boarding school, straggy lean neck, very pale' - quickly put an end to the idea. Frederick married three times. His second wife, Sophia Charlotte, was a sister of the future king of England, George I. He died on 25 February 1713.

The portrait was painted in 1688, shortly after Frederick succeeded to the throne of Brandenburg, and is the first official portrait of him as Elector. Gedeon Romandon, an Italian portrait and history painter, worked in Berlin for a number of years before his early death at the age of thirty.

Sources:     *Encyclopaedia Britannica* (eleventh edition); S.B. Baxter, *William III* (London,1966); H. and B. van der Zee, *William and Mary* (London, 1973).

## 29 *Christian V, King of Denmark and Norway (1646-99) (1696)*

BY JAN FRANS DOUWEN (1656-1727)
ROSENBORG CASTLE, COPENHAGEN
REPRODUCTION

Christian V, son of Frederick III and brother of Prince George of Denmark, succeeded to the throne in February 1670 on the death of his father. Married to a German princess (as his father had been), his sympathies were to the German rather than the Danish way of life. German was the language of the court and army, and the higher offices were filled mainly with Germans, who supplanted the old Danish aristocracy and landowners. A weak despot, King Christian's chief interest lay in military matters. Robert Molesworth, William's envoy at the Danish court, described the king as good-natured but 'often over-ruled by those about him, to whom he leaves the whole management of affairs because he neither loves, nor has a genius for, business ... he is never better pleased than when an exact chart of any country or delineation of any fortress is brought to him, his genius for the war [William's campaign in Ireland] inclining him to love fortification' (Danaher and Simms, pp. 10-11). He had considerable admiration for Louis XIV and modelled himself upon him, an emulation which Molesworth considered harmful to Denmark's interests: 'France has told this king that soldiers are the only true riches of princes, and this has made him raise more than he knows what to do with unless he disturbs his neighbours ... Denmark resembles in this point a monster that is all head and no body, all soldiers and no subjects' (Danaher and Simms, p. 12).

By the summer of 1689 it was clear to William that he needed additional

28

29

troops to conquer Ireland, most of which was under James's control. Denmark, at this time supported by France against Sweden in her territorial claims to parts of Holstein, was an obvious source of manpower. Accordingly William approached Christian with an offer of help in settling the dispute. By the time Molesworth reached the Danish court Denmark had relinquished her Holstein claims and Christian - greatly disappointed in Louis XIV - was ready to embark upon an alliance with England and Holland. By the treaty of 15 August 1689 he agreed to provide 6,000 infantry and 1,000 cavalry. The force was to be under the command of Schomberg, with discipline left to the Danish lieutenant-general, Ferdinand Wilhelm, Duke of Würtemberg-Neustadt. Although William considered the Danish terms too high, he ratified the treaty on 4 September 1689, partly out of fear that Denmark would again become France's ally if the treaty was not concluded and partly out of the need for a speedy reduction of Ireland.

After William's arrival in Ireland, the Danish troops took part in all the major engagements of the campaign and were an important part of the Williamite army. A contemporary account described them in glowing terms: 'All the Danes are comely proper men as can be seen; the foot are everything that can be wished for by a general - lusty, healthy, rugged fellows, well disciplined, well clothed, very neat and cleanly, arms as bright as silver, all firelocks ... their colour green lined with red, blue lined with white, grey lined with blue and grey lined with green, and every man a cloak or such a coat as the Dutch Guards wear, and you shall not see a man with a hole in any part of his clothing ...' (Danaher and Simms, p. 18).

Their deployment in Ireland, however, filled the Irish with dread. A Jacobite appeal to Schomberg's troops in 1689 deplored William's use of them and other mercenaries: 'To call in multitudes of strangers and foreigners, of desperate fortunes and divers nations, who are contriving your slavery, together with the old invaders of our country, the Danes, who held our ancestors in a war of three hundred years, and their insolence became intolerable to a proverb, till the very women fell upon them with the indignation of so many Judiths, it is so shameful it cannot be honourable' (Gilbert, p. 253). Despite criticisms of their rapacious behaviour (usually because they had not received their pay) and friction between Christian and William, William continued to use the Danes; after the conquest of Ireland he employed them on the Continent until the treaty of Rijswijk in 1697.

Douwen, a Dutch portrait painter, worked as court painter for the Elector Palatine in Düsseldorf for a time and together with another Dutch artist, Anton Schoonjans, painted members of the Danish royal family in 1696. The portrait is recorded in the first known inventory of Rosenborg of c.1696.

Sources:       J.T. Gilbert,ed., *A Jacobite Narrative of the War in Ireland 1688-1691* (Dublin, 1892, reprinted Shannon, 1971); K. Danaher and J.G. Simms eds., *The Danish Force in Ireland 1690-1691* (Dublin, 1962).

## 30 *Pope Innocent XI (1611-89)*

BY GIOVANNI BATTISTA GAULLI (1639-1709)
HER MAJESTY THE QUEEN, WINDSOR CASTLE
REPRODUCTION

Pope Innocent XI (Benedetto Odescalchi) succeeded to the papacy in 1676. Devout and saintly, with a high sense of duty both religious and secular, he immediately addressed himself to a reform of the church, wiped out the deficit within the Papal States, reduced rents and closed the gambling houses. His abiding dream was to unite the Christian princes of Europe against Islam, and to that end he pressed Louis XIV to conquer Constantinople and establish a Christian state there, with the dauphin as king. Louis's marked lack of enthusiasm for the idea caused Innocent great irritation; when the controversy over the *regale* arose, he seized upon it as a means of exerting his authority over the French king.

Louis XIV regarded himself as head of the church in France and believed that it had certain customs and privileges with which the pope had no right to interfere. Papal infallibility had not at this time been proclaimed; Louis believed that he too was God's representative on earth and that the pope was not his superior but his ally. Chief among the 'Gallican' traditions was the French bishops' belief that they were descended from the apostles and that their sees had been established by God; while recognising the primacy of the papacy, they maintained that the church was a decentralized institution and that their ecumenical council had primacy even over the pope.

In 1673 the expense of war had forced Louis to extend to all the dioceses of France, instead of to only half of them, the *regale,* that is, the king's right to draw revenues from vacant bishoprics and abbacies and to appoint to benefices within their gift. Bishops of dioceses which had been exempt up to 1673 had to have their oaths of allegiance registered in the *Chambres des Comptes;* bishops refusing to register would have their sees declared vacant. Two bishops refused and eventually turned to Innocent for support. Their resistance sparked off a quarrel between Louis and the pope which resulted in the French church issuing the Declaration of Gallican Liberties in 1682. This proclaimed the superiority of councils to the pope, denied papal infallibility and subordinated the pontiff's decisions (even in questions of faith) to the approval of each Church. In reply, the pope annulled the Declaration and refused to confirm Louis's clerical appointments. Neither the pontiff nor Louis, however, went so far as to make a break within the church; each wanted to avoid a schism if possible. (In the event, the quarrel lasted for years, until in 1693 Innocent's successor extended the *regale* to all France).

Another row between pope and king broke out in 1687. On this occasion it centred upon Innocent's determination to suppress the practice of *franchise*, the right assumed by ambassadors to the papal court to grant asylum to anyone who requested it within their compounds in Rome. Misuse of this privilege had made the diplomatic quarters havens for Roman criminals. All the states except France agreed to the request, whereupon Innocent refused to accept another French ambassador until Louis relinquished the *franchise.* Louis then defied Innocent's ruling and installed a new French ambassador in Rome by force of arms, whereupon the pope excommunicated both him and his advisers. Louis then seized the papal territory of Avignon and threatened a schism. Innocent, however, stood firm in his resolve.

**30**

These disputes concerning Gallican liberties and ambassadorial rights were only two among numerous differences between Innocent and Louis. Innocent regarded Louis's pretensions and thirst for power as a threat to Europe and stood firm against Louis's ambitions, despite the fact that both were united in religion. (This was virtually the only common ground they had). Innocent refused to be bullied into appointing Louis's nominee to the vacant archbishopric of Cologne in 1688. He disapproved strongly of Louis's persecution of French Protestants and regarded the revocation of the Edict of Nantes as folly. Furthermore, he supported the anti-French League of Augsburg of 1686 (aimed at checking French aggression in western Europe), acquiesced in the aims of William of Orange and was unsympathetic to James II, whom he regarded as Louis's puppet.

Innocent died on 12 August 1689, lamented by many. Gaulli, who collaborated with Bernini and whose greatest work is the frescoes in the Gesù, had an extensive portrait practice, numbering Popes Alexander VII and Clement XI among his sitters. His sensitive drawing of Innocent XI shows a frail old man, with a questioning and thoughtful gaze.

Sources:      V. Cronin, *Louis XIV* (London, 1964); J.B. Wolf, *Louis XIV* (London, 1968); J.B. Wolf, ed., *Louis XIV A Profile* (London, 1972); R. Mousnier, *Louis XIV* (The Historical Association, 1973).

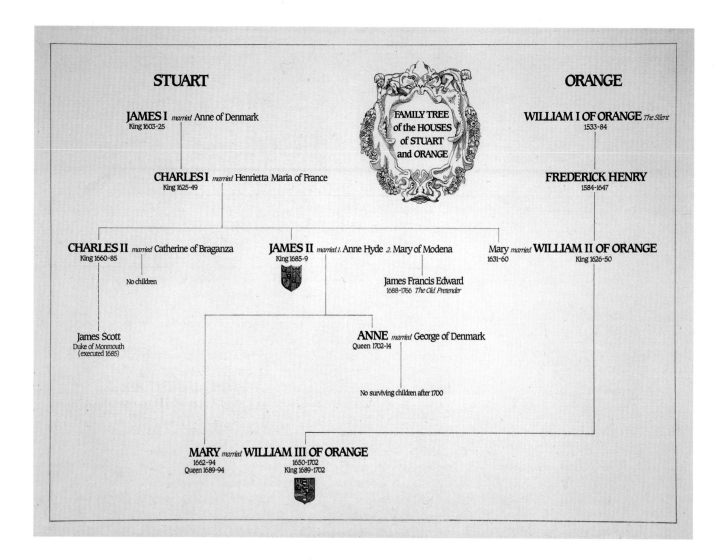

**STUART**

**ORANGE**

FAMILY TREE
of the HOUSES
of STUART
and ORANGE

**JAMES I** *married* Anne of Denmark
King 1603-25

**WILLIAM I OF ORANGE** *The Silent*
1533-84

**CHARLES I** *married* Henrietta Maria of France
King 1625-49

**FREDERICK HENRY**
1584-1647

**CHARLES II** *married* Catherine of Braganza
King 1660-85

No children

**JAMES II** *married 1.* Anne Hyde *2.* Mary of Modena
King 1685-9

Mary *married* **WILLIAM II OF ORANGE**
1631-60 King 1626-50

James Francis Edward
1688-1766 *The Old Pretender*

James Scott
Duke of Monmouth
(executed 1685)

**ANNE** *married* George of Denmark
Queen 1702-14

No surviving children after 1700

**MARY** *married* **WILLIAM III OF ORANGE**
1662-94 1650-1702
Queen 1689-94 King 1689-1702

## 2. James II and the Glorious Revolution

In William of Orange's plans to thwart the ambitions of Louis XIV, England played a crucial part. At the very least he needed England to be neutral. William's wife Mary, the elder of James II's two Protestant daughters by his first marriage, was next in line to the English throne when her father succeeded in 1685. William himself, through his mother, had a more remote claim as the grandson of Charles I. Though the English and the Dutch had long been rivals for sea power and trade, by the 1680s their common hatred of France and their common Protestant faith were tending to lessen that traditional animosity. When his father-in-law was king, William was careful to behave correctly towards him, whilst maintaining good relations with influential Englishmen who found James's policies less and less to their liking.

Though a zealous Catholic by the time he came to the throne, James promised to uphold the Church of England and was welcomed by most of his English subjects as their legitimate king. His one and only parliament in 1685 voted him a large income for life, and an attempt by the Duke of Monmouth (a bastard son of Charles II) to overthrow him received little support and was easily and ruthlessly suppressed. James then alarmed many of his subjects, however, by keeping a large army. (Following their experiences under Cromwell, most Englishmen associated a standing army in time of peace with oppression and arbitrary government). He also appointed Catholics as officers in it, despite the laws forbidding such appointments. Alarming as this was, especially in view of the current persecution of Protestants in France by his friend Louis XIV, it did not drive his subjects to positive action until the summer of 1688, when the arrest and trial of the seven bishops and the birth of a Catholic heir in what some Protestants regarded as suspicious circumstances created a crisis.

A small number of leading figures then secretly approached William of Orange to invite him to come to England to save its religion and liberties - an invitation which he accepted with the approval of the Dutch authorities.

The preparation of a large invasion force in Holland in the autumn of 1688 could scarcely be kept secret, but James could not believe that his son-in-law would risk setting out so late in the year, when the weather in the North Sea was notoriously unreliable. In the event, indeed, William only got away at the second attempt, but then favourable winds and good seamanship carried him safely past the waiting English fleet to land in Devon. Despite the assurances of those who had invited him, support was slow to materialise at first. Advancing cautiously towards London he found his way barred by James's army at Salisbury. When some of James's most trusted officers (and even his daughter Anne) deserted him, he lost his nerve and fled. On reaching London, William fulfilled his promise of calling an assembly to safeguard the religion and liberties that James's policies had endangered. The problem created by James's flight to France was eventually solved by declaring that he had thus abdicated and offering the vacant throne jointly to William and Mary, subject to important limitations on royal power expressed in the Declaration of Rights. This revolution, called glorious because it had been achieved without bloodshed (at any rate in England), immensely strengthened William's power to oppose France in Europe. It also created the Jacobite movement.

**31** obv.

**31** rev.

## 31 *Mary, Princess of Orange and her son William, 1654*

MEDAL BY P.V. ABEELE (FL. 1622-77)
HUNTERIAN MUSEUM, GLASGOW

Silver, 64 mm.
Lit:        *Medallic Illustrations*, 417-18, no. 55.
Description:   obv.  facing bust of William III as a child, wearing a plumed hat over a cap.
                    The portrait is surrounded by a border of intertwined orange and laurel.
                    legend:  (on a ribbon below the bust) WILHELMVS III D.G
                    PRINC.ARAVS.ETC [William III, by grace of God  Prince of Orange etc.]; at
                    either side: AN 1654 [year, 1654].
            rev.  bust of Mary, Princess of Orange, draped, wearing a necklet of pearls, her
                    hair put up with jewels and pearls, against a background of intertwined
                    roses and thistles.
                    legend:  MARIA D.G.PRINCEPS M.BRIT.AVRANT.DOTARIA.ETC
                    (Mary, by grace of God princess of Great Britain, dowager of Orange, etc].

This medal was produced by embossing two thin plates and then joining them, allowing higher relief than the normal technology of the period.

Mary, Princess of Orange, was the daughter of Charles I of England.  After the death of her husband, William II, power shifted away from the house of Orange to the States-General. This medal has been regarded as a possible attempt to emphasise what Mary may have considered the rights of her young son. In 1654 William would still have been wearing broadly female clothing, as was the custom of the time, and not boys' attire.  (Boys were not 'breeched' until slightly older). The same obverse was used with a portrait of his father.

The Dutch issued many medals by this method of production, the technique of which allowed much more freedom of expression than die-sinking, as can be seen from this example.

## 32 *Marriage of William and Mary, 1677*

MEDAL ATTRIBUTED TO N. CHEVALIER (D.1720)
ULSTER MUSEUM, BELFAST; HUNTERIAN MUSEUM, GLASGOW

Silver, 42 mm.
Lit:        *Medallic Illustrations*, 569, no. 236.
Description:   obv.  bust of William III in armour, wearing cravat, and with long hair.
                    legend: GVLH.III.D.G.PRIN.AVR.HOL.ET.WES.GV [William III, by
                    grace of God Prince of Orange, Governor of Holland and West Friesland].
            rev.  draped bust of Mary, wearing pearl necklet, with an elaborate hair style.
                    legend:  MARIA.D.G.AVR.PRIN.NAT.DE.IORC. [Mary, by grace of
                    God Princess of Orange, daughter of the Duke of York].

This seems to have been quite a popular medal, being still relatively common. At least two sets of dies were used for each side, as well as a cast version differing from either.

The news of the royal wedding was greeted with an enthusiasm familiar to more modern times, in part because it cemented the peace settlement between the United Provinces and England. William's wearing of armour signifies his military command. An almost identical medal exists on which the legend on the reverse indicates that the person depicted is William's mother, although the actual likeness is virtually the same as that of Princess Mary.

**32** obv.                    **32** rev.

**33** obv.

**33** rev.

## 33 *Coronation of James II, 1685*

MEDAL BY JOHN ROETTIER (FL. 1660, D. 1703)
HUNTERIAN MUSEUM, GLASGOW

Silver, 34 mm.

Lit:               *Medallic Illustrations,* 605, no. 6.
Description:   obv.   bust of James II, laureate and draped over armour.
                           legend: IACOBVS.II.D.G.ANG. SCO.FR.ET.HI.REX [James II, by grace
                           of God king of England, Scotland, France and Ireland].
                    rev.   a hand emerging from a cloud holds a crown over a laurel wreath lying on
                           a cushion.
                           legend: A.MILITARI.AD. REGIAM [from the military to the kingdom];
                           in exergue: INAVGVRAT.23.AP.1685 [crowned 23 April 1685].

The coronation medal of Charles II by Thomas Simon was somewhat old-
fashioned, especially in regard to the king's portrait. On this medal James is
shown in a similar manner to that in which his brother appeared on his later
coins (also by Roettier). The reverse makes great play of James's military
background: he had served with some distinction in the French army during the
Interregnum and was lord high admiral from 1660. The hand is that of God or
Providence, adding the crown to the laurel wreath which his military career had
already earned him.

## 34a *Touch Piece of James II, c. 1685*

BY ANON
HUNTERIAN MUSEUM, GLASGOW

Gold, 18 mm.

Lit:               *Medallic Illustrations,* 611, no. 19.
Description:   obv.   three-masted ship in full sail, with pennants flying.
                           legend: IACO.II.D.G.M.B.FR.ET.HI.REX [James II, by grace of God king
                           of Great Britain, France and Ireland].
                    rev.   St Michael, in Roman armour and with spread wings, stands with one foot
                           on a dragon which he stabs with a spear.
                           legend: SOLI. DEO. GLORIA [the glory is God's alone].

There was a belief that the kings of England and of France had the inherited
ability to cure scrofula ('the King's Evil') by their touch. Whilst it has been
suggested that the origins of the practice go back at least as far as Edward the
Confessor, it seems more likely that the power descended from the saintly Louis
IX of France. As part of the ceremony the king touched the afflicted person,
special prayers were said by the court chaplain and a coin, pierced so that it
could be worn suspended from a white ribbon, was hung around the neck of the
affected person as an amulet.

Originally in England the gold coin known as an angel (initially worth 6s.
8d., but later 10s.), which had as its obverse design St Michael and the dragon,
was presented to the participants in the ceremony of touching. When this coin
became obsolete, gold medals with the same obverse design were substituted.
These were first made for Charles II, during whose reign over 100,000 persons
were touched. In order to save money, the metal of the touch-pieces was
eventually changed from gold to silver. James and his descendants up to Henry
IX, the last of the Stuart Pretenders, continued to touch and to issue touch-
pieces. In England, however, the practice ended with the death of Queen Anne.
William III actually referred those wishing to be touched to James in exile at St
Germains.

## 34b *Touch piece of Queen Anne*

BY ANON
ULSTER MUSEUM, BELFAST

Gold, 21 mm.

Lit: *Medallic Illustrations*, 242-43, no. 28.

Description: obv. three-masted ship, with most of its sails set and flying pennants.
legend: ANNA.D:G:M:BR FET.H:REG: [Anne, by grace of God queen of Great Britain, France and Ireland].

rev. St Michael in Roman armour, wearing a cloak, tramples and stabs a dragon under his feet with a spear which terminates in a cross at the butt end.
legend: SOLI. DEO. GLORIA. [the glory is God's alone].

As the last of the Stuarts to rule England, Anne was also the last monarch to carry out the ceremony of touching. Her most famous 'patient' was the young Samuel Johnson.

## 34c *Touch-piece of James III (the Old Pretender)*

BY ANON
ULSTER MUSEUM, BELFAST

Silver, 20 mm.

Lit: *Medallic Illustrations*, 316, no. 140.

Description: obv. three-masted ship with some of its sails set.
legend: IAC.III.D.G.M.B.F.ET.H.R. [James III, by grace of God king of Great Britain, France and Ireland].

rev. St Michael, in Roman armour and with spread wings, stands with one foot on a dragon which he stabs with a spear.
legend: SOLI. DEO. GLORIA. [the glory is God's alone].

There may be significance in the fact that the ship no longer has all its sails set and that St Michael is more definitely winged. It was said that the ship was sailing against an adverse wind.

James III found himself in a more difficult position than his father over touching, as he had a legitimate rival in Queen Anne, who provided the same service. (Neither William nor Mary did so).

## 35 *James II (1633-1701)*

BY AN UNKNOWN ARTIST, AFTER SIR GODFREY KNELLER (1646-1723)
CITY OF MANCHESTER ART GALLERY

Oil on canvas 229.9 x 141 cms.

Prov: The Earl of Home (but not apparently from the Clarendon Gallery); sold Christie's, 20 June 1919(89); Leggatt's, Sir Ernst Royden; purchased from A.M. McNeill, Taynish, Spital, Wirral, October 1961.

Exh: *Kings and Queens of England*, Liverpool 1953 (23).

Lit: D. Piper, *Catalogue of the Seventeenth Century Portraits in the National Portrait Gallery* (Cambridge, 1963), p.177.

James, Duke of York, was the younger son of Charles I and his French queen Henrietta Maria, and the younger brother of King Charles II. Like his brother, he spent long years in exile following the execution of their father, serving with notable bravery in the French and Spanish armies. In September 1660 he married his mistress Anne Hyde, daughter of Edward Hyde, Earl of Clarendon and Charles II's Lord Chancellor. The couple had two daughters who survived to adulthood and ascended the throne: Mary and Anne. At the Restoration Charles II appointed him lord high admiral, a title which had originally been conferred upon him in childhood. As ruler of the king's navy he was competent and hard-working, and was instrumental in bringing about a number of much-needed reforms. In addition to this post he was a member of the privy council and Charles's deputy when he was away from London.

In 1672 he took what was undoubtedly the most momentous step of his life - conversion to Roman Catholicism. Raised as Church of England in accordance with his father's wishes, he had felt drawn to Catholicism certainly since 1668, as had Charles. The Duchess of York was similarly attracted and ceased taking Anglican communion in 1669. Early in that year both brothers planned to

35

declare their conversion and promote Catholicism in England. Charles, however, vacillated until his deathbed, repeatedly using the promise of action in the matter to wheedle money out of Louis XIV. (French subsidies enabled him to rule without a parliament). Although James was received into the Catholic church in 1672, he continued to attend Anglican services until 1676. By then, however, his conversion was common knowledge.

At Easter 1673, in the prevailing mood of anti-Catholicism, parliament passed a Test Act which excluded Catholics from holding public office. As a result of this James was forced to relinquish his position as lord high admiral. He still remained involved with affairs of government, however, and attended meetings of the privy council.

To most Englishmen of the time Catholicism was synonymous with arbitrary government and absolutism in the manner of Louis XIV, a prospect which filled many of them with dread. As heir to his brother, who had no legitimate children, James was the focus of their fears. His second marriage, to the Catholic princess Mary of Modena in 1673, added to these anxieties and brought repeated protests from the Commons. The hysteria engendered by the Popish Plot of 1678 made James all too aware of the precariousness of his own situation. Writing to his nephew and son-in-law the Prince of Orange in October of that year, he declared with foresight: 'I do verily believe that when this affair is thoroughly examined it will be found nothing but malice against the poor Catholics and myself in particular' (Ashley, p. 120). The basic details of the plot, which was a complete fabrication, were that the king and government were going to be overthrown by the Jesuits, Protestants were going to be massacred in their thousands and James would be declared king and govern by the advice of the Jesuits.

Faced with a storm of anti-Catholicism, Charles endeavoured to make James conform to the Church of England; it was that or leave court. James refused and was sent into exile in March 1679. His banishment, initially to Brussels and then to Edinburgh, lasted for three years. Shortly after he left England, the Commons made his exclusion from the throne its chief priority and in May 1679 carried an Exclusion Bill with a sizeable majority. The Exclusionists, or 'Whigs' as they came to be called, controlled the Commons but needed the consent of the Lords and king for the bill's passage; in the event, the Lords threw the bill out in 1680, after pressure from Charles. The exclusion issue remained to the fore until 1683, when the Rye House Plot, a Whig-engineered plan to assassinate Charles and James, was discovered. Thereafter the Exclusionists as a group began to disintegrate.

In May 1682 James returned from banishment and established himself at his brother's side. The upheaval of the exclusion crisis had created a deep rift within the political nation: Whigs, generally the party of Dissent and exclusion, tried to undermine the authority of the established church; Tories, who supported Anglicanism and the hereditary principle, looked to Charles to give the monarchy a strong image. Both Charles and James now began to develop a closer relationship with the Tories, who in turn did their utmost to crush the Whigs and Dissent. The Tories now regarded the main threat to the establishment as coming from Dissent, not Catholicism. As for James, the Dissenters' support for exclusion reinforced his already-held conviction that they were all ardent republicans.

James ascended the throne on 6 February 1685, without the expected civil disturbances around the country. In a speech to his privy council he declared his intentions and denied that he would use his power arbitrarily: 'I shall make it my endeavour to preserve this government both in church and state as it is by law established. I know the principles of the Church of England are for monarchy and the members of it have shown themselves good and loyal subjects; therefore I shall always take care to defend and support it. I know too that the laws of England are sufficient to make the king as great a monarch as I can wish; and as I shall never depart from the rights and prerogative of the crown, so shall I never invade any man's property' (Miller, p. 120).

James started off his reign well. Much more diligent than Charles, he devoted a lot of time to business, began repaying his brother's debts and pruned his household expenses. On the surface his position seemed secure: the Tories were his loyal friends and the Whigs were cowed. His defects, however, soon became obvious as time progressed. His view of kingship left little room for manoeuvre; he commanded and expected to be obeyed. Ruling, for him, was a one-way process; inflexible in the extreme, he completely lacked the ability to concede any ground to those who did not think as he did. His office was to be used in God's service - and that, for him, meant the advancement of Catholicism. It was not an objective which was shared or desired by the nation.

His aim above all else was the re-establishment of Catholicism in England; at this time, Catholics were only one per cent of the population. He claimed he did not wish to make Catholicism the dominant religion, hardly possible when there were so few Catholics, but wanted to place them on an equal footing with Protestants as regards freedom of worship and the holding of public office. He fully expected to win many converts from the Church of England and convinced himself of this possibility. He advocated toleration for all Christians and was opposed to persecution for conscience's sake.

During 1685 mistrust of him began to grow as he insisted on employing Catholic officers within the army. To enable them to serve he used his prerogative to waive the Test Acts of 1673 and 1678 (the latter prohibited Catholics from sitting in either house of parliament). During the spring and summer of 1686 he began to use his prerogative to an even greater extent. He viewed this as a temporary expedient, until relief could be granted by parliament. Dissenters, whom he had hitherto regarded with suspicion, now seemed like possible allies; if they were given toleration, they might perhaps become loyal subjects who would support him in his objective. By August 1686 they were able to meet freely; by the following year, persecution of them had almost ceased.

In the second half of 1686 and the early months of 1687 James's catholicising policy intensified considerably. In Ireland, Richard Talbot, Earl of Tyrconnell and Lord Deputy from January 1687, pressed forward with a vigorous catholicisation of the army, judiciary and local administration. Scotland's turn came in February 1687, when James issued a Letter of Indulgence to his subjects there granting concessions to both Catholics and Dissenters. Shortly afterwards, in April, he granted a similar general dispensation to England by his first Declaration of Indulgence. This suspended the penal laws and - when the king so decided - the Test Act. These were still only temporary measures however; James's chief anxiety was what would happen after his death. He determined therefore on a repeal carried by parliament, to make secure his life's work.

James now began one of his most questionable moves - the 'closeting' of MPs in his private apartments as he tried to persuade them to agree to repeal. These closetings, carried out during the summer of 1687, were undoubtedly deeply intimidating to those on the receiving end; those interviewed were subjected to extreme psychological pressure. James, dogged in his determination on repeal by parliament, refused to be put off. An appeal to William and Mary for support caused him further frustration; both were opposed to repeal of the Test Acts, though they were prepared to tolerate suspension of the penal laws (but not their repeal). James then decided to pack a parliament with those who supported his aims. This campaign, which dragged on from the autumn of 1687 to that of the following year, canvassed MPs, JPs, deputy lieutenants and minor officials. As with the earlier closetings, considerable intimidation was used in this exercise, which was not a success but only served to unite Anglican opinion against repeal. James, notwithstanding, refused to accept the general unpopularity of his measures.

From April 1688 James lurched inexorably towards revolution. On the 27th of that month he reissued his Declaration of Indulgence and ordered that it be read out in every church pulpit in the land. This commandment met with determined refusal by a number of bishops, seven of whom (including the Archbishop of Canterbury) were sent to the Tower but later released on bail. On 10 June an event for which James had been praying for for years took place: Mary Beatrice gave birth to a healthy son. England now had a Catholic heir to the throne; rejoicings at his birth, which were not widespread, were over-shadowed by the furore surrounding the bishops' incarceration. (Rumour claimed that the child was a changeling but this was untrue). At their trial at the end of June the bishops were acquitted, to James's fury. By this time support for their stance was widespread. James, however, still blindly refused to accept that the majority of his subjects were loyal to the Church of England. Undeterred, he pushed forward even more energetically towards packing a House of Commons to meet in November.

Though warned by the French, James refused even to consider that William had hostile intentions towards him until the middle of August. Not until the second half of September, however, did he finally accept that the army being prepared in the Dutch Republic was intended for England; he had convinced himself it was aimed at the French. With that, he lost his nerve and began a hurried retreat from his previous policies. Those who had been turned out of office were to be reinstated and a vigorous attempt was made to placate the Anglicans, clergy and laity. Such panic measures, however, did not convince the bishops, who refused to sign a document abhorring William's conduct.

William landed at Torbay on 15 November 1688. During the next few weeks there were sizeable defections and desertions to the Williamite side. On a visit to his army on the 20th of the month, James became so unnerved at its lack of morale that he had a severe nosebleed, probably from a psychological cause. (The ailment lasted for some days). As defections mounted and William drew closer to London, James at the end of November was persuaded to call a parliament for 15 January 1689. In the ensuing negotiations between the two sides William set forth his demands: the dismissal of all Catholics from office, a pardon for his followers, financial provision for his army and the placing of the Tower, Tilbury and Portsmouth in safe hands.

James received the letter containing these stipulations on the evening of 10 December; shortly after midnight he fled in secret for France. He was subsequently captured by a party of seamen and made his way back to London, where considerable sympathy was displayed for his plight - to William's discomfiture. He fled a second time on the night of 22 December (the back door of the house where he was being held was conveniently left unguarded) and finally reached France on Christmas morning 1688. Louis received him with much ceremony, placed the palace of St Germains at his disposal and granted him a substantial pension.

As late as 3 December James had still not decided whether to resist or flee. By this time the army's loyalty was uncertain, so resistance seemed out of the question. To stay would mean he would have to agree to the persecution of Catholics again, the power of the crown would be drastically reduced and there would be a parliamentary inquiry into the birth of his son. He could face none of this. Sick in body and mind and not able to think coherently, he chose temporary exile in France as the most sensible option. Shortly before he fled he sent his wife and baby son ahead.

When Tyrconnell heard of James's collapse, he began to raise more troops in Ireland and urged him to come over. Louis also pressed him to make a stand. In a state of shock at the turn of events, James was reluctant to stir and preferred to spend his time at his religious devotions. When he eventually did come, in March 1689, he found the country in a shambles: there were no carts, few horses and very little rope; trade was dead, as most of the Protestant merchants had fled to England. James's attitude to Ireland was ambivalent; the country was basically a stepping-stone in his fight to regain his English throne and he held Irish aspirations in contempt. Maintaining the English interest in Ireland was more important to him. It was with considerable reluctance that he agreed to an act in his Dublin parliament of May 1689 (the 'patriot' parliament), which declared that the English parliament had no right to pass laws for Ireland. Likewise he objected to total repeal of the Restoration land settlement; this went ahead, nevertheless.

James's feelings for the native Irish were explicit in instructions he wrote for his son in 1692: principal garrisons should never be entrusted to Irish governors or Irish troops; the sons of ancient families should be given an English education, to wean them from their hatred of the English; schools should be established to teach English and 'by degrees wear out the Irish language, which would be for the advantage of the body of the inhabitants' (Simms, p. 154); the Os and Macs should be told that the estates declared forfeit by James I and his predecessors could not be restored; no native of Ireland should be lord lieutenant.

James's defeat at the Boyne was decisive. Though many of the Irish fought valiantly, they were hampered by poor equipment and ill-trained. James, however, had nothing but criticism for his Irish army. Ungallantly he commented: 'when it came to a trial they basely fled the field and left the spoil to the enemies, nor could they be prevailed upon to rally, though the loss in the whole defeat was but inconsiderable: so that henceforth I never more determined to head an Irish army and do now resolve to shift for myself...' (Simms, p. 153). He left Ireland shortly thereafter and fled back to France. After the French navy was crushed at Barfleur and La Hogue in 1692, his hopes of regaining his lost kingdoms were doomed.

James turned more and more to religion during the remainder of his life and accepted his misfortune with resignation; he believed God was punishing him for his sins, especially those of the flesh (he had had numerous mistresses). His daily prayer was submissive and penitential: 'I give Thee O my God most humble thanks for taking my kingdom from me; Thou didst awake me by that from the lethargy of sin. Had not Thy goodness drawn me from that wretched state, I have been forever lost. I return Thee also my most humble thanks for that out of Thy infinite bounty Thou didst banish me into a foreign country where I learned my duty and how to practise it' (Ashley, p. 287). He longed for death and was ill several times between 1695 and 1701. He died on 5 September 1701.

The painting is after a portrait by Kneller in the NPG, dated 1684, which was probably finished before Charles II's death in February 1685 and showed James as Duke of York and lord high admiral, with baton and plumed helmet. The design was engraved (in reverse) by I. Beckett. A sceptre and royal regalia were added after James became king. A studio version or copy is in the collection of the Duke of Portland, Welbeck. James and his second wife, Mary of Modena, sat to Kneller about thirty-six times each.

Sources:      Piper, as above; J.G. Simms, *Jacobite Ireland 1685-91* (London, 1969); J.R. Jones, *The Revolution of 1688 in England* (London, 1972); Maurice Ashley, *James II* (London, 1977); John Miller, *James II: a Study in Kingship* (Hove, 1978).

# 36 *Armour of King James II, 1686*

London, Richard Hoden
Royal Armouries, Tower of London (II. 123. III. 1306)

Comprising a pott, breastplate, backplate and long elbow gauntlet, all of steel, total weight 37 lb 2 oz. The buff coat is associated, weight 8lbs.
Purchased by the Tower Armouries from the maker in 1686. The buff coat is from the collection of Sir Anthony Cope, Bart., at Eversley Manor, Hants; purchased at Pearson and Harris, Winchester, 14 July 1949 (253).

Exh:      *Parliament and the Glorious Revolution, 1688-1988,* Banqueting House, London 1988.

Lit:       J. Hewitt, *Official Catalogue of the Tower Armouries* (1859), class II, no. 23, p. 9.
Viscount Dillon, *Illustrated Guide to the Armouries, Tower of London* (1910), class II, no. 22, p. 192, repr. pl. 25 .
C.J. Ffoulkes, *Inventory and Survey of the Armouries of the Tower of London* (1915), vol. 1, class II, no. 123, p. 138, repr. pl. XIX.
A.R. Dufty and W. Reid, *European Armour in the Tower of London* (1968), repr. pl. LXVII.

The armour is decorated with punched, engraved and gilt bands of trophies. The faceguard of the helmet is fretted and engraved with the initials IR (Iacobus Rex) and with the Royal Arms and their supporters, the lion and unicorn. It is marked only with the stamped crowned IR of the Arsenal of King James II. Its attribution to the maker, Richard Hoden, is based upon the record of payment for it, which was discovered by H.L. Blackmore:

14 December 1686

Recived into his Ma.$^{ts}$ Stores of Armour w.$^{th}$ in ye Office of Ordnance

from Richard Hoden Armourer, The Armour hereafter menconed being for

his Ma. owne Body viz.$^t$

| Harquebus Armo$^r$ | Breat carbine Proof) | |
| white parcell gilt | Back Pistoll Proofe) | for all w.$^{ch}$he |
| & chased & lyned w.$^{th}$ | Pott Pistoll Proofe) | is allowed |
| Crimson Sattin | Long Elbow Gauntlett) | £100.00.00 |

(PRO, WO 51/33, p. 137).

This is the last of the British royal armours, of which a series survive from the time of King Henry VIII onwards. Unlike its predecessors, most of which were complete armours, it is in the form of a harquebusier or light cavalry armour. Armours of this type were the last to be worn by British troops until the nineteenth century. This armour differs only from those of contemporary cavalry in its fine decoration.

Source:        C. Blair, *European Armour* (1957).

## 37 *Mary of Modena (1658-1718)*

BY JOHN SMITH, AFTER SIR GODFREY KNELLER (1646-1723)
NATIONAL GALLERY OF IRELAND, DUBLIN

Mezzotint 36.4 x 26.6 cms (plate 35 x 25.6).
Lit:        Adrian Le Harivel,ed., *National Gallery of Ireland*
           *Illustrated Summary Catalogue of Prints and Sculpture* (Dublin, 1988), p.324, repr.

Mary Beatrice d'Este of Modena, second wife of James II, was the daughter of Alfonso IV of Modena, of the house of d'Este. Lord Peterborough, sent by James to view her as a possible bride, described her at the age of fifteen as 'tall and admirably shaped, her hair black as jet, so were her eyebrows and her eyes, but the latter so full of light and sweetness, as they did dazzle and charm too ... in the whole turn of her face, which was of the most graceful oval, there were all the features, all the beauty, that could be great and charming in any human creature' (van der Zee, pp. 87-8). Deeply religious and having had a very sheltered upbringing, her desire in life was to be a nun; she had never heard of England nor of the Duke of York (as James was then) when Peterborough met her in 1673. She was horrified at the thought of marriage and had hysterics for two days. In the end Pope Clement V had to be called upon to persuade her, which he did by pointing out that marriage, for her, would be a worthier sacrifice than the cloister and that she could regard her life as being consecrated to bringing England back to the Catholic faith. The marriage took place in Modena on 30 September 1673, with Peterborough acting as proxy for the Duke of York.

On her journey to England she stayed at Versailles, where Louis XIV received her warmly and was greatly impressed by her beauty. She landed at Dover on 21 November and was met by the Duke, at the first sight of whom she burst into tears. (She later confessed that she had not loved her husband initially but had grown to do so as time went by). A second marriage was performed at Dover by the bishop of Oxford, under the authority of the king's signet, before the couple progressed to London.

James's marriage to a Catholic princess came as a blow to his daughter Mary; likewise to the nation in general, who regarded the union as a dangerous new Catholic influence, engineered by Louis XIV (who had played a part in the marriage negotiations and had contributed to the bride's dowry). To help counterbalance the new Catholic threat there were renewed calls for Mary to be married to her cousin William of Orange, who was regarded as the rising Protestant champion. A month after the wedding, parliament had in fact called upon Charles II to declare his brother's proxy marriage void and had been adjourned in consequence. Charles did not publicly acknowledge the royal wedding until September 1674.

Mary Beatrice found favour at court and grew deeply attached to her stepdaughters Mary and Anne; in the country at large, however, she shared her husband's unpopularity and was regarded as a symbol of his subservience to France. The couple's first child Catherine Laura was born on 16 January 1675 but died on 3 October following. Their second child Isabel, born on 28 August 1676, died on 2 March 1680. Their son Charles, born on 7 November 1677, died of smallpox on 12 December of that year. Two more children followed before the birth of the Prince of Wales on 10 June 1688: Elizabeth, born in 1678, and Charlotte Margaret, born on 15 August 1682, died on 6 October following. A fifth daughter, Louisa Mary, born on 28 June 1692, died in 1712.

After her flight to France with the Prince of Wales on 10 December 1688 Mary Beatrice settled at St Germains and made a highly favourable impression on the French court at large, by her attitude of calm dignity and regal bearing. Although initially cherishing the hope of a restoration to the throne, she eventually became reconciled to her position and turned to religion for

**37**

consolation. During James's absences she lived at the nunnery of the Visitation (her favourite order) at Chaillot, near Paris. She took a deep interest in James's Irish expedition of 1689 and carried on an active correspondence with the English Jacobites, to whom she gave large sums of money. After James's death on 6 September 1701 she lived in retirement at St Germains or Chaillot. Her death, on 7 May 1718, was deeply regretted by many, not least by an entourage of English Jacobites whom she had helped to support.

The engraving is after a three-quarter length oil of c.1685 at Chirk Castle, Wales. Kneller painted Mary Beatrice several times before and after her accession as queen; versions include a full-length at Hampton Court. She also sat to Lely shortly after her arrival in England and to Wissing about the time of her accession in 1685; versions by the latter are in the NPG, the SNPG, at Petworth and Drumlanrig. The portrait shows her as fetching and attractive, fully justifying Peterborough's description above.

Sources:     *DNB*; D. Piper,*Catalogue of the Seventeenth Century Portraits in the National Portrait Gallery* (Cambridge, 1963); H. and B. van der Zee, *William and Mary* (London, 1973).

38

## 38 *The Execution of the Duke of Monmouth, 25 July 1685*

ENGRAVING PUBLISHED IN AMSTERDAM BY ADRIAAN SCHOONEBEEK; TEXT IN
DUTCH AND FRENCH
ULSTER MUSEUM, BELFAST
REPRODUCTION

James Scott, Duke of Monmouth, a bastard son of Charles II, was unwisely
persuaded by Whig friends to lead a Protestant rebellion against James II in
England, to coincide with another in Scotland. Landing at Lyme Regis on 11
June 1685 with a few followers, he was joined by large numbers of country
people and was proclaimed king at Taunton and Bridgewater. His rustic army
was cut to pieces at Sedgemoor by royal troops whose second-in-command was
Churchill, future Duke of Marlborough (another royal officer was Sarsfield, who
was wounded and left for dead).

When caught and taken to the Tower, Monmouth pleaded with James for his
life but was beheaded (very incompetently - the executioner took five strokes of
the axe) shortly after. His unfortunate followers in the West Country were
hunted down and cruelly dealt with by Judge Jeffreys - one reason why William
of Orange, landing in the same area three years later, found the people there slow
to join him at first.

Adriaan Schoonebeek published four sets of engravings depicting events in
Great Britain and Ireland and in the career of William of Orange 1685-95, under
the general title of *Le Théâtre d'Angleterre*. Many of the prints were copies or
adaptations of existing works by de Hooghe and other artists - a common
practice before the age of copyright.

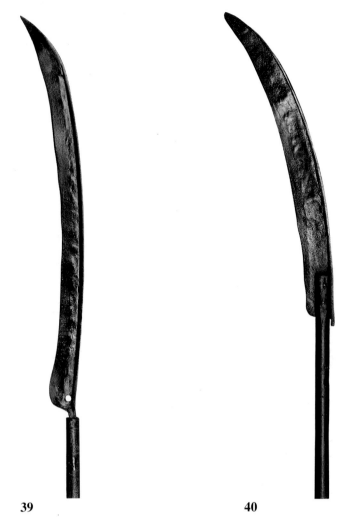

**39** *Scythe blade, seventeenth century*

ENGLISH
ROYAL ARMOURIES, TOWER OF LONDON (VII.960)

Length of head 99 cms.
Iron head.
Said to have been taken from the Duke of Monmouth's troops in 1685.
Exh:    *Parliament and the Glorious Revolution, 1688-1988,* Banqueting House,
London 1988.

Iron scythe blade with the tang straightened and set into a modern wooden haft.
The back of the blade has been stretched and folded to stiffen it. Near the tang is
the maker's mark and a circular hole through the blade.

 The men who joined the Duke of Monmouth in his abortive attempt to seize
the throne in 1685 were short of weapons; many agricultural implements like this
are reported to have been used.

**40** *Scythe blade, seventeenth century*

ENGLISH
ROYAL ARMOURIES, TOWER OF LONDON (VII.961)

Length 73 cms.
Iron head.
Said to have been taken from the Duke of Monmouth's troops in 1685.
Exh:    P*arliament and the Glorious Revolution, 1688-1988,* Banqueting House,
London 1988.

Iron scythe blade, the tang of which is missing. The blade is held in a modern
wooden haft by two nails.

39                                                    40

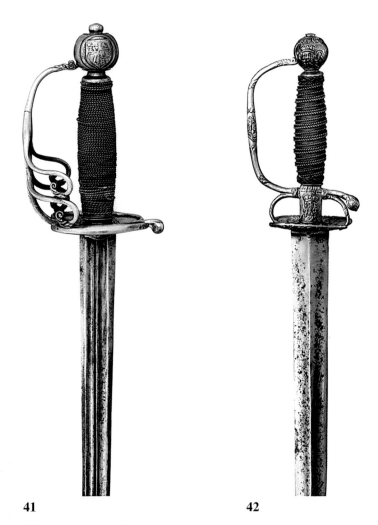

**41**                                         **42**

# 41 *Horseman's sword*

THE HILT ENGLISH, BETWEEN 1702 AND 1714, THE BLADE PROBABLY GERMAN
ROYAL ARMOURIES, TOWER OF LONDON (IX.1010)

Length overall 109.2 cms, blade length 91.9 cms, height 0.878 kg.
Silvered cast brass hilt, steel blade.
Purchased at Sotheby's, 16 April 1957 (98).

Lit:    A.R. Dufty, *European swords and daggers in the Tower of London* (1974), p. 24,
          repr. pl. 49b.
          A.V.B. Norman and G.M. Wilson, *Treasures from the Tower of*
          *London* (1982), p. 52.

The hilt, of cast brass with traces of silvering, consists of a pommel, knuckle-guard and a short rear quillon supporting an oval side shell on each side. The knuckle-guard is linked to each shell by a small scroll-guard. A second scroll on each side links the centre of the knuckle-guard to the end of the other scroll on the same side. The pommel and shells bear, in low relief, the arms of the house of Stuart and of the City of London. The straight two-edged blade has two deep fullers and a prominent central full-length rib. The name ANDREA is stamped on each side of one fuller; the other has what appears to be traces of the name FERRARA.

The royal arms are those used by James II until the loss of his throne in 1688 and by Queen Anne from 1702 to 1714. Comparable hilts are known. One bears the monogram of Queen Anne, the others carry the regimental devices of the Royal Horse Guards, as used between 1661 and 1703, and of Schomberg's Horse, as used from 1693 to 1711.

Andrea dei Ferari was a sixteenth century bladesmith working at Belluno. His name, which appears on a large number of blades (many of a much later date) seems to have been widely forged.

**43** obv.

**43** rev.

# 42 *Smallsword, c. 1690*

ENGLISH
ROYAL ARMOURIES, TOWER OF LONDON  (IX.1372)

Length overall 99 cms, blade length 81.5 cms, weight 0.67 kg.
Gilt cast brass hilt and steel blade.
Acquired in 1974 from the Williams collection.

The hilt is of gilt cast brass. The pommel bears portraits of William and Mary, identified by the letters WR and MR. The guards consist of a knuckle-guard and single rear-quillon mounted on a quillon block supporting the arms of the hilt. Separate double shell-guard. The grip is bound with a pattern of three different wires, including a herringbone effect, and has a wire Turk's head at each end. The parallel-sided quillon block is typical of this kind of sword in the late seventeenth century and, like the pommel, bears portraits of William and Mary. The shell-guards are also decorated with relief portraits of William and Mary, flanked by putti blowing trumpets. These portraits of the king and queen are again identified by the letters WR and MR.

The smallsword first appeared in the 1640s and was in use for about a century and a half, with only gradual changes. The associated blade is double-edged and of flattened diamond section.

Source:          A.V.B. Norman, *The Rapier and Small Sword 1460-1820* (London, 1980).

# 43 *The Popularity of William, after the Peace of London, 1674*

MEDAL BY ANON
PHOTOGRAPH

Silver, 41 mm.
Lit:              *Medallic Illustrations,* 562-63, no. 226.
Description:     obv. to the left a man in armour, with sword held over his right shoulder, reaches out towards an orange held out by a hand from the clouds; to the right a Belgic lion, holding its bundle of arrows and with an arrow protruding from its back, does the same.
legend: HINC HOSTES DEBELLO [Henceforth the enemy is overcome];
on a tablet below: WIE SAGH SOO VER D'ORANGIE STER 1674 [Who ever saw the star of Orange so high ?].
rev. crowned shield with the arms of William, surrounded by a heraldic garter.
legend: GERMINI QUOD AVRIACO FIDAT LEO BELGICVS GALLO LAESVS. [let the Belgian lion, wounded by the cock, trust the Orange];
on the garter: HONI SOIT QVI MAL Y PENSE ['Evil be who evil thinks'].

The obverse uses the design of contemporary Dutch coins, which featured both the knight and the Belgic lion to symbolise the United Provinces, which were saved from France (here shown as a cock) by the house of Orange in the person of William. The sparing of the country was the consquence of the treaty of London, signed by England and Holland in 1674, by which France was forced to give up almost all the territory she had gained in the United Provinces. The treaty made William extremely popular; not only did he receive the positions of Stadtholder, Captain and Admiral-General of the provinces of Holland and Zeeland, but he was also given sizeable sums of money by some of the provinces. The type of reverse of this medal is discussed in no. 14.

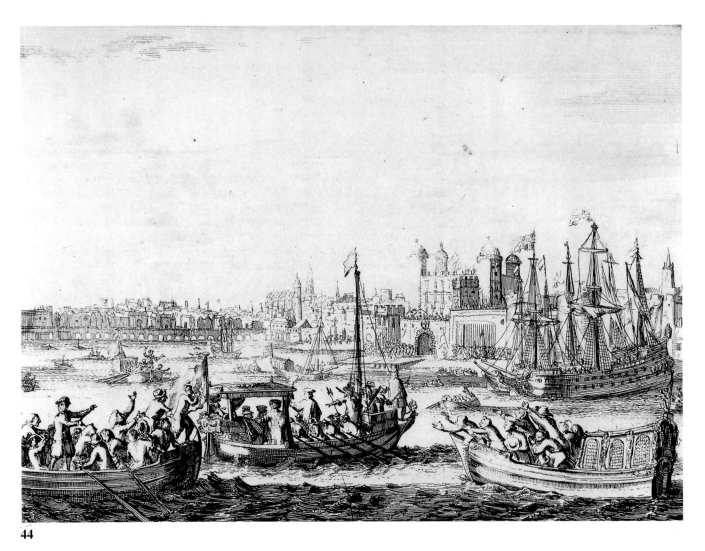

**44** *The seven bishops on their way to the Tower, 18 June 1688*

By P. Pickaert (1670-1732), published in Amsterdam by Adriaan Schoonebeek; text in Dutch and French
Ulster Museum, Belfast
Reproduction

In April 1688 James published his 'gracious Declaration to all his loving subjects for Liberty of Conscience' (the Declaration of Indulgence) and ordered it to be read in every church in the country.

Despite their support for James as the legitimate monarch the leaders of the Church of England, considering the order unlawful, refused to have the Declaration read. Seven of them, led by Archbishop Sancroft, petitioned him to withdraw the order. When they persisted in their disobedience he had them arrested and sent to the Tower. Two days later James's queen gave birth to an heir. The bishops were subsequently tried and acquitted, amid scenes of great rejoicing. Coming when it did, after a number of other moves against the exclusive power of the established church, the arrest of the bishops was a major blunder.

Though they felt obliged to disobey James on that occasion, Sancroft and four others later refused as a matter of conscience to swear allegiance to William and Mary and were deprived of their sees. The non-jurors, as they and the clergy who did likewise were called, survived for a time as a separate Anglican communion.

**45**                                                            **46**

## 45 *Mary of Modena with the Prince of Wales*

BY J. GOLE (1660-1737)
BRITISH MUSEUM, LONDON

Mezzotint 18 x 23 cms; Dutch text.

The Prince is shown in leading-strings, holding a windmill toy and playing with
a spaniel. The windmill, which appears again and again in the Williamite prints
of the period, is a reference to the popular belief that the child was really a
miller's son who had been smuggled into the queen's bedroom in a warming pan
and produced as an heir.

Source:       *Catalogue of Prints and Drawings in the British Museum,* Div. 1, vol. 1(1870)
              no. 1164.

## 46 *The cradle of the Pretender*

BY AN UNKNOWN ARTIST
BRITISH MUSEUM, LONDON

Mezzotint 18 x 23 cms; Dutch text.

The child is shown in his cradle with a windmill toy. On the table is an orange.
Behind Queen Mary of Modena is the Jesuit Father Petre, James II's confessor,
with his hand around her neck in a scandalously familiar manner - a reference to
the scurrilous gossip of the time.

Source:       *BM Catalogue,* vol. 1, no. 1116.

47

## 47 *L'Europe Allarmée pour le fils d'un meunier*
*(Europe alarmed over a miller's son)*

BY ROMEYN DE HOOGHE (1645-1708)
ATLAS VAN STOLK, ROTTERDAM

Print with contemporary colouring 62.2 x 51 cms; Dutch text.

This typically complicated broadside shows the infant Prince of Wales in his
cradle, with a windmill and other toys, surrounded by those conspiring to pass
him off as the true heir. Seated at the foot of the cradle are (1) 'the first mother'
and (2) Father Petre. To the right of it are (3) 'the second mother' (Mary of
Modena) and (4) a Catholic prelate with armour under his robes and treading on
a naked sword to indicate an appeal to force. The 'seller of red hats' (7) is the
pope, while in the wings (8) in armour with eagle crest, is the Emperor Leopold
reminding them of his power. Behind the second mother is (10) James II, 'dean
of the Jesuits', (12) the midwife begging him not to stop half-way, and a doctor
of the Sorbonne assuring them all of a dispensation for lying. The Portuguese
Jewess (13) - Queen Catharine of Braganza, widow of Charles II - laments that
she never thought of manufacturing an heir (Charles had no legitimate children).
In the background are Irish papists with torn flags preparing to depart, and
Quakers setting out for Pennsylvania. The owls and bats on top of the pillars are
symbols of darkness, as is the inscription above them. In the far distance are the

46

**48**

ships of William's invasion fleet, whose approach threatens to undo the conspiracy.

Another version of this print has text in both Dutch and French.

Source:     *BM Catalogue,* vol. 1, no. 1158.

## 48 *The Prince of Great Britain, James Francis Edward Stuart (1688-1766)*

BY JOHN SMITH, AFTER SIR GODFREY KNELLER (1646-1723)
NATIONAL PORTRAIT GALLERY, LONDON

Mezzotint, image 33.6 x 25.6 cms.

James Francis Edward Stuart, Prince of Wales, known as the Chevalier de St George and the 'Old Pretender,' was the only son of James II by his second wife, Mary of Modena. Born on 10 June 1688, his birth caused great despondency among Protestants; James's Protestant daughters by his first marriage, Mary and Anne, were therefore postponed in the line of succession. For Catholics the birth was an occasion of much jubilation and rejoicing; the infant would be raised as a Catholic and continue the catholicising of England started by his father. In Ireland there was much celebration, with a vice-regal procession from Kilmainham Hospital to Dublin castle, where high mass was said, firework displays were staged on the Liffey and the streets ran with wine.

The baby's birth was a month premature and immediately gave rise to rumours that he was not the king's son but a fraudulent changeling, smuggled into the lying-in chamber in a warming-pan, on instructions from the Jesuits. The fact that the child was a healthy boy took everybody by surprise; Mary Beatrice had had children but they had died in infancy and she had not given birth for six years. Events around the birth helped fan the flames of suspicion: almost all of those present in the room were Catholics and those who should have been there as witnesses, notably the Archbishop of Canterbury, the Earls of Clarendon and Rochester (staunch Anglicans and uncles of Mary and Anne) and the Dutch ambassador, were excluded. The most important absentee, however, was Anne herself, who had gone to Bath for a cure. (Williamite sources claimed that Anne's visit to Bath had been at the insistence of her father; James, however, maintained that he had wanted her to postpone her visit until after the baby was born). Her letter to Mary, written on her hasty return to London, reveals her dismay and surprise at the turn of events: 'My dear sister can't imagine the concern and vexation I have been in, that I should be so unfortunate to be out of town when the Queen was brought to bed, for I shall never now be satisfied whether the child be true or false. It may be it is our brother, but God only knows, for she never took care to satisfy the world, or give people any demonstration of it ... 'tis possible it may be her child; but where one believes it, a thousand do not' (van der Zee, p. 233).

From Holland, Mary bombarded Anne with enquiries about the birth and drew up a list of eighteen detailed questions for her to answer. Anne eventually replied, stating that there had been no screen in the room and that 'When she was in great pain ... the Queen desired the King to hide her face with his head and periwig, which he did, for she said she could not be brought to bed and have so many men look on her ... as soon as the child was born, the midwife cut the navel-string ... and then she gave it to mrs. Labaudie, who as she was going ... to carry it into the little bedchamber, the King stopped her, and said to the Privy Councillors, that they were witnesses there was a child born, and bid them follow it into the next room and see what it was, which they all did' (van der Zee, pp. 235-6). Anne was in fact unable to furnish her sister with any concrete proof of a plot to substitute a fraudulent child; her sole negative evidence was that she had never heard of anyone who had felt the child stir before birth and that she had not seen the queen engorged with milk afterwards.

Williamite propaganda usually portrayed the prince as the son of a miller, sometimes depicting him with a little windmill on his head; the Dutch engraver de Hooghe entitled one of his productions 'L' Europe allarmée pour le fils d'un meunier' (see no. 47).

The baby was baptised in St James's Chapel on 15 October 1688, with the Pope and the Queen-Dowager (Catharine of Braganza, Charles II's widow) as god-parents. A week later James summoned fifty-four lords temporal and spiritual to a council at Whitehall, to tell them plainly that the child was his. Forty witnesses gave evidence, including the Queen-Dowager, and the king himself supplied graphic details of the birth. The assembled body thereupon accepted the evidence and declared the child to be his legitimate son. (Behind James's highly unusual step of calling a council to judge the legitimacy of his heir lay the fact that William was preparing to invade England. By acting thus, James hoped to have the support of his subjects when he went to fight him). On 10 December following, his kingdom all but lost, James sent his wife and baby son to France. The next day he too fled, a confused and broken man. The young prince was raised in France at the exiled Jacobite court.

The question of the succession was settled in 1701 by the Act of Succession, which named the house of Hanover heir after Anne to the English throne. To William's fury, Louis XIV nevertheless proclaimed the chevalier James III of England and VIII of Scotland on James II's death on 6 September of that year. One of William's last acts of state, shortly before his death in 1702, was to give his assent to the Abjuration Bill, which excluded the Pretender Prince of Wales from the crown. A Stuart king never sat on the throne again. In 1715 the chevalier made an unsuccessful attempt to regain the crown; in 1745 his son Charles Edward (Bonnie Prince Charlie) also tried and failed.

The German painter Godfrey Kneller came to England in 1676 and achieved considerable success as a portraitist, being appointed principal painter to the king in 1688, jointly with John Riley. In 1692 he was given a knighthood. His portrait (now lost) of the young prince was painted on 21 June 1688, when the baby was only eleven days old. Although a supporter of the Revolution, Kneller was convinced that the child was legitimate. His opinion, in fractured English, is an

**49**

interesting recollection of the event: 'Wet de devil de Prince of Wales te son of a brickbat woman, begot it is a ly. I am not of his party, nor shall not be for him, I am satisfet wit wat ye parliament has done, but I must tell you wat I am sure of, and in what I cannot be mistaken. His fader and moder have sate to me about 36 times a piece, and I know every line and bit in their faces. Begot I could paint King James just now by memory. I sayh this child is so like both, yt there is not a feature in his face, but wat belongs either to his fader or his moder; this I'm sure of, and be got, I cannot be mistaken. Nay, ye nails of his fingers are his moders ye Queen yt was' (Killanin, p. 18).

Sources:    *DNB;* Lord Killanin, *Sir Godrey Kneller and his times* (London, 1948);
            H. and B. van der Zee, *William and Mary* (London, 1973).

## 49 *'The Portsmouth Captains', 1688*

BY ROBERT WHITE (1645-1703)
NATIONAL ARMY MUSEUM, LONDON

Engraving 38 x 28 cms.
Exh:    *1688 Glorious Revolution?* National Army Museum 1988(81).

In September 1688 James II ordered five Irish recruits to be added to each company of the regiment of which his son the Duke of Berwick was colonel. When the lieutenant-colonel, John Beaumont, and five of his captains refused to receive the recruits, Berwick was sent down to Portsmouth (where the regiment was stationed) to enforce the order. When the officers asked to resign their commissions rather than obey, they were arrested, court-martialled and ca-shiered.

The background to this incident was the catholicisation of the Irish army by Tyrconnell, who had got rid of most of its Protestant officers and men. Many of James's English officers feared that the king would try to fill the English army with Irish Catholics, and that this was only the start of the process. If James had any such intention he gave it up when he saw the strength of feeling against it within the army.

When William of Orange came to the throne Beaumont was reinstated as colonel of his old regiment and served with it in Ireland, where he fought at the battle of the Boyne.

## 50 *William and Mary invited to England, 1688*

MEDAL BY ANON
HUNTERIAN MUSEUM, GLASGOW

Silver, 62 mm.
Lit:         *Medallic Illustrations*, 634-35, no. 58.
Description:  obv. conjoined busts of William and Mary, both draped, he over armour.
                legend: (above) ATAVUM PRO LIBERTATE FIDEQUE [for the liberty and faith of our ancestors]; (across, below): M. WILH. HENR. ET MARIA D. G. AUR. PRINC. ETC. REFORMATIONIS VINDICES [William Henry and Mary, by grace of God Prince and Princess of Orange etc., maintainers of the Reformation].
              rev. draped female standing facing, holding up a scroll with her right hand and resting her left on a cap of liberty, which sits on an open book on an altar; at her feet lie a papal cap, with a snake crawling out of it, a cross of Lorraine, a monstrance and other liturgical items; at the top a rayed eye looks down.
                legend: IAM MIHI ROMA MINAX. FISTULA DULCE CANIT [now the flute of overbearing Rome sounds sweet to me]; in exergue: REFORMATIO ANGLIAE MDCLXXXVIII [the reformation of England, 1688]; (on the scroll): LITTERAE FAGEL [the letters of Fagel]; (on the altar): SS FIDES [the most holy faith].

**50** obv.

**50** rev.

The obverse portraits on this medal are small in relation to the flan. The medallist also seems to have aimed for serene and open expressions, as befits religious saviours. The reverse may be interpreted as showing Religion, under the eye of Providence, trampling the snake of Discord which is emerging from the papal tiara. The cross of Lorraine is a form particularly associated with France. All the symbols of the Catholic faith are cast down. The open book is frequently used as indicating the Protestant attitude to the Bible. Fagel acted as one of William's moral mentors and published a series of influential works. The sweet-sounding flute may perhaps relate to what was seen as the siren-song of James's Declaration of Liberty of Conscience.

The invitation alluded to here is that issued at the end of June 1688 by seven leading members of the aristocracy and Church of England, who urged William to invade and rescue lost liberties and religion.

## 51a *Landing of William III at Torbay, 1688*

MEDAL BY G. BOWER (FL. 1650-90)
ULSTER MUSEUM, BELFAST; NATIONAL MUSEUM OF IRELAND, DUBLIN

Silver, 48 mm.
Lit:         *Medallic Illustrations*, 639, no. 64.
Description:  obv. bust of William in armour, wearing cravat and sash.
                legend: GVILMVS. III. D. G. PRIN. AVR. HOL. ET. WES. GVB [William III, by grace of God prince of Orange, Governor of Holland and West Friesland (?)]; on the truncation of the arm: 1688.
              rev. in the right foreground a Roman warrior is raising the collapsed figure of Justice, who has her attributes of blindfold, sword and scales lying at her feet. To the left a figure on a prancing horse, representing William, points the way with his sword to some horsemen. The background is filled with soldiers drawn up in ranks, the beach, the sea and a large number of ships.
                legend: .TERRAS.ASTRAEA.REUSIT. [? Justice revisits the earth].

At this stage William had no British titles. These medals are casts from a much rarer struck prototype. As a cast this is the commonest of the several medals issued to mark the landing at Torbay. Struck examples have an edge inscription: NON.RAPIT.IMPERIUM.UIS.TUA.SED.RECIPIT [you did not seize power by force but received it], making the point, to those who might have been alarmed by a large army and fleet from a recently hostile foreign power, that William had come by invitation.

**51a** obv.

**51a** rev.

**51b** obv.

**51b** rev.

## 51b *Landing of William III in England, 1688*

MEDAL BY R. ARONDEAUX (FL. 1680-1710)
ULSTER MUSEUM, BELFAST

Silver, 49 mm.

Lit:       *Medallic Illustrations*, 639-40, no. 65.

Description:  obv.  William III in Roman armour, draped and wearing laurel wreath, holding sword upright in his right hand, tramples upon a snake representing discord, grasps the hand of a female wearing three crowns, to represent England, Scotland and Ireland. A burning tripod altar is between them. An orange tree stands behind the female, with roses and thistles entwined about the stem; a shield with the royal arms hangs from the tree. A large moon is in the background, symbolising Britain's emergence from a period of darkness, contrasted with the rising sun behind William. Behind William can also be seen figures representing Father Petre and James II, the former carrying an infant (the Prince of Wales) holding a toy windmill. legend: DEO VIN DICE   IUSTITIA COMITE [God our protector, Justice our companion ?].

              rev.  soldiers disembarking from several small boats, some with sails as well as oars; cavalry advancing up the beach, led by a figure on a prancing horse. Behind is a fortified harbour with a tower from which flies a flag. Behind this again is a breakwater, over which can be seen the sails of a large number of ships. legend: CONTRA INFANTEM PERDITIONIS [Against the child of perdition]; in the exergue: EXPEDITIO NAUALIS PRO LIBERTATE ANGLIAE MDCLXXXVIII [Naval expedition for the liberty of England, 1688].

The place shown on the reverse is definitely not Torbay and must be intended to represent the idea of invasion rather than being an actual attempt to depict an event. The fact that the infant prince is holding a windmill alludes to the Williamite belief that he was in fact the illegitimate son of a miller.

## 52 *Zee Tocht Uyt Hellevoetsluys Door S.K.H. Wilhem Henrik.*
### *(William's departure from Hellevoetsluys)*

BY ROMEYN DE HOOGHE (1645-1708)
ATLAS VAN STOLK, ROTTERDAM

Print with contemporary colouring 51.6 x 61.8 cms; Dutch text.

Having accepted the invitation to go to England and having got the support of the Dutch authorities, William and his advisers prepared a formidable army and a large fleet to transport it. By the end of October 1688 some 250 cargo ships and three squadrons of warships were waiting at Hellevoetsluis for a favourable wind. Aboard were 11,000 troops and 3,000 horses, large supplies of money to buy provisions in England, dies for the minting of coins and a printing press to produce proclamations and propaganda.

    The fleet sailed on 11 November but almost immediately ran into a westerly gale which forced it back to port. Hundreds of horses which had been drowned had to be replaced before the final departure on 11 November. Believing that William would scarcely be so foolish as to set out so late in the year, James II behaved complacently until the last moment. Then luck (or as contemporaries thought, Providence) was on William's side: a favourable easterly wind took the invasion fleet safely across and kept the English ships in harbour.

52

**53** *William's invasion, his departure from Holland, arrival in England and entry into London, in eight scenes*

BY ROMEYN DE HOOGHE (1645-1708)
ATLAS VAN STOLK, ROTTERDAM

Print with contemporary colouring 53.5 x 61.5 cms; text in English and Dutch.

This is a superb example of the work of de Hooghe as William's propagandist. Both the scenes selected and the captions attached to them are designed to present the Prince of Orange as the welcome saviour of England's religion and liberties. In fact, despite the assertion (VII) that on arrival he was 'complimented by the most eminent Lords etc.,' William was received very cautiously; nor was his entry into London the grand occasion depicted, for he preferred to enter without public ceremony.

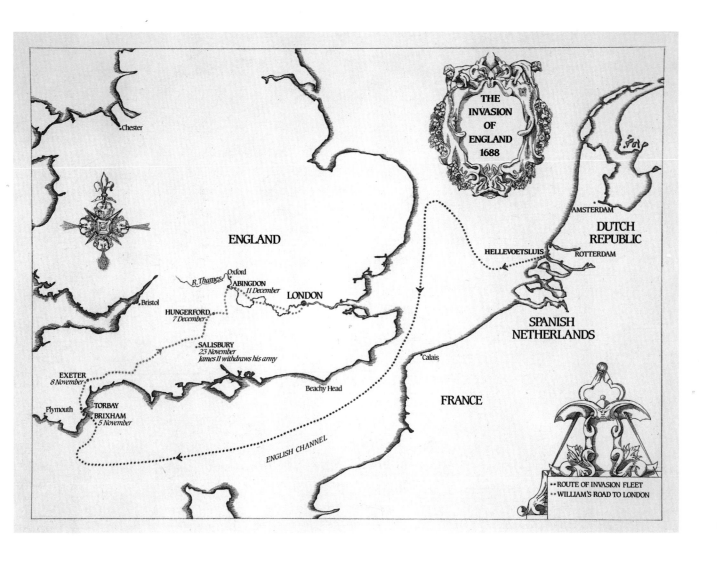

THE
INVASION
OF
ENGLAND
1688

Chester

ENGLAND

AMSTERDAM

DUTCH
REPUBLIC

HELLEVOETSLUIS    ROTTERDAM

R. Thames    Oxford
**ABINGDON**
*11 December*    **LONDON**

**HUNGERFORD**
*7 December*

Bristol

SPANISH
NETHERLANDS

**SALISBURY**
*23 November*
*James II withdraws his army*

Calais

**EXETER**
*8 November*

Beachy Head

FRANCE

Plymouth    **TORBAY**
**BRIXHAM**
*5 November*

ENGLISH CHANNEL

•• ROUTE OF INVASION FLEET
•• WILLIAM'S ROAD TO LONDON

**53**

**54** *The declaration of His Highness William Henry ...*
*Prince of Orange, etc. of the reasons inducing him, to appear in*
*armes in the kingdome of England, for preserving of the Protestant*
*religion... Printed at The Hague by Arnout Lhers... 1688*

THE QUEEN'S UNIVERSITY, BELFAST

folio:  4 pp.
Lit:  D. Wing, *Short-Catalogue of Books Printed in England, Scotland, Ireland, Wales*
*and British America ... 1641-1700,* 2nd ed., 3 vols., New York 1972-1988, W2328.

This pamphlet contains the original declaration of 10 October 1688 with the
additional declaration of 24 October 1688. Official and unofficial versions of the
declarations were published in 1688 in Dutch, English and French and in a
variety of formats.

    The English printer of the declaration, who took a considerable risk, was
later rewarded handsomely by William.

**55** *Some Reflections upon his Highness*
*the Prince of Oranges Declaration. London, printed ...*
*MDCLXXXVIII [1688]*

THE QUEEN'S UNIVERSITY, BELFAST

quarto:  12 pp.
Lit:  Wing, *Short-Catalogue,* S4589.

This pamphlet gives a Jacobite view of the Glorious Revolution.

**56**

## 56 *Queen Anne (1665-1714)*

BY JOHN SIMON, AFTER EDMUND LILLY (FL. 1702-16)
NATIONAL GALLERY OF IRELAND, DUBLIN

Mezzotint 39.3 x 38.8 cms (plate 34 x 25.5), published 1702.

Lit:     Adrian Le Harivel, ed., *National Gallery of Ireland Illustrated Summary Catalogue of Prints and Sculptures* (Dublin, 1988), p. 353, repr.

Anne, second daughter of James II and his first wife Anne Hyde, was born on 6 February 1665 and was raised at Richmond with her sister Mary. A sickly child, she was afflicted with eye trouble from infancy and was reserved and taciturn by nature - the exact opposite of Mary.  She was also markedly stubborn in temperament; according to the Duchess of Marlborough  (her best friend for many years), her 'positive sticking to any point which she had once affirm'd, or desir'd to be believ'd, was a peculiarity of Temper, which had, from Her Infancy, been observ'd in Her' (Gregg, p. 7). Nevertheless, despite their varying natures, the sisters remained close as they were growing up; Mary's removal to Holland in 1677 caused considerable sadness to both of them. However, they corresponded regularly and in 1678 Anne and her step-mother the Duchess of York (Mary of Modena) paid Mary a visit which went exceedingly well. William took great trouble to please his guests and James was delighted that his favourite daughter was happy in her marriage. In 1679 and 1681 Anne was permitted to visit her father in exile in the Spanish Netherlands and in Edinburgh. James seems to have enjoyed having her with him and appears to have been a fond and indulgent parent.

Shortly after Anne's marriage to the Prince of Denmark on 28 July 1683 the couple moved into the Cockpit, a suite of apartments in Whitehall which Charles II gave to Anne as her town house. The couple's friends, known as 'the Cockpit circle', included John and Sarah Churchill (the future Duke and Duchess of Marlborough), Colonel John Berkeley and his wife Barbara Villiers (whose sister Elizabeth was William III's mistress), Sir Benjamin Bathurst and his wife, the Duke of Grafton and the Marquis of Ossory. Anne was delivered of her first child, a stillborn daughter, on 12 May 1684. This was the beginning of a long line of tragedies in the Denmarks' efforts to have children. Between 1684 and 1700 Anne conceived seventeen times (including twins) but had numerous miscarriages and still births; her longest surviving child, the Duke of Gloucester, died in 1700 aged eleven. Her repeated failure to have healthy children was to blight her life, both physically and emotionally.

James II's accession in 1685 altered considerably Anne's social and political position; she was now heiress presumptive after Mary (who was still childless after eight years of marriage) and was the highest ranking Protestant member of the royal family living in England. As such, she became the focus of much Protestant attention. Hitherto not at all interested in national affairs, she now became much more politically aware and zealous in her attachment to the Anglican church. As James strove to secure civil liberties for his co-religionists during late 1685, so Anne daily attended divine service in the Chapel Royal at Whitehall. James hoped Anne would become a convert, as her mother had done years before, and in 1685 published papers of religious devotion written by Charles II and Anne Hyde (Anne's mother, the first Duchess of York), which he presented to Anne. This, however, was the extent of his persuasion at that time. Anne remained unmoved after reading her mother's papers and commented drily in a letter to Mary: 'Nobody has yet said anything to me about religion. The K[ing] only gave me those papers to read which were writ by the late King, and my mother, concerning which I am of your opinion: and indeed, they will do them no service, if they have no greater influence on other people than they have had on us; and I trust in God they will not' (Brown, p. 16).

The Catholic faction around James (Scots, Irish and Jesuit advisers) also entertained hopes of converting Anne and tried to frighten her by putting about a rumour that James planned to legitimise his two Catholic sons by Arabella Churchill, the Duke of Berwick and Henry Fitzjames. In the autumn of 1686 Tyrconnell, Sarah Churchill's brother-in-law, also tried by suggesting that if Anne became a convert she might procure the succession. By early 1687, however, those who had thought Anne amenable to persuasion were realising that this was not the case; in her choice of religion she was as intractable as her father.

In March 1687 Anne's relationship with her father underwent a change, when he forbade her to pay Mary a visit. He had initially given permission for Prince George to visit Denmark and Anne to go to Holland but, fearing that a meeting between Mary and Anne would unite the sisters more strongly than ever in their adherence to Protestantism, forbade them to meet. Anne was outraged at this attack on her liberty and believed Catholic politicians to be behind it. In a letter to Mary, she voiced her fears for the future of the country: 'Things are come to that pass now, that, if they go on much longer, I believe in a little while no Protestant will be able to live here. The K[ing] has never said a word to me about religion since the time I told you of; but I expect it every minute, and am resolved to undergo anything rather than change my religion: nay, if it should come to such extremities, I will choose to live on alms rather than change' (Brown, p. 25).

James's refusal to permit the visit had important consequences. Anne now made no attempt to conceal her growing hatred for her step-mother Mary Beatrice and her Catholic evangelism, and began to assume a higher profile as a Protestant defender, both at court and within the Anglican church. Most importantly, she entered into a correspondence with William and Mary, which she herself described as treasonous in its denunciation of the king and queen. She made it plain to William, via Marlborough, that she would stand by the Protestant cause whatever happened. Although it is not clear how early she knew of William's projected invasion, she was prepared for it whenever it came.

News of Mary Beatrice's pregnancy in November 1687 was an enormous blow to Anne, for both personal and political reasons. During 1687 she had suffered a series of devastating losses: on 21 January she had had a miscarriage, in February her two surviving daughters died of smallpox and on 22 October she miscarried a stillborn son. The fact that her stepmother was now pregnant again, when many thought her incapable of having more children, filled her with rage and envy. It also fired national resentment within the country at large, which had banked on the accession of James's Protestant daughters. Inflamed by fears for her religion and the thought of a Catholic tyranny under a Stuart male line (and perhaps partly blinded by the trauma of her personal losses), Anne now became the chief perpetrator (and perhaps the originator) of the rumour that Mary Beatrice's pregnancy was false.

Anne's letters to Mary during March 1688 are full of innuendo. 'I must tell you I can't help thinking Mansell's [Anne and Mary's code name for their father] wife's great belly is a little suspicious. It is true indeed she is very big, but she looks better than ever she did, which is not usual ... Her being so positive it will be a son ... give some cause to fear there may be foul play intended' (Brown, p. 34). Writing a week later, she claimed she thought the forthcoming child *would* be a boy 'there being so much reason to believe it is a false belly. For, methinks, if it were not, there having been so many stories and jests about it, she should, to convince the world, make either me or some of my friends feel her belly; but quite contrary, whenever one talks of her being with child, she looks as if she were afraid one should touch her. And whenever I happen to be in the room as she has been undressing, she has always gone into the next room to put on her smock. These things give me so much just cause for suspicion that I believe when she is brought to bed, nobody will be convinced it is her child, except it prove a daughter. For my part, I declare I shall not, except I see the child and she parted' (Brown, p. 35). Anne assured William Lloyd, Bishop of Worcester, that Mary Beatrice had allowed her to feel her abdomen during her previous pregnancies. However, later in the year, when questioned by her uncle the Earl of Clarendon, the princess stated that her stepmother never allowed her such liberties. To compound the confusion, James II's *Memoirs* claimed that Anne *had* felt the baby move and had declined to attend the council held in October 1688 to judge the legitimacy of the new heir, as this would have entailed swearing she had felt the child stir (many of the women present at the council had seen her do it). To swear to such effect would have shown up her own questionable role in the whole affair.

Speculation also surrounds Anne's absence at the child's birth on 10 June. On 16 April 1688 she suffered yet another miscarriage and, failing to recover with her usual ease, left London at the end of April for a cure at Bath. Contrary to rumours that the king had ordered her to go, she went voluntarily, apparently glad of the excuse to be far from London. (Tunbridge Wells, her favourite spa, was much closer to the capital). It seems likely that Anne had already decided in her own mind that the baby, if a boy, would be a fraud - and absence from the event would justify her position. On her return to London on 18 June she wrote to Mary, 'For my part, except they do give very plain demonstrations, *which is almost impossible now,* I shall ever be of the number of unbelievers' (Gregg, p. 58). With the blind obstinacy that was part of her nature, she was determined to regard her half-brother as an impostor, and clung to the belief all her life. (The child of course was genuine: rather than a Catholic plot to foist a fraudulent changeling on the nation, the plot was Protestant-inspired, to discredit the birth. A number of Protestants who should have been at the birth chose to be out of town; those who could not avoid being there took care to stand where they could see nothing, rather than witness an event which would decide the fate of the kingdom. The majority of eye-witnesses were therefore Catholics).

At the end of June, Anne and her advisers learnt of the general details of the invitation to William. Although Sarah Churchill claimed in her *Conduct* that her actions and Anne's were spontaneous and unpremeditated, the Churchills and the princess in fact planned at least three months before he invaded England to join William. When rumours began to spread in the middle of September about the invasion, Anne refused to be drawn or comment on the matter and declined to show public support for her father once the council had authenticated the prince's birth.

After the Prince of Denmark and Churchill had defected to the Orange side on 24 November, James on his way back to London from Salisbury ordered that Sarah be placed under house arrest. Hearing of the imminent return of her father, Anne (still at the Cockpit) panicked, sent for Sarah and declared 'that rather than see her father, she would jump out a window' (Gregg, p. 65). Early in the morning of 26 November Anne and Sarah escaped in disguise from Whitehall, fled to the home of Bishop Compton and eventually made their way to Castle Ashby, the home of Compton's nephew the Earl of Northampton. James was devastated at Anne's desertion; broken in spirit at her flight he appeared, according to a court observer, to have lost his faculties.

After the Revolution the latent hostility between William and Anne quickly rose to the surface. William mistrusted the Churchills and disapproved of Anne's friendship with Sarah. He also resented Anne's better hereditary claim to the throne. Anne's consent to the succession settlement was begrudged; she was initially opposed to William's being king for life and had hoped to follow Mary in the succession. To this end she tried to rally the Tories behind her, and only reluctantly agreed to give up her rights to William after a struggle. Her political stature increased after the birth of the Duke of Gloucester (the longed-for Protestant heir) on 27 July 1689 but tensions remained within the royal family. By nature Anne and Mary were incompatible; as Sarah Churchill (now the Countess of Marlborough) commented, 'It was indeed impossible that they should be very agreeable companions to each other because Queen Mary grew weary of anybody who would not talk a great deal; and the Princess was so silent that she rarely spoke more than was necessary to answer a question' (Gregg, p. 75). By 1692 the sisters were deeply estranged, partly because of Anne's clinging to Sarah against William and Mary's wishes. Anne at this time was desperately looking forward to a 'SunShine day' when she would ascend the throne and referred to William as 'that Monster' and 'that Dutch abortive.'

After Mary's death in 1694 relations between William and Anne improved. William realized he needed to repair the rift between his sister-in-law and himself, and invited Anne to keep court at St James's 'as if she were a crowned head.' Though the reconciliation was at best superficial, it lasted for the remainder of the king's life, despite various setbacks. (Anne was anxious to gain control of James's Irish estates, which he had settled upon his children when Duke of York but which William had granted to Elizabeth Villiers. William ignored Anne's wishes and she never succeeded in getting control of her father's private property).

Anne succeeded to the throne on 8 March 1702 and made her first speech to parliament three days later, in which she stressed her nationalism ('I know my own heart to be entirely English', *DNB*) and her adherence to William's foreign policy. From the beginning of her reign she was determined not to allow herself to be bullied by any party or politician, despite her sex; to the end of her life she remained her own woman. Hard-working and with an excellent memory, she aimed at political moderation and never attempted to challenge the supremacy of parliament. She saw her role as being the mother of her people. With that in mind, she chose as her coronation text a passage from Isiah: 'Kings shall be thy nursing Fathers, and Queens thy nursing Mothers', an ironic quotation considering her many tragic pregnancies, but one which contained the dominant theme of her reign - her desire to 'make my Country and my freinds easy' (Gregg, p. 402). On her death on 1 August 1714 she was succeeded by George I, of the house of Hanover.

The English portrait painter Edmund Lilly received considerable patronage during Anne's reign. This portrait of the queen was copied in enamel by Charles Boit and the engraving produced from that. A full-length of the queen, by Lilly, dated 1703, is at Blenheim, with versions elsewhere. Anne also sat to Kneller, Dahl, Lely, Riley, Wissing and Murray. After her coronation, her state portraits for official dispersion appear to have been produced mainly by Kneller's studio.

Sources:   *DNB*; D. Piper, *Catalogue of Seventeenth Century Portraits in the National Portrait Gallery* (Cambridge, 1963); B.C. Brown, ed., *The Letters of Queen Anne* (London, 1968); H. and B. van der Zee, *William and Mary* (London, 1973); E. Gregg, *Queen Anne* (London, 1980).

57

## 57 *George, Prince of Denmark (1653-1708)*

BY PIETER SCHENK, AFTER SIR GODFREY KNELLER (1646-1723)
NATIONAL GALLERY OF IRELAND, DUBLIN

Mezzotint 35.6 x 27 cms (plate 33.5 x 25.4), published 1705.
Lit:    Adrian Le Harivel, ed., *National Gallery of Ireland Illustrated Summary Catalogue of Prints and Sculptures* (Dublin, 1988), p. 319, repr.

George, Prince of Denmark, younger brother of the Danish king Christian V, was born on 23 April 1653. His early years were spent in naval and military service and his chief interests were soldiering and horses. Negotiations for his marriage to Anne began early in 1683 and were carried out in secret, to avoid interference from the Prince of Orange, who had suggested Prince George of Hanover as a suitable match for Anne. (William's opposition to the union was twofold: Denmark at the time was an ally of France and Louis XIV, in sponsoring the match, wanted to see England and Denmark allied against the Dutch. Furthermore, as George was a king's son, he would take precedence over William at the English court). The wedding took place on 28 July 1683. According to the diarist John Evelyn, the groom 'had the Danish Countenance, blound; a young gentleman of few words, spake French but ill, seemed somewhat heavy; but reported Valient' (Gregg, p. 35).

The prince was good-natured, mild-tempered and honest but somewhat dull and plodding, qualities which drew forth from Charles II his famous quip, 'I have tried him drunk and I have tried him sober and there is nothing in him' (Gregg). Nevertheless, Anne considered him the best of husbands; they were devoted to each other and he stayed faithful to her all his life. As the match was French-inspired, it was generally believed that he would become a convert to Catholicism. However, he had been raised a strict Lutheran and remained so after his marriage, although paying occasional conformity to the Anglican church. Within their marriage Anne remained the dominant partner; the prince supported her in her opposition to her father and acquiesced in her actions prior to the Revolution.

On 18 November 1688 the prince accompanied his father-in-law to Salisbury to join the army (he had refused a formal command but had offered to accompany the king as an uncommissioned volunteer). At the same time Anne wrote to William, sending him good wishes for his success and promising that Prince George would join him soon. On the evening of 24 November, the prince and the Duke of Ormonde defected to the Orangist camp, a desertion made light of by James, who said of his son-in-law's departure, 'A good trooper would have been a greater loss' (van der Zee, p. 257). For his loyalty to William, the prince was given a peerage and British citizenship.

William, however, had little time for his brother-in-law and treated him with coldness. Although Prince George accompanied the king to Ireland (he wished to join the campaign and paid his own expenses), William did not want him and only took him along as a gesture to please Anne - and possibly to ensure her loyalty. William refused to consult him in military matters and gave him no recognition for his services at the Boyne and at Limerick. According to Sarah Marlborough, 'the King never took more notice of him that if he had been a page of the back stairs nor was he ever once named in any gazette ...' (Hamilton, p. 275). After such rude treatment it was impossible for him to serve under William again. Nevertheless, both he and Anne were anxious to find an arena where he could win military glory, so he decided to join the navy as a volunteer. When he told William of his plans before the king left for the Continent in January 1691, William made no comment and the prince accordingly assumed he agreed to the idea. However, William had instructed the queen that the prince was not to be allowed to serve. In May 1691 the prince (acting on his own initiative) made plans to sail on the *St Andrew* and sent his luggage on board. Mary was forced to forbid him to go (persuasion was of no avail) and the royal sisters had a bitter quarrel as a result. By the summer of that year the relationship between Anne and Mary was a mere formality, with little affection on either side. Relations between the king and the Prince and Princess of Denmark remained strained until after Mary's death in 1694, when a superficial 'truce' took place which endured until William's death.

After Anne's accession to the throne in 1702 the prince received many of the honours she felt he was due. In April of that year he was appointed generalissimo of her forces, and in May and June was created lord high admiral, lord warden of the Cinque ports and captain-general of the London Artillery Company. During the winter of 1707 his health began to suffer (he had severe asthma) and there was much Whig criticism of the naval administration of which he was titular head; by October of the following year there were calls for his resignation. That this would have taken place remains uncertain, for he died on 28 October 1708.

The portrait is after a three-quarter length oil by Kneller, painted c. 1690. The prince also sat to Riley, Dahl and Wissing.

Sources:  *DNB;* B. C. Brown, ed., *The Letters of Queen Anne* (London, 1968); E. Hamilton, *William's Mary* (London, 1972); H. and B. van der Zee, *William and Mary* (London, 1973); E. Gregg, *Queen Anne* (London, 1980).

**58**                                                    **59**

## 58 *Plug bayonet, 1687*

ENGLISH
ROYAL ARMOURIES, TOWER OF LONDON (X.236)

Length overall 43.8 cms, blade length 29 cms, weight O.34 kg.
Brass quillons and pommel, wooden grip, steel blade.
Inscr:  'GOD SAVE: IAMES: THE 2' and 'ANNO:DOMINI:1687' on blade.
        Presented by Mr. F.H. Cripps-Day in l942.
Exh:    *Parliament and the Glorious Revolution, l688-1988,*  Banqueting House, London
        l988.

The bayonet has a polished wooden grip with a long brass pommel decorated
with baluster mouldings and a tang-button. The grip has two pairs of finely cut
lines around it, one next to the pommel, the other next to the swelling of the grip.
The quillons are recurved with bulbous terminals. The single-edged blade has a
false rear-edge.

Highly decorated plug bayonets like this were often carried by infantry
officers. Patriotic inscriptions on weapons appear to have been popular at this
period; examples are known which carry inscriptions to William and Mary
and Anne.

## 59 *Plug bayonet, late seventeenth century*

BRITISH
ROYAL ARMOURIES, TOWER OF LONDON (X.71)

Length overall 45.5 cms, blade length 30.3 cms, weight 0.28 kg.
Steel and brass with a wooden grip.

Wooden grip with a brass pommel and spherical tang button. The grip is
swollen towards the blade and has a brass ferrule. The short cast-brass quillons
have bulbous terminals. Straight single-edged blade stamped with a mark. The
back of the blade is sharpened for 13 cms from the point.

The plug bayonet was designed to be simply stuck (plugged) into the muzzle
of a musket. Whilst it afforded the musketeer a greater degree of self-protection
than hitherto, and led to the demise of the pike as an infantry weapon, it had the
disadvantage of rendering the musket temporarily unusable as a gun.

60 obv.

60 rev.

61 obv.

61 rev.

## 60 *The reception by Louis XIV of James II*

MEDAL BY J. SMELTZING (FL. 1685, D. 1695)
HUNTERIAN MUSEUM, GLASGOW

Silver, 59 mm.

Lit:             *Medallic Illustrations*, 654-55, no. 13.

Description:   obv.   draped and laureate bust of James II, a small rose underneath.
                      legend:  * IACOBVS II D. G. BRITANNIARUM IMPERATOR* [James II, by
                      grace of God ruler of Britain].
               rev.   a rayed sun partially hidden by the moon, below it a cloud and a shore,  with
                      two distant ships on the sea.
                      legend:  ORBATA LUCE LUCIDUM OBSCURAT [deprived of light
                      she obscures the bright]; in exergue:  LUD:XIV GALL:REX ADMITTIT
                      IAC:II BRIT:REGEM FUG:VII IAN:MDCLXXXIX. [Louis XIV, king
                      of France, allows in James II, the fleeing king of Britain, 7 January 1689].

This is a somewhat ambiguous medal by Smeltzing, who went to France in 1670
and worked for a time at the mint, before returning to Leyden. James is laureate,
a sign of military victory, and there appears to be no hint of caricature in the
portrait. This is somewhat at odds with the slightly cryptic reverse. Louis XIV
was, of course, the sun and one presumes that James is represented by the moon.
An eclipse seems to be taking place, with the lesser body obscuring the brighter
and casting the world into darkness.

## 61 *Coronation of William and Mary, 1689*

MEDAL BY J. ROETTIER
ULSTER MUSEUM, BELFAST

Gold and silver, 34 mm.

Lit:             *Medallic Illustrations*, 662-3.
                 H. Wollaston, *British Official Medals for Coronations and Jublilees*
                 (London, 1978).

Description:   obv.   conjoined busts of William and Mary, both draped.
                      legend: GVLIELMVS. ET. MARIA. REX ET. REGINA. [William and
                      Mary, king and queen].
               rev.   Jupiter, in the upper right portion of the flan, throwing a thunderbolt from
                      a cloud, at a figure representing Phaeton, who is falling from a two-horse
                      chariot in the bottom left, surrounded by solar rays.
                      legend, above NE TOTVS ABSVMATVR. [that everything may not be
                      ruined]; in exergue INAVGVRAT. II. AP. 1689 [crowned 2 April 1689].

This is the official coronation medal and the only one of the series which has
conjoined busts, emphasising the joint sovereignty of the two monarchs.  Orders
were given that 515 were to be struck in gold and 1,200 in silver, together with
an unknown quantity in lead.  The reverse is extremely explicit, to anyone with
knowledge of the myth of Phaeton.  The unfortunate son of  Helios, on
discovering his parentage, asked his father if he could guide the chariot of the
sun for the day, but was too weak to manage the immortal horses, which bolted.
The world was in danger of being burnt up until Jupiter felled him with a
thunderbolt.  Given Louis XIV's association with the sun, the message is clear.

The medallist was in fact a supporter of James, and it was suggested later
that the allegory was double-edged, in that William's overweening pride was
being attacked.

There is also significance in the fact that none of the countries over which
the new monarchs  would rule are mentioned.  Archbishop Sancroft refused to
conduct the coronation, since he regarded himself as still being under oath of
allegiance to James. William's position in particular was not derived from any
right of birth, but from other claims which required the dignity of anointment
for support.

J. Roettier was chief engraver at the mint, but his sons James and Norbert
claimed to have produced the dies without their father, who had signed his medal
for James's coronation, whereas this piece is without signature.

**62** obv.

**62** rev.

## 62 *Coronation of William and Mary, 1689*

MEDAL BY G. BOWER (FL. 1650-90)
ULSTER MUSEUM, BELFAST

Silver, 53 mm.

Lit:         *Medallic Illustrations*, 668, no. 38.

Description:   obv. conjoined busts of William and Mary, he in armour wearing laurel wreath, both draped

legend:GVIELMVS.ET.MARIA.DG.MAG.BRI.FR.ET.HIB.REX.ET.REĠINA [William and Mary, by grace of God, king and queen of Great Britain, France and Ireland].

           rev. William and Mary sit facing under a canopy, each holding a sceptre and orb. Two bishops support a large crown over them. They are sitting on a platform raised on three steps with drapes either side.

legend: *IDOLOLATRIA. SERVITVTE. PROFLIGATIS. RELIGIONE. LEGIB. LIBERTAT. RESTITVTIS [idolatry and slavery cast down, religion, laws and liberty restored]; in exergue 1689.

This example is a cast from a struck medal, which is much rarer. It has been pierced for wear. It is possible that the omission of Scotland from the list of titles is deliberate, as it was slightly slower to ratify the new monarchs. There is nothing oblique about the reverse legend, and it makes a clear statement of the anti-Jacobite case without recourse to mythology. The market aimed at was Britain, and as the piece must have been a commercial venture rather than officially sanctioned, it indicates that this was expected to be a commercially successful design.

## 63 *Krooning Van Willem De III En Maria, Tot Konig En Koningin Van Engeland, Enz In Westmunsters Abdy Den 11/21 April 1689*

BY ROMEYN DE HOOGHE (1645-1708)
ATLAS VAN STOLK, ROTTERDAM

Print with contemporary colouring 51.4 x 61.2 cms; Dutch text.

James II's flight to France (which William facilitated at the second attempt, after the first had failed) created a problem for those who did not wish to have a change of ruler and an opportunity for those who did. When William rejected a proposal that he should rule as regent, and when Mary rejected any suggestion that he should rule only as her consort, parliament was obliged to declare that James had abdicated and thus made the throne vacant. The crown was then offered jointly to William and Mary, who accepted the Declaration of Rights limiting its powers to some extent. The joint reign of William III and Mary II officially began on 13 February 1689. In the event of Mary's death, William was to be king for his own life.

## 64 *Mary II (1662-94)*

BY AN UNKNOWN ARTIST, AFTER WILLEM WISSING (1655-87)
NATIONAL PORTRAIT GALLERY, LONDON

Oil on canvas 39.4 x 32.4 cms.

Lit:     David Piper, *Catalogue of Seventeenth Century Portraits in the National Portrait Gallery* (Cambridge, 1963), pp. 225-6

Mary, eldest daughter of James, Duke of York and his first, Protestant wife Anne Hyde, was born on 30 April l662. Her childhood years were spent at Richmond Palace in the company of her sister Anne (two years her junior) and a number of playmates, including Sarah Jennings (the future Duchess of Marlborough) and Frances Apsley, her closest friend. To avoid the possibility of James influencing his daughters towards the Catholicism to which he had become converted, Charles II declared Mary and Anne to be children of the state; both girls were accordingly raised apart from their father, in their own household at Richmond, under the guidance of two Anglican chaplains. Their upbringing, therefore, was strongly Protestant. James was permitted to have his daughters stay with him at St James's fairly frequently, however, and visited them regularly at Richmond. The young girls' part in the political game and in the Protestant-Catholic

KROONING VAN WILLEM DE III. EN MARIA, TOT KONING EN KONINGIN VAN ENGELAND, ENZ. IN WESTMUNSTERS ABDY DEN 11/21 APRIL 1689.

Rang der hooge en laage Staats perçoonen, geleidende haare Maiesteiten naar de Abdy, om gekroond te worden.

63

controversy then current assumed considerable importance in 1671 when James's other children, Edgar and Catherine, died; as survivors, Mary and Anne stood second and third in line to the throne. The disposal of Mary's hand became a matter of great political consequence.

Plans for a marriage between Mary and her cousin William were mooted in 1674, when Charles and James sent Lord Ossory to The Hague to sound out William's views on the subject. William, however, was less than enthusiastic, being too caught up in military matters and fighting the French; as he succinctly put it, 'I cannot leave the battlefield nor believe that it would be agreeable for a lady to be where the battlefield is' (van der Zee, p. 94). Three years later he considered the matter again. Impressed by accounts of Mary, he travelled to London in October 1677 to ask James for her hand. James demurred, whereupon William urged his suit with the king. After a frustrating and tantalising delay, during which William threatened to give up the idea and go home, Charles gave his consent, despite the fact that he had promised James that he would never marry off his nieces without their father's consent. (Behind Charles's agreement lay his hope that this Protestant alliance would allay his subjects' fears concerning his friendship with Louis XIV and its cloaked objective, the conversion of England to Catholicism). Mary's reaction to the news of her forthcoming marriage was to weep for a day and a half. Louis's reaction was one of rage, and he immediately stopped the secret subsidies which enabled Charles to rule without a parliament.

The wedding took place on 4 November 1677, William's birthday. The couple appeared an ill-matched pair; Mary was 5 feet 11 inches, a statuesque beauty with raven hair; William was half a foot shorter, sallow and slightly stooping, with a noticeably hooked nose which gave him an aquiline appearance. The ceremony was a subdued family affair (crowded gatherings brought on William's asthma), which Charles tried to enliven by ribald jokes. The couple left for Holland on 19 November but were forced to turn back and stay at Canterbury for some days because of bad weather. They finally left England's shores on the 28 November. Mary was heartbroken at leaving her family, especially Anne, who was seriously ill with smallpox, and her stepmother the Duchess of York (Mary of Modena), to whom she was deeply attached.

Despite her unhappiness when first married, Mary quickly grew to love William deeply, as can be seen from her correspondence to Frances Apsley when William went to fight the French in February 1678: 'I suppose you know the prince is gone to the army, but I am sure you can guess at the trouble I am in, I am sure I could never have thought it half so much. I thought coming out of my own country, parting with my friends and relations the greatest that ever could, as long as they lived, happen to me, but I am mistaken that now till this time I never knew sorrow, for what can be more cruel in the world than parting with what one loves?' (Hamilton, p. 65). About this time it was announced that she was pregnant; sadly, she miscarried in late April. In August of the same year her hopes of a child were raised again, only to be dashed in early 1679. (She never ceased to hope for a family but may have been rendered barren by an infection which started after her first miscarriage).

Mary soon settled in Holland and grew to love the Dutch people for their homely life-style and lack of ostentation. Her own life was a relatively quiet one, as William was often away for lengthy periods on campaign. The couple met as often as possible during his absences, however, and appear to have had a caring and stable relationship - contrary to some reports, which said that William was unkind to his wife and treated her with coldness. William seldom looked at other women, having little interest in them and being too caught up in military matters to spare the time; however, he did have a relationship for many years with one of Mary's ladies-in-waiting, Elizabeth Villiers, which caused considerable tension between the couple in 1685. Mary, for her part, promptly despatched 'squinting Betty' (as she was called) back to England.

Mary remained on good terms with her father, despite his displeasure at the friendship and hospitality she showed towards Monmouth, Charles II's illegitimate son, in 1684. However, after his abortive attempt to usurp James in January 1685, William and Mary quickly distanced themselves from him and William mollified his father-in-law by offering to send Dutch troops to help quell Monmouth's uprising. Tension between father and daughter grew, however, in the following year; James regularly complained that rebels to his reign were being harboured in the Dutch Republic. His refusal to intervene on William's behalf when the principality of Orange was seized by Louis XIV in October 1686 strained relations even further and rankled deeply with Mary, who complained: 'The only thing I ever asked the King, my father, to do was to use his influence with the King of France to prevent the seizure of the Principality of Orange. But my father preferred to join with the King of France against my husband' (van der Zee, p. 209).

During 1687 James tried to convert his daughters to Catholicism. He initially had hopes of Anne; had he been successful, William feared, he would thereafter have attempted to alter the succession to exclude Mary (at this time his daughters were his sole heirs). Anne, however, clung tenaciously to her religion and made a point of being defiantly zealous in her attachment to it. In November of that year he corresponded with Mary on the subject, and in February 1688 began sending her books. These she dutifully read, in addition to her mother's papers on her conversion, but remained unshakeable in her adherence to the established church.

The birth of the Prince of Wales in July 1688 forced the issue of the catholicising of England to a climax; once the invitation by the Seven reached William, his subsequent plans to invade England forced Mary to make up her mind as to the legitimacy of her new half-brother. Once she had convinced herself that her father had tried to deceive the nation she could then support William's dethroning of James with a clear conscience. This she did, though not without considerable heart-searching and anguish. The fact that by this stage she felt there was no other way to save church and state probably helped ease her

**64**

torment (she had always been a dutiful daughter and her father's favourite). During August 1688 William and Mary were forced to dissemble with James and Mary Beatrice. William tried to reassure James that the massing of troops in Holland was because of the French and, on a more personal level, Mary tried to hide her coolness towards the birth of the Prince of Wales in her letters, with little success; Mary Beatrice complained that her 'dear lemon' (her pet name for her step-daughter) showed no interest in the baby and never asked after him. Mary Beatrice's last plea to her, shortly before the invasion in November 1688, caused Mary considerable heartache: 'I am much put to it what to say, at a time when nothing is talked of here but the Prince of Oranges coming over with an army ... The second part of this news I will never believe, that is, that you are to come over with him; for I know you to be too good, that I dont believe you could have such a thought against the worst of fathers, much less perform against the best, that has always been kind to you, and I believe has loved you better than all the rest of his children' (van der Zee,p. 247).

Mary's arrival in England in February 1689 was both pleasurable and painful: 'When I saw England, my native country, which long absence had made me a stranger to, I felt a secret joy, which doubtless proceeded from a natural sympathy, but that was soon checked with the consideration of my father's misfortunes which came immediately into my mind. The joy of seeing the Prince again, strove against that melancholy, and the thoughts that I should my husband see owned as the deliverer of my country, made me vain; but alas, poor mortal! thought I then, from whom has he delivered it but from my father. Thus were my thoughts taken up, and while I put the best face on, my heart suffered a great deal ...' (Hamilton, pp. 206-7).

Mary found it difficult to settle into her new position as queen and into the worldliness of court life, where little time was given up to religious devotions; in Holland she had lived quietly and had become extremely devout. William too found it difficult to settle in; he was not a good mixer and living at Whitehall was bad for his health. Because of this the court soon moved to Hampton Court, where Mary could pursue her interests in gardening and architecture. The couple also made Holland House, Kensington (renamed Kensington Palace) their London home. William's journey to Ireland in 1690 to supervise military operations there caused Mary considerable worry, for she dreaded the thought of a confrontation on the battlefield between her husband and her father; furthermore, she would have to reign alone, for which she felt ill-equipped. In the event, she was left in control of the country, but could only deal with matters which required immediate attention; she could summon parliament in an emergency but could not give commissions or appoint bishops. A cabinet council of nine was set up to advise her.

Mary found the council meetings a considerable ordeal; the council, for its part, expected to find a puppet who would be easily manipulated. Instead they found a woman of spirit who, despite her lack of confidence, refused to be browbeaten and who was prepared to make decisions; one of her first acts was to approve a warrant for the arrest of her uncle Clarendon, who was involved in a plot against William. When William returned to London in September 1690 he expressed himself well pleased with her governance, a sentiment echoed by both houses of parliament the following month. During William's absences in the next four years she again assumed the regency and acted with commendable good sense, although beset by political and personal problems (she and Anne were estranged because of the latter's friendship with Lady Marlborough, whose husband was suspected of treason). By 1694 she had become extremely popular in her own right, for her concern for others and her open friendly manner; there was a saying at court that the queen talked as much as the king thought and the princess [Anne] ate.

On 20 December 1694 she fell ill; a week later, it was evident she had contracted smallpox. She died on 28 December, aged thirty-two. Her death was an immense blow to William, to the nation and to the Dutch. At St Germains, James forbade mourning and showed no signs of sorrow at the news; some of his courtiers, however, appeared in black, claiming they were mourning a relative. She was given a state funeral on 5 March 1695, although she had left instructions that she wanted to be buried without 'extraordinary expense;' she had always hated pomp and show. The year after her death Bishop Burnet, who knew her well and loved her dearly, published an essay to her memory. His comment on the couple succinctly sums up Mary's contribution to the age and to the nation:

'... while *He* went abroad with the Sword in *His* Hand, *She* stayed at home with the sceptre in Hers; *He* went as the Arbiter of Europe, to force a just, as well as general peace. *She* stayed to maintain Peace and do Justice at home. *He* was to conquer Enemies, and *She* was to gain Friends.'

Willem Wissing, born in Amsterdam, studed at The Hague and came to England in l676, where he was one of Lely's later pupils. He found particular favour with James II, who sent him to Holland in l685 to paint portraits of the Prince and Princess of Orange. Versions of the l685 portrait of Mary are at St James's Palace, at Cirencester House and in the collection of the Earl of Clarendon, among others. This portrait of Mary is a variation of her l685 portrait and was probably painted after Wissing's death. It is probably contemporary, however.

Sources:    G. Burnet, *An Essay on the Memory of the Late Queen* (London, l695); *DNB;* The Hon. B. Bathurst, *Letters of Two Queen*s (London, l924); Piper, as above; E. Hamilton, *William's Mary* (London, l972); H. and B. van der Zee, *William and Mary* (London, l973).

# 65 *William III (1650-1702)*

ATTRIBUTED TO THOMAS MURRAY (1663-1735)
NATIONAL PORTRAIT GALLERY, LONDON

Oil on canvas 243.5 x 151.7 cms.

William III, Prince of Orange, was the posthumous son of William II of Orange, who died of smallpox at the age of twenty-four. The young prince's passage to manhood was watched over with considerable fondness by the Dutch people; at the age of ten, he was regarded as 'the heir to the name and affection of the people of this country [the Dutch Republic]... If this affection and love, which at the moment fills the people, lasts and grows stronger, it can be said that as long as he has the drive, the ambition and the will to be sovereign of the State, he could well succeed' (van der Zee, p. 28). Although barred from the stadtholdership that his family had held for several generations, his training from the age of sixteen, when he was made a child of state, was geared in that direction. In 1668 he assumed his hereditary title of First Noble of Zeeland, a gesture of challenge to the leadership of the Grand Pensionary of Holland, Johan De Witt, who was anti-Orange and determined to keep William in a position of subordination.

In the same year he assumed his majority and began to administer his own affairs with a competence impressive in one so young. Sir William Temple, English ambassador at The Hague, found him 'a most extreme hopeful prince, and, to speak more plainly, something much better than I expected, and a young man of more parts than ordinary, and of the better sort ... loves hunting as much as he hates swearing ... [In other words] A Prince of many virtues' (van der Zee, p. 48). In 1670 he paid his first visit to England, where he was welcomed warmly by Charles II (his uncle) and made a favourable impression. (The dissipation of the English court, however, made him feel ill at ease). Charles, who had not met William since he was a boy of ten, expressed great satisfaction with his nephew but was somewhat surprised and dismayed to find that his young kinsman, far from being pliant and susceptible to influence, was both an ardent Protestant and a Dutch patriot. (A few months later Charles entered into an alliance with France, the so-called secret treaty of Dover, whereby both countries pledged to attack the Dutch after Charles, a Catholic at heart, had announced his conversion).

The attack on the Dutch Republic finally came in the spring of 1672. Shortly before this, William had been appointed captain - and admiral-general (the highest posts in the army and navy) for a single campaign, to the delight of the general public at The Hague. The Dutch now turned to their new captain - general for help against the forthcoming French invasion; with very little experience and few advisers, William was now in the position of guardian of his country. When the invasion came early in June the Republic collapsed before the French and lost three provinces within a fortnight. In the chaos which followed, the Dutch turned against De Witt and his policy of appeasement (he and his brother were lynched) and appointed William Stadtholder and captain - and admiral-general of the whole Republic for life. In the ensuing war with France, which dragged on until 1678 (the English ended hostilities by the peace of Westminster of February 1674), William became the liberator of his country, a tried and tested leader - a constitutional monarch in all but name - and a lifelong enemy of Louis XIV. To contain France became his chief concern and the basis of his foreign policy.

William's marriage to Mary in 1677 forced him of necessity to take a deeper interest in English politics. In August 1681 he visited England again, largely in a bridge-building capacity; relations between himself and his uncles had become strained because of the exclusion crisis. Charles was angered at William's ambiguous attitude towards excluding James from the succession and furious at the recent Dutch Insinuation, which urged Charles to accept exclusion. (William, in fact, had been closely involved in the drafting of the Insinuation, a plea for unity between king and parliament). William's visit was not a success on account of the political and personal tensions of the exclusion issue; nevertheless he learnt something of interest: that Charles was sceptical of his brother's ability to keep the crown. (He is reported to have commented, 'My brother will lose his kingdom by his bigotry and his soul for a lot of ugly trollops' (van der Zee, p. 193)). His scepticism was to be prophetic.

James II's accession in February 1685 made Mary heiress presumptive and William heir presumptive by marriage. William's concern now was to improve his strained relationship with his father-in-law. Accordingly he requested Monmouth to leave The Hague, where he had been a guest of the court; the presence of the young man, Mary's cousin and Charles II's favourite (but illegitimate) son, who himself had hopes of the English throne, was now a political embarrassment. As a test of William's good intentions towards him, James demanded that William change his attitude towards France (he needed Louis's support) and cashier the officers in the English regiments in the Dutch Republic whose loyalty to James could not be depended upon. William agreed to the latter but equivocated with the former. James, nevertheless, was reasonably satisfied with his son-in-law's submission to his interests, assuring him 'for the time to come, the same confidence will be established between us, as our near relation and the good of our family requires' (Baxter, p. 202). Family feeling was important to James, and although his attitude to his son-in-law and nephew by blood was ambivalent - he refused William the style of Royal Highness, not wishing to emphasize his connection to the English throne, and never gave Mary an allowance - on the surface he claimed friendship and fondness for him.

James's determination to pursue a catholicising policy in England inevitably drew William deeper into the arena of English politics, for he wanted his support in this. In November 1686 James sent the Quaker William Penn to meet William and try to obtain his support for the repeal of the penal laws and Test Acts. William, however, refused to support James as he considered the Acts a safeguard for the Protestant religion. He feared that James's measures would spark off a rebellion which could lead to the establishment of a republic; like all the Stuarts, he overestimated the strength of English republicanism. As diplomatically as possible he tried to warn James of the dangerous path he was following, maintaining 'that the Romish religion could not become dominant without the King's breaking the laws and his own promises and without (he feared) one day causing disorders which would imperil the monarchy; ... that it would be better to assure the Catholics of a reasonable liberty ... as for himself ... he would maintain the Catholics in an honest liberty, as they have in this country [the Dutch Republic], but he could never agree or consent to allow them to become dominant' (Miller, p. 176).

William kept himself well informed of events in England by the use of special missions, entrusted to his close advisers Dijkvelt and Zuylestein. These reconnaissance exercises were undertaken in 1685, 1687 and 1688. Dijkvelt's mission of February - May 1687 is seen as marking the start of the process which led to invasion; during his stay he met moderates and Protestants of various kinds and reassured them of William's steadfastness to his religion and his good intentions towards them. Zuylestein, William's cousin, visited England in August 1687 and laid the foundations for the setting up of a clandestine intelligence system. Over the next year an elaborate underground was established, with mail being carried initially by merchant ships and diplomats and later by fast yachts and small vessels which operated special courier services. Gradually William built up a sizeable body of agents in high places, who were able to supply him with details of James's privy council meetings. Books and pamphlets from the Dutch Republic were smuggled in and distributed by the thousand; answers and rejoinders, refutations and restatements poured

**65**

from the presses in an intense war of propaganda.

William's last special mission was in June 1688, when Zuylestein came ostensibly to convey William's congratulations on the birth of the Prince of Wales but in reality to carry preparations for the invasion further along. Though there is considerable speculation about the timing of William's decision to invade, it seems that he had made up his mind by the end of April 1688. By this time the rift between himself and his father-in-law was complete. Furthermore, he felt he had no choice but to act and speedily, before the European war that was threatening actually broke out. The invitation from the seven leading members of the aristocracy and Church of England at the end of June, to come and save England, spurred him on. (The invitation was in fact a letter of association by the seven, a commitment on their part to act in support of William *whenever* he decided to come.) Despite repeated warnings by the French, James refused to believe an invasion was imminent until near the end of September.

William invaded with ease on 5 November 1688 and succeeded in an almost bloodless take-over as James, crippled with indecision and totally demoralised, fled to France. While William stated in his declaration that he had come only to secure a free parliament and would not take over unless invited to do so by parliament, the possibility of dethroning his father-in-law was undoubtedly in his mind. (Mary, in her *Mémoire*, spoke of William going to dethrone her father). After considerable political haggling, during which William rejected both the idea of a regency and of his being Prince Consort to Mary, the throne was declared vacant and the crown offered jointly to William and Mary on 13 February 1689, with administration vested in the former for life. The coronation took place on 11 April 1689, with king and queen swearing to govern according to the statutes agreed in parliament and to uphold the Protestant religion, rather than, as was customary, to uphold the law made by their ancestors.

Although William had invaded England to rescue lost liberties and religion, acquiring the throne of England was more of a means to curtail French aggression than an end in itself. He needed England in his lifelong struggle against Louis XIV; in bringing about the Revolution, he was following his basic belief that England was of central importance in the European fight against French supremacy. Halifax noticed this during conversations he had with him in the spring of 1689, remarking astutely that 'Hee hath such a mind to France, that it would incline one to think hee tooke England onely in his way' (van der Zee, p. 280). William, however, could not have dared embroil his new kingdom in a costly European war; it was James and Louis who brought this about by James's invasion of Ireland in March 1689, aided and abetted by the French. Parliament immediately gave William the freedom to act and England declared war on France in May. The ensuing struggle in Ireland was but one episode in the long war of the Grand Alliance, which ended with the treaty of Rijswijk of 1697. Nevertheless, Jacobite defeat in Ireland was of major importance, for it cemented the Revolution of 1688 and ended (in a real sense) James's chance of reclaiming his kingdom; it also ensured the Protestant succession which has continued ever since.

As a king William was not popular. His taciturn and reserved ways did not please the English in general and he 'used noe arts' to make himself liked. During the early years of his reign he suffered from acute homesickness and was only too glad to escape each spring to the Continent, to continue the struggle against Louis XIV and then to spend a few months hunting at Het Loo. His physical appearance, short, with round shoulders and a marked hunch of his back, was the butt of numerous jibes, some extremely cruel viz.,'He has gotten in part the shape of a man, but more of a monkey, deny it who can, and behaves like one',(*Poems on Affairs of State,* vol. 5, p. 41). His obvious preference for Dutch company (his two chief favourites were Dutchmen) was a major irritant and created considerable ill feeling. According to Bishop Burnet, who knew him well, 'The King was thought to love the Dutch more than the English, to trust more to them and to admit them to more freedom ... and the English being of more lively temper than the Dutch, grew to expresss a contempt and aversion for them, that went almost to a mutiny' (van der Zee, p. 285). By 1698 English jealousy of the Dutch was at its height; any popularity William might have had was in decline. In 1700 his grants of forfeited Irish land to favoured individuals, almost all of whom were foreigners, were cancelled by parliament, to his fury and mortification.

William died on 8 March 1702 (OS), of complications from a broken collarbone caused by his horse stumbling on a mole hill; he had however been in poor health for some time. (Thereafter, the Jacobites had a new hero to toast - the 'little gentleman in black velvet' - namely the mole.) Mourning in the country was half-hearted and he was buried with little ceremony, unlike Mary, who had been greatly loved. Although he has often been called the Protestant Champion, William was not a religious fanatic; his fight was against the hegemony of France above all else. By his actions he propelled England into Europe, where he created a new balance of power by the Grand Alliance. To the chagrin of the English, who had offered him their country, he remained above all else a Dutchman.

The portrait, which shows William in coronation robes, relates to the standard state portrait of the king by Kneller, which originated in 1690 and which was virtually mass-produced by Kneller's studio. Thomas Murray, to whom the painting is attributed, studied under John Riley and established an independent practice by 1682, when he painted portraits of the Duke and Duchess of Albemarle (at Welbeck). In 1697 he executed replicas of Kneller's royal portraits for the Merchant Taylors' Hall.

Sources:     G. de'F. Lord et al., eds., *Poems on Affairs of State*, (New Haven, 1963-75); S.B.Baxter, *William III* (London, 1966); M.A. Thomson, 'Louis XIV and William III, 1689-97,' R. Hatton and J.S. Bromley, eds., *William III and Louis XIV* (Liverpool, 1968); J.R. Jones, *The Revolution of 1688 in England* (London, 1972);H. and B. van der Zee, *William and Mary* (London, 1973); J. Miller, *James II: a study in Kingship* (Hove, 1978).

# 3 James II and Ireland

In his kingdom of Ireland, where the large majority of his subjects were of his own faith, James carried his catholicising policies farther and faster than in England. Irish Catholics hoped, as Irish Protestants feared, that a Catholic king would upset the Restoration settlement by which Protestants (especially the Anglican variety) held most of the country's land and enjoyed a monopoly of political power. James proceeded cautiously enough at first, appointing the Protestant Earl of Clarendon as his lord lieutenant. Later, however, under the influence of his old companion Richard Talbot, whom he created Earl of Tyrconnell and commander of the Irish army and later (in 1687) lord deputy in Clarendon's place, large numbers of Protestant judges, officials and army officers were replaced by Catholics. In 1687 the existing town charters, which excluded Catholics from local offices and also ensured the election of Protestant MPs by the Irish boroughs, were called in and replaced by new ones which gave the king the right to appoint and dismiss councillors; Catholics or (as in Belfast) Presbyterians largely replaced Anglicans. Though this created much alarm and despondency among Protestants, what James himself called the 'stubborn people' of Londonderry alone seriously challenged his right to make these changes, but in vain. Catholic worship, which had been subject to many restrictions and occasional persecution during the previous reign, was openly supported and encouraged. Increasing numbers of Protestants, fearing worse, fled to England, where their refugee tales fell on sympathetic ears and did James much harm.

Tyrconnell's actions ensured that when the Williamites triumphed in England and later - though rather less easily - in Scotland, Ireland remained under the control of James's supporters. The only exceptions were Londonderry and Enniskillen. Believing the rumours of an intended massacre of Protestants which circulated in the north late in 1688, the inhabitants of both towns refused to accept garrisons of Catholic troops, thus in effect rebelling against royal authority. They subsequently declared their support for William and put their faith in deliverance from England.

In France meanwhile, James had recovered his nerve and, supported by Louis XIV , decided to recover his throne too. His arrival in Ireland in March 1689 with supplies and French advisers created tremendous enthusiasm among his supporters. It soon became apparent to them, however, that their king's interest in Ireland was as a stepping stone to England. In fact his first hope was to cross from the north of Ireland to Scotland, where he had many supporters among the Highland clans. Londonderry, however, refused to submit even when James himself appeared before its walls. The resulting siege lasted for 105 days and ended with the relief of the city by the Williamites on 28 July. At the same time the Enniskillingers, whose raiding activities had done much to distract the besiegers of Derry, inflicted a crushing defeat on another Jacobite army near Newtownbutler. William was thus left with a bridgehead and local support in the north, though James retained control of most of the country during the latter part of 1689 and the first half of 1690.

One of James's first acts on arriving in Ireland was to summon a parliament to settle the affairs of the kingdom. Following the changes made by Tyrconnell and the flight of many important Protestants, this assembly was overwhelmingly Catholic in its membership (though it included four Church of Ireland bishops). Understandably determined to redress old wrongs and settle old scores, by reversing the Restoration land settlement and confiscating the property of Williamite fugitives, it acted as if the war was already won. As a result, the Jacobites lost the chance to prepare as thoroughly as they might have done against the inevitable Williamite invasion.

## 66 *Richard Talbot, Earl and Duke of Tyrconnell (1630-91)*

BY AN UNKNOWN ARTIST, ENGLISH SCHOOL, SEVENTEENTH CENTURY
NATIONAL GALLERY OF IRELAND, DUBLIN

Oil on canvas 118 x 91 cms.
Prov:    Formerly at Malahide Castle.
Lit:      David Piper, *Catalogue of the Seventeenth Century Portraits in the National Portrait Gallery 1625- 1714* (Cambridge, 1963), p.354.
        *National Gallery of Ireland Illustrated Summary Catalogue of Paintings* (Dublin, 1981), p. 45, no. 4167.

Richard Talbot was the youngest of eight sons of Sir William Talbot, a lawyer and landowner from a prominent Irish Catholic family. In 1647 young Talbot served in Preston's Catholic army. Two years later he helped defend Drogheda against Cromwell and was one of the few to escape (though badly wounded) when the town was stormed. In the early 1650s he went abroad to serve in the armies of France and Spain. While in Flanders, he met and became a close friend of the Duke of York, who appointed him commander of his regiment. Thereafter the lives of both were bound together, to no small advantage for Talbot, who used his influence over James to further both his own interests and those of his class, the Old English Catholic gentry of Ireland.

At the Restoration Talbot settled in England and became a leading member of the Duke of York's household. He also acquired considerable estates in Ireland under the Restoration settlement, despite the fact that he subsequently became a prime mover in attempts to have the land acts repealed. His motive for this was his desire - in fact, his lifelong ambition - to see the Catholic gentry returned to their former prominence. For his efforts in this direction he soon gained the reputation of Catholic champion, and in 1670 became chief spokesman for the Catholic gentry who had suffered under the Acts of Settlement and Explanation.

During the next two years, at Talbot's instigation, an enquiry commission headed by Prince Rupert examined the feasibility of altering the settlement. By early 1673, however, the English parliament felt uneasy about the work of the commission, as did the Protestant landowners of Ireland. Parliament accordingly requested the king to abandon the enquiry and dismiss Talbot, who had 'notoriously assumed to himself the title of agent of the Roman Catholics of Ireland' (McGuire, p.77). Charles agreed and Talbot left court to go into exile abroad.

Shortly before the death of Charles in 1685 he was permitted to return to England. On James's accession he was created Earl of Tyrconnell and lost no time in trying to persuade the king to overturn the settlement and restore the lands and status of the Catholic Irish gentry. James had considerable reservations about this: where he was concerned, nothing should be done to put Protestants on the defensive or make them fearful for their security and estates.

In June 1686 Tyrconnell returned to Ireland to take command of the army. This was a considerable snub to Clarendon, the lord lieutenant, for the post was traditionally held by the viceroy. Tyrconnell thereupon began a purge of the army: Catholics replaced Protestants in large numbers, so that by the following October two-thirds of the force were Catholics. Other changes too were brought about: Catholics were appointed judges and Catholic bishops were given payment from government funds. Clarendon was forced to acquiesce in these policies, such was the extent of Tyrconnell's influence upon the king.

In January 1687 Tyrconnell replaced Clarendon as viceroy - not styled as lord lieutenant, however, but as lord deputy, a lesser title. (Clarendon had been kept in the dark about being replaced until the last possible moment). There was much consternation among Protestants at news of the appointment and many

**66**

families prepared to leave for England. Tyrconnell's arrival was delayed because of bad weather, which was commemorated in Wharton's famous song *Lilliburlero*:

> Arra! but why does he stay behind?
> O by my sowl! 'tis a Protestant wind;
> But see de Tyrconnell is now come ashore,
> And we shall have commissions galore;

When he arrived, he lost no time in pursuing his policies to the full: the catholicisation of the army was intensified, more Catholic judges were appointed and the Catholic church was given additional government funds. A number of Catholics were made privy councillors.

In June l687 he pressed for, and got, a royal warrant empowering him to issue new charters to cities and corporate towns. This was a crucial factor in his long-term strategy, for it would enable him to create a Catholic parliament to modify or repeal the land settlement. A few months later he was summoned to Chester to meet the king (his enemies at court were discrediting him and claiming that his measures would be disastrous for the Irish economy). James, after initial coldness, gave him his backing but refused to call an Irish parliament to investigate the land settlement until he had first summoned an English one. By mid l687, therefore, Tyrconnell ruled Ireland almost unchecked.

After James's flight to France in December l688, Tyrconnell had two options: to reach an accommodation with William or declare for the exiled James. He chose the latter. In emotional language he urged James to come to Ireland and fight for his lost kingdoms, pressing him 'to consider whether you can with honour continue where you are when you may possess a kingdom of your own, plentiful of all things for human life' (Miller, p.220). James came (extremely reluctantly) and awarded Tyrconnell a dukedom for his services.

With the calling of the Dublin parliament of May l689 Tyrconnell achieved his goal. Largely Catholic, mostly Old English gentry, it repealed the Restoration land acts and attainted some 2,400 Protestant landowners. On paper, the Protestant ascendancy was broken. The legislation, however, came to nothing with James's defeat at the Boyne.

In battle on that fateful day, Tyrconnell fought bravely although weakened by ill health. When defeat became obvious he urged James to return to France. He and the Jacobite leaders and army retreated to Limerick, where considerable dissension arose over future policy. Tyrconnell, considering the situation to be hopeless, thought it advisable to strike a bargain with William. Sarsfield and his die-hard supporters wanted to fight on. In the event the Irish army rallied, successfully defended Limerick and badly deflated Williamite morale. In the second week of September Tyrconnell went to France to report to James, leaving Berwick in command of the army. He returned in January l69l as lord lieutenant. Although he brought with him the earldom of Lucan for Sarsfield, the relationship between the two men was fraught: Sarsfield resented Tyrconnell's claim to be commander-in-chief and there was considerable friction between them.

Tyrconnell was present at the battle of Aughrim on 12 July l69l. On l0 August he suffered a stroke and died four days later (rumour had it that he was poisoned). He was buried in an unmarked grave in Limerick Cathedral. His second wife, Frances Hamilton, widow of George and sister-in-law of the Jacobites Richard and Anthony Hamilton, outlived him by forty years.

Versions of the portrait include another in the NGI, after Rigaud, one in the NPG by an artist of the French school, and one at Rudding Park. The painting shows Tyrconnell wearing the blue ribbon of the Garter over his left shoulder. Tyrconnell received the Order of the Garter from James at Versailles on or before 16 November l690: the portrait type therefore probably originated in France between November and December of that year. The fortress in the right background is possibly meant to be Limerick.

Sources:    *DNB*;  Piper, as above; J.G. Simms, *Jacobite Ireland 1685-91* (London, l969); J. Miller, *James II: a study in kingship* (Hove, l977); J. McGuire, 'Richard Talbot, earl of Tyrconnell (l603-91) and the Catholic Counter Revolution,' C. Brady, ed.,*Worsted in the Game Losers in Irish History* ( Dublin, l989).

## 67 *Sir Neil O'Neill, second baronet of Killelagh (?1658-90), as an Irish chieftain (1680)*

BY JOHN MICHAEL WRIGHT (1617-94)
TATE GALLERY, LONDON
REPRODUCTION

The painting shows O'Neill wearing the costume of an Irish chieftain and is highly unusual for that reason. The only other known depiction of Irish dress is Marcus Gheeraerts's portrait of Captain Thomas Lee of l594 (also in the Tate Gallery), which shows Lee bare-legged like an Irish kern and wearing a fancy dress derived from a costume book. The closest comparable illustration of an

Ulster chieftain's dress is that published in John Derricke's *Image of Irelande* of 1581. This shows a chieftain wearing a conical plumed hat similar to O'Neill's; also a quilted leather doublet, fringed cloak and tights. O'Neill's smocked shirt is Italian in style, and is either an invention of Wright's or an extremely ornate example by an Irish seamstress.

The dog gazing devotedly at O'Neill and wearing a padlocked collar inscribed with his master's name is an Irish wolfhound, a prized breed whose export was forbidden in 1652. MacLysaght, quoting the letter of an English visitor to Ireland in the 1690s, furnishes an amusing account of the breed: 'They were as quiet among us as lambs without any noys or disturbance. I enquir'd the use of them and was told that besides the ornament that they were, they kill'd as many deer as pay'd verie well for their keeping ... I am well assur'd that a dog of this kind which my Lord Duke of Ormond had in the castle of Dublin when he was Lord Liut. walkt into the stable yard where a little curr kept a barking and yelping at him, which he never regaurded but walkt forward with a careless pace, untill the curr snapt him by the heeles, which made the grehound give him a patt with his fore foot which layd him on the ground, and then standing over him pist upon him; the same dog being provokt by a small setting dogg which belongd to the Duke tooke him by the back and layd him gently upon a coale fire in the state roome and walked unconcernedly away' (pp. 336-7).

The most unusual feature of the painting is the inclusion of the suit of Japanese armour. James I owned two such suits (now in the Tower of London), which had been sent to him by the Shogun of Japan in 1614 - but that shown in Wright's painting is not like either of them. Wright may have seen such a suit among a collection of rarities which a Jesuit called Tomson showed to John Evelyn in 1664. Wright, a fellow Catholic, may have known Tomson; he certainly knew of Japan, as he had two books relating to the country in his library.

The fact that O'Neill chose to be represented wearing an Irish chieftain's dress says a great deal about his feeling of Irishness and his devotion to Catholicism. By the late seventeenth century Gaelic Ireland had been largely destroyed by successive periods of English colonisation. O'Neill's wearing of Irish dress is both a nostalgic longing for a vanished age and an emotional commitment to an Irish ideal, which for him culminated in his fight for the Jacobite cause at the Boyne. The inclusion of Japanese armour lying at his feet is pointed in its symbolism; in 1680 Catholics were rigorously persecuted in Japan. By towering over the arms of the persecutors of his religion, O'Neill probably wished to be seen as a defender of Catholicism. The conical-shaped mountain in the background is probably Slemish, which was close to his Antrim estates. (For information on O'Neill, see no. 173).

Wright, one of the leading portrait painters of the seventeenth century, worked in Italy during the late 1640s and became a member of the Roman Academy of St Luke. A keen antiquarian, he was appointed Antiquary to Archduke Leopold, governor of the Spanish Netherlands, in 1653-4 and settled in Flanders. He returned to Commonwealth England in 1656 and, despite being a Catholic, quickly established a reputation; by 1658 he was regarded as one of the best painters in England. He received a number of royal commissions under Charles and James but lost favour under William and Mary.

Wright is known to have painted two versions of the Irish chieftain (or Irish Tory as the picture is also called). One is in the Tate Gallery and the other is in the Sutherland collection at Dunrobin Castle. He also painted a Highland laird, Sir Mungo Murray, in Scottish dress, of which there are three known versions: one in the SNPG, one at Holyrood House and one in the collection of Lord Brocket. The portraits of O'Neill and Murray, alike in format and subject matter, were companion pieces.

Sources:    E. MacLysaght, *Irish Life in the Seventeenth Century* (Cork, 1950);
            S. Stevenson and D. Thomson, *John Michael Wright The King's Painter*,
            SNPG, July-September 1982; J. Fenlon, 'John Michael Wright's 'Highland laird'
            identified,' *Burlington Magazine*, October 1988.

**67**

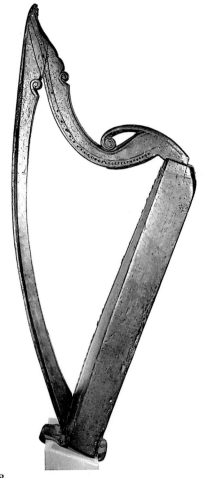

**68**

## 68 *The Mullagh Mast harp, c. 1700*

NATIONAL MUSEUM OF IRELAND, DUBLIN (249-1944)

Large high-headed harp with a one-piece willow soundbox.
Height 157 cms.

The soundbox has thirty-four string-holes, of which the lower nine are fitted with triangular copper plates, pierced for the strings and ten of the remainder with brass string-shoes. The neck has thirty-three tuning-pin holes; no strings or tuning-pins remaining.

The soundbox is decorated on the front and sides with roughly-incised trellis and, below in front, with scrolls and arcs. There are traces of three heart-shaped mounts, probably of metal, on either side of the string-holes. The top of the forepillar and the neck are decorated with carved scrolls.

The back of the soundbox has a printed label: 'Brought To Taymouth Castle FROM THE MARQUIS OF BREADALBANE's APARTMENTS AT HOLYROOD PALACE MAY 16 1860.' Under the neck is a hand-written label inscribed, 'this harp found in Mulagh Mast, Co. Kerry.'

Photo Pieterse-Davison International, Dublin

**69** *Royal charter of James II to the Corporation of Dublin, 27 September 1687*

DUBLIN CITY CORPORATION

Parchment; first membrane (of fifteen), illuminated with gold and silver leaf and colours; in Latin; issued at Dublin.

The replacement of existing borough charters by new ones in 1687 gave Catholics (or, in Belfast, Presbyterians) control of local government and prepared the way for the election of a Catholic parliament. However, ten of the twenty-four aldermen appointed for Dublin under the new charter were Protestants; the arms of all twenty-four, along with those of the lord deputy, the sheriff and the recorder, appear on the document.

This first membrane has a portrait of James II in oils within the initial letter of his name, his royal coat of arms and the arms of the kingdoms of England and Ireland. On a side panel are the arms of Tyrconnell (now very indistinct) and those of the City of Dublin.

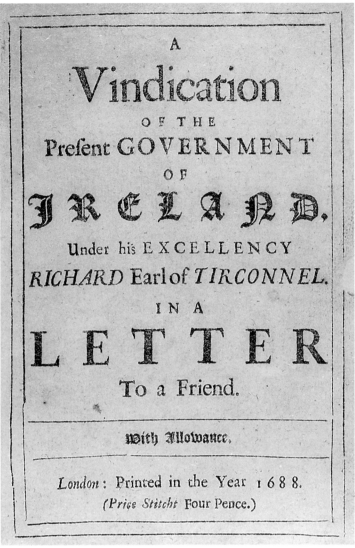

**70**

**70** *A vindication of the present*
*government of Ireland under his Excellency Richard Earl of*
*Tirconnel...London: printed... 1688*

THE QUEEN'S UNIVERSITY, BELFAST

quarto: [1], 21 pp.
Lit:     Wing V524.

This is a Jacobite attempt to allay Protestant fears by referring, among other things, to Tyrconnell's English ancestry and his English wife. The pamphlet provoked a Dublin reply, *A letter from a gentleman in Ireland to his friend in London,* 1688.

**71** *The Popish champion: or,*
*A compleat history of the life and military actions of Richard Earl of*
*Tyrconnel, generalissimo of all the Irish forces now in arms... As*
*also a brief description of the kingdom of Ireland... London, printed*
*for John Dunton...MDCLXXXIX[1689]*

THE QUEEN'S UNIVERSITY, BELFAST

quarto: [4], 58, [2] pp.
Lit:     Wing P2944.

This pamphlet is dedicated to the officers in William's army.

72

### 72 *King James II landing at Kinsale in Ireland*

<small>Print published in Amsterdam by Adriaan Schoonebeek</small>
<small>Ulster Museum, Belfast</small>
<small>Reproduction</small>

Following his panic flight to France in December 1688 James recovered his nerve and determined to recover his thrones with Louis XIV's help. His springboard was Ireland, where Tyrconnell and the Catholics controlled the country. In March 1689 James landed from a French ship at Kinsale, accompanied by French advisers. He was greeted with great enthusiasm. Schoonebeek's print emphasises the religious aspect of the reception by putting Catholic clergy in the foreground.

### 73 *The journal of the proceedings*
*of the Parliament in Ireland. With the establishment of the forces there... London: printed for Robert Clavell... MDCLXXXIX[1689]*

<small>The Queen's University, Belfast</small>

quarto: 20 pp
Lit:     Wing I422A.

The journal, which was licensed on 7 July 1689 and published before 13 September of that year, covers the period between 7 May and 11 June 1689. The proceedings of James's Irish parliament were destroyed by order of the Irish parliament of 1695.

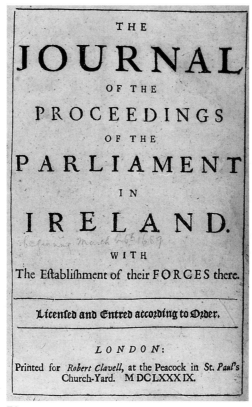

THE

# JOURNAL

OF THE

## PROCEEDINGS

OF THE

## PARLIAMENT

IN

## IRELAND.

WITH

The Eſtabliſhment of their FORCES there.

*Licenſed and Entred according to Order.*

LONDON:

Printed for *Robert Clavell*, at the Peacock in St. *Paul's* Church-Yard. MDCLXXXIX.

**73**

**74** *A list of such of*
> the names of the nobility, gentry and commonalty of England and Ireland... who are all by an Act of a pretended Parliament assembled in Dublin... the 7th of May, 1689... attainted of high treason... London, printed for R.Clavel... and J. Watts... 1690

THE QUEEN'S UNIVERSITY, BELFAST

quarto: 70 pp.
Lit:    Wing L2409.

Licensed  26 March 1690; *Term Catalogue,* May 1690 (ref. E.Arber, ed., *The Term Catalogues, 1668-1709 AD*, 3 vols., London, 1903-6).

**75** *Ireland's lamentation: being a short*
> ...account of the scituation, nature, constitution and product of Ireland. With... relation of the... miserable sufferings of the Protestants there... to the latter end of April, written by an English Protestant that lately narrowly  escaped with his life from thence. London, printed by J.D. and sold by Rich. Janeway... 1689

THE QUEEN'S UNIVERSITY, BELFAST

quarto: [2], 36 pp.
Lit:    Wing I1025.

Licensed 18 May 1689. The author gives a hostile, and sometimes amusing, account of King James's progress from Cork to Dublin: 'At Carloe he was slabber'd with the kisses of the rude Country Irish Gentlewomen, so that he was forced to beg to have them kept from him...'

The printer J.D. is perhaps John Darby, whom the bookseller and publisher John Dunton described as 'the religious printer. He goes to Heaven with the Anabaptists but is a man of general charity.'

76

### 76 *Cruelty of King James and Comte d'Avaux to Irish Protestants*

PRINT PUBLISHED IN AMSTERDAM BY ADRIAAN SCHOONEBEEK
ULSTER MUSEUM, BELFAST
REPRODUCTION

Protestant refugees fleeing from Ireland to England brought exaggerated tales of persecution with them. Avaux, Louis XIV's ambassador to James in Ireland, was credited with advising the extermination of the Protestants. In fact this fearsome scene of hanging men and burning houses was adapted by Schoonebeek from an engraving of the siege of Bonn, and was not a representation of events in Ireland.

### 77 *A True narrative of the*
*murders cruelties and oppressions, perpetrated on the Protestants in Ireland, by the late King James's agents, since his arrival there...*
*London: printed for Richard Baldwin... 1690*

THE QUEEN'S UNIVERSITY, BELFAST

quarto: [6], 30 pp.
Lit:     Wing T2804.

Published before May 1690 (see *Term Catalogues*) and dedicated to 'Gilbert [Burnet], Lord Bishop of Sarum.' Richard Baldwin was an extensive publisher of political pamphlets and broadsides. According to John Dunton, 'He was a true lover of King William; and... always voted on the right side.'

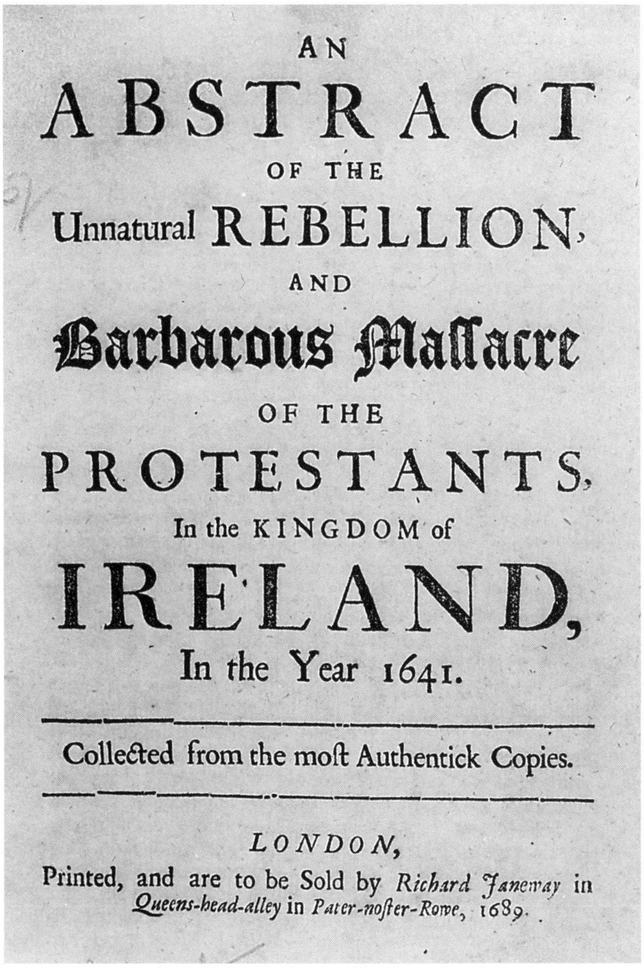

AN
ABSTRACT
OF THE
Unnatural REBELLION,
AND
𝖇𝖆𝖗𝖇𝖆𝖗𝖔𝖚𝖘 𝕸𝖆𝖘𝖘𝖆𝖈𝖗𝖊
OF THE
PROTESTANTS,
In the KINGDOM of
IRELAND,
In the Year 1641.

Collected from the moſt Authentick Copies.

LONDON,
Printed, and are to be Sold by *Richard Janeway* in
*Queens-head-alley* in *Pater-noſter-Rowe,* 1689.

78

## 78 *An Abstract of the unnatural*
*rebellion, and barbarous massacre of the Protestants, in the*
*kingdom of Ireland in the year 1641... London, printed by Richard*
*Janeway... 1689*

THE QUEEN'S UNIVERSITY, BELFAST

quarto: 31 pp.
Lit:    Wing A146.

The pamphlet is an obvious attempt to use the events of 1641 to stir up anti-Catholic feelings in 1689: '... it must not, be accounted a work improper at this time. ' The printer Richard Janeway became notorious as a fanatically Protestant publisher.

## 79 *View of Londonderry from the north-east, c.1685*

ATTRIBUTED TO THOMAS PHILLIPS (C.1635-93)
BRITISH LIBRARY, LONDON

Ink and colour wash on linen-backed paper 47.5 x 91 cms, on sheet 53.3 x 97.7 cms.
Lit:    R. Loeber, 'Biographical Dictionary of Engineers in Ireland, 1600-1730,' *The Irish Sword,*
        vol. xiii, (1977-9), 283.
        S. Tyacke, *London Map-sellers 1660-1720* (Tring, 1978), p.45, no.174.

In the wake of persistent rumours from Paris of an imminent French invasion of Ireland, Thomas Phillips, the Second Engineer of Great Britain, was ordered to Ireland on 24 August 1684, to survey the fortifications of the kingdom and to make recommendations for their improvement. In the course of his tour in the early part of 1685 he executed a number of plans and views of the principal Irish forts.

79

This unsigned view, which is accompanied by a signed plan of Londonderry's fortifications, was probably prepared for Charles II. It is typical of Phillips's working, as opposed to presentation, pieces. By the time he had returned to England in June 1685 the invasion scare had passed, and his radical recommendations were never acted on. As a recent author has remarked, had action been taken, the outcome of the Irish campaigns after 1689 might well have been different: a country of heavily fortified towns and harbours in Jacobite hands would have been more difficult for William to conquer.

Phillips, perhaps the most accomplished British-born military engineer of the seventeenth century, prided himself on his skill as a surveyor and draughtsman. Like a growing number of his contemporaries, he believed that only the state had sufficient funds to finance thorough surveying and for almost all of his career he was in official employment.

His Londonderry plans of 1685 were engraved for commercial publishers, to illustrate the course of the 1688-9 campaigns. He initially refused to serve in Ireland in 1689, however, probably because of personal differences with the Duke of Schomberg. By doing so, he temporarily forfeited his position as second engineer. In 1690 he acted as engineer to Marlborough in Ireland and was probably responsible for the plans of Cork and Kinsale which can also be seen in this exhibition.

Sources:     *DNB*; British Library Add. MSS 61343 A and B (plans of Cork and Kinsale, 1690), 63760-1, 63770 (papers of Richard Graham, Viscount Preston, Envoy Extraordinary in Paris 1682-5), K. Top. LIV. 31 (plan of Londonderry, c.1685); E. Chappell, ed., *The Tangier Papers of Samuel Pepys [Publications of the Navy Records Society, vol. 73]* (London, 1935); Loeber, as above.

## 80 *Alexander MacDonnell, third Earl of Antrim (1615-99)*

BY AN UNKNOWN ARTIST
VISCOUNT DUNLUCE

Oil on canvas  63.2 x 51.7 cms.

Alexander MacDonnell, a foremost Jacobite from an ancient Gaelic and Catholic family, was the younger son of Randal, first Earl of Antrim. He commanded a regiment of Irish troops during the 1641 rising and was attainted by Cromwell, but was restored in 1660. In 1683 he succeeded his brother. James II appointed him a privy councillor and lord lieutenant for Co. Antrim. In 1689 he sat in James's parliament in Dublin.

**80**

In the winter of 1688 he was ordered to raise a regiment of Catholic Irish and Scots, to take over Mountjoy's garrison duties in Londonderry. This took some time, as he wanted the regiment to look impressive and determined upon recruits over six feet tall. When his force eventually reached Derry on 7 December the town was without a garrison, as Mountjoy had left on 23 November on Tyrconnell's orders. The sight of Antrim's Redshanks (bare-legged Highlanders with a fearsome reputation) terrified the citizens. After confused debate as to whether to admit them, thirteen young apprentices closed the town gates. Derry thereafter became the main centre of Protestant resistance to James II in Ireland.

Antrim's regiment served throughout the war in Ireland, till the capitulation of Limerick, playing an undistinguished part in the battle of the Boyne. In 1689 he was outlawed in England and his estates were declared confiscated. They were restored to him in 1697, however, under the terms of the second (civil) article of Limerick, whereby pardon and property rights were offered to those holding out in Limerick or any other Irish garrison, provided they remained in Ireland and submitted to William. There was considerable discussion in the Commons about Antrim's restoration and whether a small hill outside Limerick, surrounded by a ditch (which is where he was positioned at the time of the capitulation) constituted a garrison. In the event, his restoration went ahead. Had it not, the 'omitted clause' of the treaty, whereby the terms covered those under the protection of the Irish army in certain counties, would have been his second line of defence. The last years of his long life were taken up with securing his pardon and restoration. This involved much travelling to London to mobilise influential friends on his behalf. He died in June 1699, while returning from London, and was buried at Holywell, Flintshire.

Sources:    G.E.C., *The Complete Peerage* (London, 1910); J.G. Simms, *The Williamite Confiscation in Ireland 1690-1703* (London, 1956).

**81**

## 81 *Sir William Stewart, first Viscount Mountjoy (1653-92)*

By an unknown artist
National Trust
Reproduction

Mountjoy, only son of Sir Alexander Stewart and grandson of Sir William Stewart, succeeded his grandfather as second baronet in 1662 and inherited considerable property in counties Donegal and Tyrone. In 1682 he was created Baron Ramelton and Viscount Mountjoy and in 1684 was appointed master-general of the ordnance for life. He was also made a privy councillor and served as colonel of a regiment of foot. Though a Protestant, he kept his offices under James II, being described by Clarendon as 'very industrious in the king's service' *(DNB)*. In 1686 he served on the Continent, where he was seriously wounded at the capture of Buda in September. He returned to Ireland in 1687 and was made a brigadier-general.

His regiment, largely Protestant, was stationed in Derry when William landed at Torbay on 15 November 1688. Tyrconnell, anxious to replace three Irish regiments he had despatched to James's army in England, thereupon ordered Mountjoy and his troops to Dublin. The Earl of Antrim was ordered to take over Mountjoy's duties in Derry and raise a force of Catholic Irish and Scots. This, however, took some time and the force failed to reach Derry by the appointed date of 20 November. On 23 November Mountjoy marched south, leaving Derry without a garrison, an error of judgement on Tyrconnell's part which George Walker lauded as the work of the Almighty: 'it pleased God so to infatuate the Councils of my Lord Tyrconnell that ... he took particular care to send away the whole regiment quartered in and about Londonderry' (Macrory, p. 122). When Antrim finally arrived at Derry he found the gates shut against him.

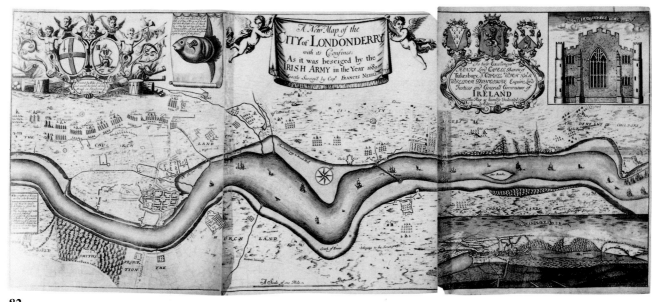

**82**

When Mountjoy reached Dublin Tyrconnell promptly sent him back to Derry with six companies of his regiment, to reoccupy the city. After negotiations with the military government there (composed of members of the former Protestant corporation, led by Colonel Philips), it was agreed that two of Mountjoy's companies (all Protestant), under the command of Lundy, should be admitted. Mountjoy's two sons were to remain within the city as hostages (he had promised to procure a general pardon for Ulster's rebellious inhabitants within fifteen days). He then went to Newtownstewart to meet delegates from Enniskillen, whom he advised to trust to the king's protection. He planned to go to Enniskillen himself but was summoned by Tyrconnell to return to Dublin.

Meanwhile news had arrived that James had fled to France. Tyrconnell, suspicious of Mountjoy's loyalty and anxious to get him out of the way before he became a leader of the Protestant rebels, sent him to France with a letter for James. Mountjoy refused to sail until Tyrconnell had agreed to certain conditions: no more levies should be made, no additional troops sent to Ulster, no more arms and no fresh commissions issued. Mountjoy was accompanied by Sir Stephen Rice, who carried a secret letter denouncing him as a traitor. On their arrival in Paris Mountjoy was thrown into the Bastille, where he remained until 1692, when he was exchanged for Richard Hamilton (who had been wounded and captured at the Boyne). He subsequently joined William's army as a volunteer and was killed at Steenkirk on 3 August 1692.

The portrait was probably painted when he was in his early thirties.

Sources:  *DNB*; J.G. Simms, *Jacobite Ireland 1685-91* (London, 1969); P. Macrory, *The Siege of Derry* (London, 1980).

## 82 *A New Map Of The City of Londonderry*
*with its Confines; As it was besieged by the Irish Army in the year 1689. Exactly Survey'd by Capt. Francis Nevill. c. 1694*

National Library of Ireland, Dublin

Engraving in three parts, each 50.5 x 40.5 cms.

Taken together, the three parts of the map show the river Foyle from above the city down to the fort at Culmore and the dispositions of the besiegers (identified by the names of the colonels). The nature of the ground, plantations, roads and pathways are indicated.

The left-hand section, containing the city itself, is headed by a cartouche bearing the legend *Printed by Edw: Sandys and are to be Sold at his House in Stephens Greene Dublin* surmounted by an elaborate display of the arms of the city topped by those of the bishop of Derry, all above the motto VITA VERITAS VICTORIA (Life, Truth, Victory). Alongside, in the top right-hand corner, is a picture of a monster fish with the caption:'This Fish was taken on ye

N:W: Side of ye Key of Derry on ye Lords day while the people were at Church by a Ship boy not long before the Shuting ye Gates; It was 4:foot long 2 foot broad, & 5 foot 3 inches from poynt to poynt of the finns;'

The middle section, headed by the title of the whole map, includes 'The Boome' across the river. The right-hand section has at top a cartouche, surmounted by three coats of arms, with the dedication 'To their Excellencyes Henry Lord Capell Baron of Tukesbury, Sr. Cyrill Wych Knt., & William Duncombe Esquire, Lords Justices and Generall Governours of Ireland This Map is humbly Dedicated by Edwin Sandys.' To the right of the cartouche is a picture of 'The East End of the church' [St Columb's]. In a panel at the bottom of the section is a view entitled 'The N:W: Prospect of the City' which shows the trajectories of the Jacobite artillery.

Francis Nevill (c.1648-1727) was a civil engineer. Little is known about his early life, but in 1689 he was acting as engineer to the corporation of Derry. On return from an official mission outside the city he was refused re-entry and soon after was taken prisoner by the Jacobites and sent to Dublin, where he managed to escape. Returning when the siege was over, he made a survey of the damage which was presented to the Irish Society. He also prepared a map of the siege which was subsequently published as part of a tract entitled *A Description of Londonderry as it was closely besieged by ye Army in April, 1689. A Description of the Towne and Workes about it. A Description of the Enemy's Camp.* This provided the material for Sandys's publication, the dedication of which places its date of publication between July 1693 and May 1695, when Capel, Wyche and Duncombe governed Ireland as lords justices.

Nevill became a burgess of the Corporation in December 1689. He was the architect and builder of the Town House (1692) which replaced the one destroyed in the siege.

Source:     R. Loeber, *Biographical Dictionary of Architects in Ireland 1600-1720* (London, 1981).

## 83 *'Londonderri': the siege of 1689*

BY OR IN THE STYLE OF ROMEYN DE HOOGHE
ULSTER MUSEUM, BELFAST

Engraving 24 x 56.5 cms; Dutch text; published by J. Tangena at Leyden.

In the key below, places and incidents are identified numerically 1-16 and alphabetically A-L. Numbers 1 and 2, on either side of the river Foyle, are separately identified as 'London' and 'derry', in the manner of Buda and Pest. (An English adaptation of this plate, gives 'Londonderry' as the key to 1 and 2 combined). From this, and also from the position of the windmill (not to mention the Vesuvius-like mountain in the background to right) it is obvious that the scene was composed from descriptions and maps.

**84**

'Londonderri' was the top half of a plate of which the lower part was a view of the siege of Bonn. The publisher, Johannes Tangena, was himself an engraver. He used the same plate, with adaptations, for a view of the siege of Athlone.

Source:     T.P. O'Neill, 'Dutch Engravings of the Williamite War, 1689',
            *Irish Book*, vol. 1, (1959-62).

## 84 *Jean-Bernard-Louis Desjean, Sieur de Pointis (1645-1705)*

By Henri Bonnart (1642-1711)
Bibliothèque National, Paris
Reproduction

Pointis was a French naval officer and artillery expert who was sent to Ireland in January 1689 to report on the situation there prior to the French decision to intervene. He was at the siege of Derry when news came that a relief force was being sent from England, and was entrusted with making a boom to block the river Foyle. According to his own account, his boom was made of beams studded with iron clamps through which ran a thick rope holding the beams together. The first boom, made of oak which would not float, was broken up by the tide. A second, made of fir, was more successful. Placed across the deep-water channel about two miles down-river from the city, with covering batteries at both ends, it was regarded as a formidable obstacle by the Williamites until forced on 28 July 1689.

Pointis had been badly wounded earlier in the siege, at Pennyburn on 25 April, but escaped probable death by refusing to be operated on by surgeons. He became famous later as the leader of a French expedition that captured the Spanish port of Cartagena in South America with an immense amount of treasure. He died at Gibraltar in 1705.

Source:     R. Loeber, 'Biographical Dictionary of Engineers in Ireland, 1660-1730,'
            *The Irish Sword*, vol. XIII, (1977-9).

**85**

## **85** *George Walker (1645?-90)*

BY AN UNKNOWN ARTIST
NATIONAL PORTRAIT GALLERY, LONDON

Oil on canvas 126.4 x 101 cms.

Donated by Olivia Charlotte, Lady Ardilaun, in 1924.

Prov:  Formerly in the Bantry collection at Macroom Castle. According to the donor, it is
not known when the picture came to Macroom, but it was certainly before 1800. It
perhaps belonged to an ancestor, Captain Richard Hedges, who fought at the Boyne
(where Walker was killed) and who bought the Macroom estates about 1703.

 Lit:  David Piper, *Catalogue of the Seventeenth Century Portraits in the National Portrait
Gallery 1625-1714* (Cambridge, 1963), pp. 365-6.

George Walker, soldier and militant Anglican priest, was born c. 1645, although
the *DNB*, Macaulay and other sources record his year of birth as 1618. His early
years are obscure but he is known to have matriculated at Trinity College,
Dublin in 1662, after which he took holy orders and was appointed to the
parishes of Lissan and Desertlyn in Co. Londonderry and Armagh diocese. In
1674 he assumed the rectorship of Donoughmore, near Dungannon, Co. Tyrone.
At the end of 1688, when the threat to Irish Protestants had become a reality
under Tyrconnell's administration and Derry's thirteen young Protestant
apprentices had closed the gates of the town to Catholic troops, he raised a
regiment at Dungannon and during the spring of 1689 saw service against the
approaching Jacobite army around Strabane and Coleraine.

On 13 April, receiving intelligence that the Jacobites were nearing Derry, he
hastened to warn Lundy, governor of the town and commander-in-chief of the
entire north-west. Lundy, however, refused to accept the seriousness of the
threat or take offensive action against the enemy. On the evening of the same
day, the council of war appointed him commander in the field and ordered 'all
officers and soldiers, horse, dragoons and foot, and all other armed men
whatsoever of our forces and friends, enlisted or not enlisted' (Macrory, p. 173)

to take the field at Cladyford, Lifford and Long Causey on the 15th. The ensuing encounter between Protestant and Jacobite forces ended in the rout of the former at Cladyford and Lifford and a retreat to Derry. So anxious was Lundy to save his own skin that when he got safely back to the town he ordered the gates to be closed, thereby excluding many of his own troops, to the number of between 4,000 and 8,000 men. Many of these were subsequently killed by the Jacobite forces. Others, however, managed to break into the town, among them Walker, with 'much difficulty and some violence upon the Centry' (Macrory, p. 180).

Though Lundy and the council of war eventually agreed to surrender the town, the vast majority of soldiers and citizens opposed this course of action. Rallied by Adam Murray, a young Ulster Scot who had commanded a force of yeomanry at the battle of Cladyford and Lifford, they deposed Lundy and the council and elected Major Henry Baker and Walker (who also held the rank of major) governors of the town. Walker and Baker immediately arranged for Lundy's escape, on the grounds that (to quote Walker) 'the Commission he bore, as well as their respect for his Person, made it a duty in them to contribute all they could to his safety' (Macrory, p. 190). Had he not escaped he would undoubtedly have been lynched as a traitor, his vacillation and lack of leadership having branded him as such to many of Derry's inhabitants.

Throughout the siege, which lasted until 28 July (OS), Walker acted as joint governor, first with Baker and after he died, with John Mitchelburn. Without doubt, his organisation and courage helped keep spirits high during the crisis. He was not above subterfuge when trying to raise the morale of his troops, as he recorded in his account of events: 'The men complain of want of Powder but by the contrivance of their Officer [ie., himself] a Bag of Mustard Seed was laid upon the carriages, which by its resemblance easily obtained the credit of a Bag of Powder and immediately gave motion to the Souldiers' (Macrory, p. 198). After the siege had been broken, Walker offered General Kirke (commander of the relief expedition to Derry) the command of his regiment. Kirke, however, declined and out of respect for Walker allowed him to dispose of his regiment as he thought best.

On 9 August Walker sailed for Glasgow, bearing with him a loyal address from Derry to the king. He was given a hero's welcome in Scotland and England, a gift of £5,000 from William and the promise of the bishopric of Derry once it fell vacant. In addition, the king commissioned Kneller to paint Walker's portrait. Other honours followed: the Irish Society gave him a banquet, Oxford and Cambridge awarded him honorary degrees and he was given the thanks of the House of Commons. Between these various activities, he prepared for publication his personal account of the siege, which appeared in September and went through several editions. (He was subsequently forced to publish a vindication of it, however, as it provoked fierce criticism from Derry's Presbyterians, who claimed that it failed to do justice to the part they had played in the defence of the town).

Walker returned to Ulster after his London visit and was about to become bishop of Derry when William invaded Ireland. He was one of the first to greet the king when he landed at Carrickfergus on 14 June and accompanied him to the Boyne, where he was killed (some said) when tending the wounded Schomberg. He was buried where he fell. Thirteen years later his widow had his body removed and buried at Donoughmore. A memorial pillar topped by a statue of him in clerical dress, erected in Derry in 1828, was blown up in 1973.

Walker's renown gave rise to many prints, the most important of which is by P. Vandrebanc, after the Kneller portrait. This portrays him as older and with heavier features than the NPG painting, which is probably posthumous and idealised.

Sources:    Piper, as above; *DNB*; Rev. P. Dwyer, A.M., ed.,*The Siege of Londonderry in 1689* (London, 1893; reprinted Wakefield, 1971); P. Macrory, *The Siege of Derry* (London, 1980).

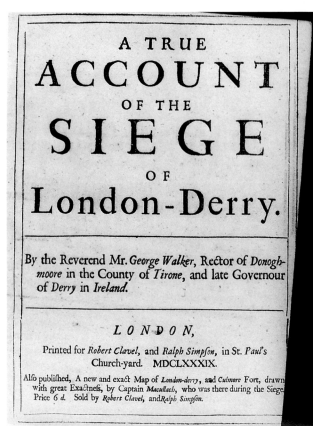

**86**

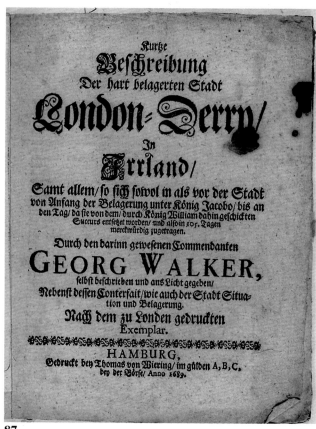

**87**

## 86 *Walker, George (1618-90)*
*A true account of the siege of London-Derry... London, printed for Robert Clavel and Ralph Simpson... MDCLXXXIX[1689]*

quarto:  59, [1] pp.
Lit:    Wing W350.

Licensed 13 September 1689; entered in Stationers' register on 14 September 1689; first appears in *Term Catalogue* in November 1689 but already as '3rd edition corrected.' This is the first edition. Ralph and Richard Simpson were the publishers of a number of controversial pamphlets on the siege of Londonderry

## 87 *Walker, George (1618-90)*
*Kurtze Beschreibung der hart belagerten Stadt London-Derry / in Irrland... Hamburg, gedruckt bey Thomas von Wiering... 1689*

quarto:  44 pp., folding plate.

This is a slightly abridged and adapted translation from the London edition of *A true account of the siege of London-Derry*, 1689. In addition to being a printer and publisher, Thomas von Wiering described himself as a block cutter (ref. Benzing, *Die Buchdrucker des 16. und 17. Jahrhunderts im deutschen Sprachgebiet*, 1963).

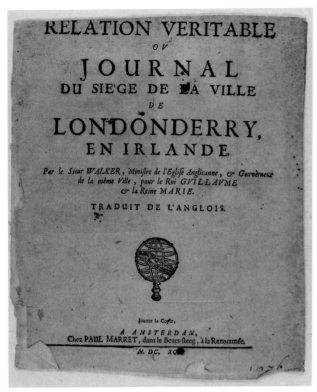

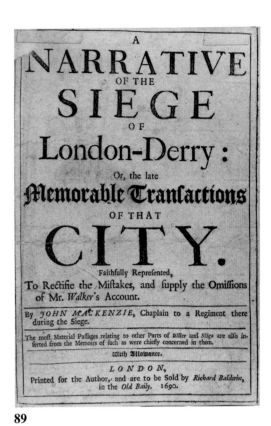

88              89

## 88 *Walker, George (1618-90)*

*Relation veritable ou journal du siège de la ville de Londonderry, en Irlande... Traduit de l' Anglois... A Amsterdam, chez Paul Marret... MDCXC[1690]*

THE QUEEN'S UNIVERSITY, BELFAST

quarto: 44 pp., folding plate.

This pamphlet is a straight translation of the London edition of *A true account of the siege of London-Derry,* 1689.

## 89 *Mackenzie, John*

*A Narrative of the Siege of London-Derry: Or, the late Memorable Transactions of that City Faithfully Represented, To Rectifie the Mistakes, and supply the Omissions of Mr.Walker's Account. By John Mackenzie, Chaplain to a Regiment there during the Siege. London 1690*

ULSTER MUSEUM, BELFAST

octavo: [6], 64 pp.

John Mackenzie of Derryloran was the Presbyterian chaplain in Walker's own regiment during the siege. Like many of the Presbyterian defenders, he felt that Walker had attempted to steal all the credit for himself and the Episcopalians. For example, Walker had praised the conduct of the eighteen clergy of the established church who had taken part (five were killed) and named them all in an appendix, whereas he professed not to have been able to learn the names of any of the seven Nonconformist clergy, depite the fact that Mackenzie was a chaplain in his own regiment.

In his *Narrative* Mackenzie suggested that Walker had never been a governor of the city at all, only a kind of quartermaster (and a corrupt one). He also accused him of cowardice and drunkenness - 'guilty of shedding no other blood to stain his coat but that of the grape' - and, worse still, of having plotted to betray the place like another Lundy. Mackenzie's hero was Adam Murray, a Scots settler who proved to be a dashing leader of cavalry.

Not surprisingly, more pamphlets followed on both sides, until Walker's death at the Boyne put him beyond the reach of his critics. Discounting its personal venom, the *Narrative* is a valuable record that does indeed supply many omissions in Walker's hastily written account.

## 90 *James Fitzjames, Duke of Berwick (1670-1734)*

BY SIR GODFREY KNELLER (1646-1723)
THE EARL OF ROSEBERY, DALMENY, NR. EDINBURGH

Oil on canvas 124.4 x 99 cms (sight).

James Fitzjames, Duke of Berwick was the son of James, Duke of York, afterwards James II, and Arabella Churchill (sister of John Churchill, later Duke of Marlborough), James's mistress for a number of years. James and Arabella (described by the Count de Grammont as 'a tall creature, pale-faced, nothing but skin and bone ... an ugly skeleton') had three other children: Henry, grand prior of France and Duke of Albemarle, Henrietta and another daughter who became a nun. Born at Moulins in France on 21 August 1670, Fitzjames was educated in France by the Jesuits. His military career began at the age of sixteen with service under the Duke of Lorraine in Hungary, fighting the Turks. There he quickly distinguished himself and showed that he had both courage and common sense. In the spring of 1687 he visited England where his father, now king, created him Duke of Berwick, Earl of Teignmouth and Baron Bosworth. He later returned to Hungary and served another campaign under Lorraine. In 1688 James summoned him to England and appointed him governor of Portsmouth. At the Revolution he fled to France to join his father.

In February 1689 he and his brother Henry accompanied James to Ireland, where they landed at Kinsale on 12 March. The French fleet which had brought James consisted of twenty-two ships, officers, men and ammunition, together with a number of James's Irish, Scots and English supporters, including the Duke of Powis, Lord Thomas Howard and Colonel Patrick Sarsfield. Berwick worked hard at raising troops among the Irish Catholics. Henry's performance, however, was not so impressive: according to the French ambassador d'Avaux, he was a 'quarrelsome young sot ... [who] got so drunk every day after his arrival in Ireland that he was incapable of mounting a horse all that summer.' Berwick subsequently served at the siege of Derry and commanded a force against the Enniskillingers. He later fought at the Boyne, and after Tyrconnell's departure for France on 12 September 1690 to report on the Irish situation to James was placed in supreme command of the Jacobite forces in Ireland. This was an unpopular choice with the army, which was hostile to Tyrconnell, considered Berwick too young and too much under Tyrconnell's thumb, and wanted Sarsfield as leader.

On Tyrconnell's return in January 1691 Berwick left Ireland for France. He had a distinguished military career in the army of Louis XIV and was made a marshal of France in 1706. Although he was implicated in the assassination plot on William's life in 1696, he later refused to become involved in the attempt by his half-brother, the 'Old Pretender,' to regain the English throne in 1715. His first wife (whom he married against his father's wishes) was Sarsfield's widow Honora.

The portrait, painted when he was in his early twenties, shows him as handsome and vigorous, with a commanding presence and confident gaze.

Sources: *DNB*; J.G. Simms, *The Williamite Confiscation in Ireland 1690-1703* (London, 1956); J.G.Simms, *Jacobite Ireland 1685-91* (London, 1969).

## 91 *Anthony Hamilton (1646?-1720)*

BY ALEXIS-SIMON BELLE (1674-1734)
DUKE OF HAMILTON, LENNOXLOVE

Oil on canvas 72.4 x 58.4 cms.

Anthony Hamilton was the third of the six sons of Sir George Hamilton and a grandson of James, first Earl of Abercorn. Born probably at Roscrea, Co. Tipperary, he spent his early years in France, where his family settled in 1651. After the Restoration they moved to England and were given new lands in Ireland and other royal favours.

**90**

Photo G R Studios, Edinburgh

**91**    Photo G R Studios, Edinburgh

In l668 Anthony joined his brother George's troop of Catholic ex-soldiers bound
for service in France. The previous year, all Catholics in Charles's Royal Guards
- George Hamilton among them - had been cashiered for refusing to take the
Oath of Supremacy. (Five of the Hamilton brothers were Catholic; only James,
the eldest, became a Protestant). In l671 Anthony and his younger brother
Richard joined a regiment of foot which George raised in Ireland for the service
of Louis XIV. All three served on the Continent during the Anglo-Dutch war of
l672-4, fighting in the Anglo-French alliance; George was later killed fighting
against the Dutch. His widow Frances (née Jennings, whose sister Sarah
married John Churchill, Duke of Marlborough) subsequently married Richard
Talbot, afterwards viceroy of Ireland and Earl and Duke of Tyrconnell. This
alliance was to be fruitful for the military careers of the Hamilton brothers; both
Anthony and Richard, despite indifferent abilities as soldiers, were always to
remain in Tyrconnell's favour, even after their dismal efforts at Derry
and Enniskillen.

About l678 Anthony left France. After an unsuccessful attempt at farming
in Ireland, he fled to England to avoid his creditors and resumed his military
career. He returned to Ireland as lieutenant-colonel of Sir Thomas Newcomen's
regiment of foot and in l685 was appointed governor of Limerick. The following
year Richard was appointed to the Irish privy council and was made brigadier of
a regiment of dragoons which he had raised and brought from England. In late
l686 Anthony too was made a privy councillor. Promotion to colonel followed
in February l687, after Tyrconnell became lord lieutenant. Two years later
Tyrconnell promoted him to brigadier.

In July l689, now major-general, he and his regiment of dragoons joined
Mountcashel's forces in an attack on Enniskillen, the second centre of Protestant
resistance in the north. In the battle of Newtownbutler his regiment suffered
severe losses; he himself was wounded and fled in panic as far as Navan,
Co. Meath. He was subsequently court-martialled but was acquitted; his
subordinate officer, however, was convicted and executed, a verdict greeted with
disgust by many. D'Avaux, the French ambassador who accompanied James to
Ireland, maintained that Anthony did not merit his high rank and had been
promoted to major-general only to please Tyrconnell. His brother Richard's
failure at the same time to take Derry was also severely criticised by d'Avaux.

Anthony, Richard and their youngest brother John, a brigadier, fought at the
Boyne, where Richard was wounded and captured. Anthony and John went to
Limerick with other Jacobites and endured the siege. All three were outlawed in

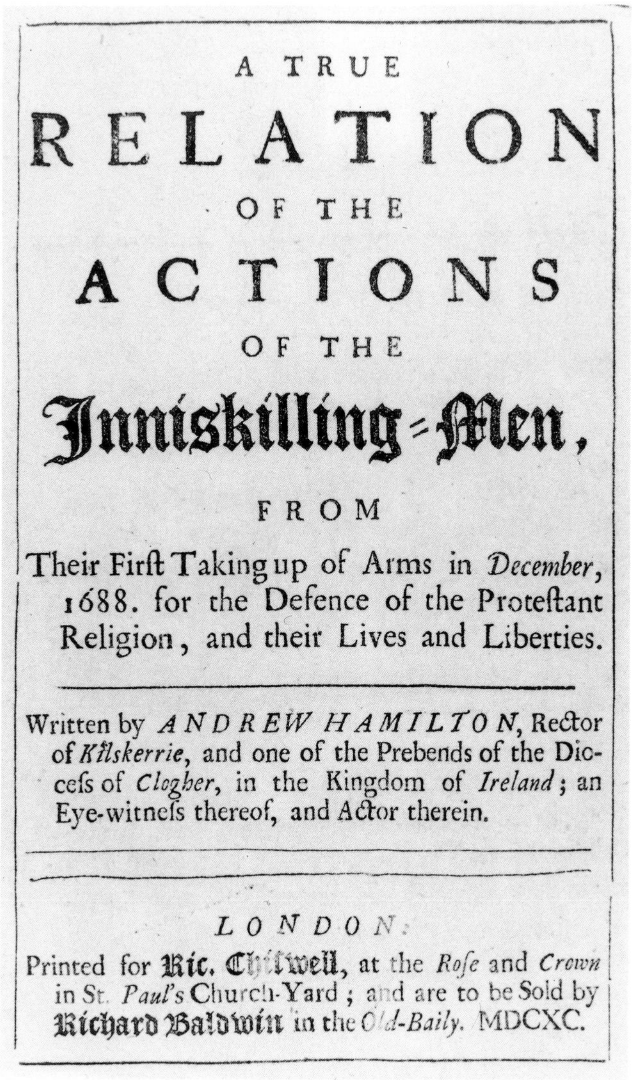

A TRUE

# RELATION

OF THE

# ACTIONS

OF THE

## Inniskilling-Men,

FROM

Their First Taking up of Arms in *December*,
1688. for the Defence of the Protestant
Religion, and their Lives and Liberties.

Written by *ANDREW HAMILTON*, Rector
of *Kilskerrie*, and one of the Prebends of the Dioces of *Clogher*, in the Kingdom of *Ireland*; an
Eye-witness thereof, and Actor therein.

*LONDON:*

Printed for **Ric. Chiswell**, at the *Rose* and *Crown*
in St. *Paul's* Church-Yard ; and are to be Sold by
**Richard Baldwin** in the *Old-Baily.* MDCXC.

**92**

1691. John died in the same year. Richard and Anthony went to France, where the former died in extreme poverty in December 1717. Anthony, who obtained the title of count at an unknown date, spent the rest of his life at the court of the exiled King James at St Germains, where he became a notable author (his *Mémoires du Comte de Grammont*, based on his brother-in-law's recollections of the scandalous court of Charles II, was particularly admired). He died on 21 April 1720.

The French portrait painter Alexis-Simon Belle, whose family were Protestant craftsmen probably from the north of France, worked for the Jacobite court with his master François de Troy. After his marriage in November 1701 he settled in Paris. He became highly popular with the French and Polish royal families, being first employed by the French court in 1722. His work is decorative and somewhat florid, with much attention paid to rich materials.

Sources:    *DNB*; R. Clark, *Anthony Hamilton His Life and Works and His Family* (London, 1921); J.G. Simms, *Jacobite Ireland 1685-91* (London, 1969); information on the artist from Fabienne Camus.

## 92 *Hamilton, Andrew (d. 1691)*

*A true relation of the actions of the Inniskilling-men, from the first taking up of arms in December 1688... London: printed for Ric. Chiswell... and are to be sold by Richard Baldwin... MDCXC [1690]*

THE QUEEN'S UNIVERSITY, BELFAST

quarto: [3], ix, 65, [1] pp.
Lit:    Wing H476.

94

Published between 15 January (Licence) and February (*Term Catalogue*) 1690. The pamphlet covers the period up to August 1689. Hamilton gives the Church of Ireland view. The Presbyterian version of the events, *A further account of the history of the Inniskilling men*, was written by William MacCormick and published in 1691 (before November, *Term Catalogue*).

### 93 *More Good News From Ireland,*
*giving a faithful account ... of the English army there under the command of his grace Duke Schomberg (London, 1689)*

ULSTER MUSEUM

The 'good news' of this Williamite pamphlet was of Schomberg's successful landing in Co. Down and easy advance into Ulster.

### 94 *Victory of the Enniskillen garrison over the Irish*

PRINT PUBLISHED IN AMSTERDAM BY ADRIAAN SCHOONEBEEK
ULSTER MUSEUM, BELFAST
REPRODUCTION

This picture of an engagement outside the walls of a fortified town was almost certainly adapted from an existing print and has nothing to do with Enniskillen. It does, however, illustrate how pikemen, musketeers and cavalry of the time fought, as well as the fame of the Enniskillingers.

### 95 *Londonderry relieved, 1689*

MEDAL BY ANON
ULSTER MUSEUM, BELFAST

Silver, 45 mm.
Lit:     *Medallic Illustrations*, 697, no. 97.

96

Description: obv. bust of William III, laureate and draped over armour, on a pedestal, with a laurel wreath being held over it jointly by, on the left, a draped female with a cornucopia representing Plenty, and on the right another female, wearing armour and a plumed helmet and carrying a book with an olive branch, representing Pallas. Above are the rays of the sun. Behind is a battle scene with ships advancing on a town.

legend: (on the pedestal) WILHELM: MAXIMUS IN.BELGICA LIBERATOR IN.BRITANNIA RESTAURATOR [William the Great, in the Netherlands a liberator, in Britain a restorer]; (below, in italic script): LIB: LONDONDERRY 1689 [Londonderry freed, 1689].

rev. bust of Louis XIV in armour with a *fleur de lis* on his shoulder, being crowned with a broken laurel wreath by a female representing Germania who holds a burning city and has a burning torch at her feet. On the right a similar female representing Gallia, with an empty basket at her feet. Both have shackles on their legs and are draped in tattered short dresses decorated with the symbols of their countries. Behind are burning towns and scenes of siege; above are clouds and bolts of lightning.

legend: (on pedestal) LUDOVIC MAGNUS INGERMANIA BARBARVS IN.GALLIA TYRRANUS [Louis the Great, in Germany a barbarian, in France a tyrant]; (below in italic script): OBS: MOGUNT; ET BONAE [sieges of Mayence and Bonn].

Making a contrast between Louis and William was commonplace and this medal is a quite successful exploitation of the form. The two portraits, deliberately formal, are both quite accurate and alike, in itself a subtle comment. The addition of the legends about Londonderry, Mayence and Bonn (the latter two cities Louis had lost in 1689), seems almost an afterthought, the main points being made by the depictions of the personifications. It was well known that France was over-stretched financially, hence the empty basket. The ragged clothing of Germania and Gallia perhaps allude to the fact that Louis was responsible for the war that was impoverishing Europe. All this is in contrast with William, who is not a besieger or a loser of cities but a bringer of relief and prosperity. Pallas is a goddess who has many attributes: she is associated with war and virginity (or purity), but more relevant here is her patronage of wisdom and truth.

## 96 *Londonderry relieved and the French and Irish army under the Duke of Berwick beaten*

PRINT PUBLISHED IN AMSTERDAM BY ADRIAAN SCHOONEBEEK
ULSTER MUSEUM, BELFAST
REPRODUCTION

The engagement depicted in the foreground of this print does not illustrate any particular incident in the siege, least of all the way it ended, and may have been adapted from an existing engraving. The ships on the river in the background do appear to represent the breaking of the boom, however.

## 97 *The Freke porringer and cover 1685-6*

BY JOHN CUTHBERT, DUBLIN
ULSTER MUSEUM, BELFAST

Silver, height 15.3 cms. hallmarks on base and lid; the arms of Freke engraved on the bowl. Purchased London 1959.

The octagonal bowl has scroll handles and each face is engraved with chinese-style birds and foliage. The domed lid has a ridged octagonal border and a hollow acanthus finial. It is probable that the porringer belonged to Elizabeth Freke, who married her cousin, Percy Freke of Rathbarry Castle, Co.Cork. In her diary, an inventory of October 1686 records a 'large silver porringer' among other items in her 'uper closett over the hall', at Billney, her own house in Norfolk.

Source:    'The Diaries of Miss Elizabeth Freke', *Cork Historical and Archaeological Society Journal*, 2nd Series, vols. 16, 17 and 18 (1910-12).

## 98a-b *Pair of candlesicks, c. 1685-7*

BY JOHN SEGAR, DUBLIN
NATIONAL MUSEUM OF IRELAND, DUBLIN (5/6-1962)

Silver, height 15.5 cms.
Exh:    *The Company of Goldsmiths of Dublin 1637-1987*, NMI 1987 (9), repr. p. 7;
        UM April-June 1989.

Chased in the Chinese manner with plants, fruit, flowers and birds, most of which are exotic, and with a human figure on each, in different types of oriental costume. Stamped with the maker's mark IS (John Segar), the harp crowned and the date letter G for 1685-7.

    While these candlesticks are a pair and part of a toilet set, the decorative figures on each are different, though executed in the same style.

## 99 *Tankard c. 1690*

BY CHARLES BEKEGLE, CORK
NATIONAL MUSEUM OF IRELAND, DUBLIN (58-1946)

Silver, height 17.8 cms.

The cylindrical body narrows slightly upwards and has a reeded rim and base. The lid is stepped and has a flange with serrated foliate decoration at front and a thumbpiece in the form of a double volute with a shell and a leaf feature. The handle has a shield-shaped terminal below. Stamped on the lid and under the rim twice with the maker's mark CB (Charles Bekegle) and a castle.

**97**

**98a-b**

**99**

# 4. The Propaganda War

Propaganda in various forms played an important part in the struggle between William and James. Of the two, William was much the more conscious of the need to win hearts and minds to his cause, since (however the fact was disguised) he had usurped the crown. James relied, to the point of complacency, on his position as legitimate ruler by divine right. The fact that William got control of London early on put James at a great disadvantage (the French, on whom James then had to rely, had other priorities). Williamite propaganda was also much more effective and attractive than that of the Jacobites, for William could call upon the most gifted artists of the day in these matters, such as his favourite medallist Arondeaux and, above all, the great engraver and designer Romeyn de Hooghe.

The war of words and images was waged principally in England and on the Continent. In Ireland minds were already firmly made up, on both sides, according to religious belief. Since the religious issue was the most important one so far as propagandists were concerned, events in Ireland nevertheless figured prominently in their work. James's reliance on Irish Catholics was a gift to Williamite propagandists, who exploited traditional prejudices against both their religion (the connection between Catholicism and persecution and Catholicism and absolutism was emphasised) and their Irishness - either fearsome or laughable, according to the effect intended. The song *Lilliburlero*, which sang James out of three kingdoms, cleverly used both. In propaganda terms Ireland was one of the James's greatest liabilities.

Propaganda items ranged from luxury goods of high quality such as expensive books, medals and engravings for the richer members of society who might influence politics, to humble household objects such as plates and playing cards. At the lowest level both sides produced scurrilous attacks on the character and morals of their opponents. Mary of Modena, James's queen, was portrayed as the object of the lusts of Father Petre, her husband's Jesuit confessor, or Louis XIV. William's hunched appearance - 'he has gotten in part the shape of a man, but more of a monkey, deny it who can' - was ridiculed by the Jacobites, who also accused him of homosexual practices with his male favourites. These attacks were more effective in the later years of William's reign, after Mary's death, when the Dutch king with his Dutch favourites and his cold, reserved manner was deeply unpopular with his English subjects, who had forgotten how much they owed to him.

**100**

## 100 *The Usurpers Habit*

By an unknown artist
British Museum, London

Print 40.6 x 30.5 cms (mount); English text.

This engraving shows Louis XIV seated at a table, the cover of which is embroidered with dancing devils and fires. His habit (i.e., dress) is covered with representations of places he has seized. His hat, which has a model of the town of Limerick, lies on the table; an onlooker with a lantern remarks, 'He begins to unrigg [undress]', a reference to the surrender of Limerick on 3 October 1691. A key below names twenty-four towns and fortresses wrongfully in Louis's possession. They include William's principality of Orange and the following Irish places in addition to Limerick : Athlone, Charlemont, Sligo and Galway. There are twelve lines of verse, viz.

> 'How proudly Lewis sitts upon his Throne
> Embroidered o're with Towns were not his own
> As Aesops Jay did from the feathered Race
> Snatch Plumes to look with more Majestick grace
> But all the Birds affronted at the Theif
> Of's borrowed feathers did him soon bereave
> So that proud Monarch must his fate Deplore
> And all his Thefts and conquests soon restore
> Mons, Strasbourg, Nice & Other Towns Hee Stole
> Will follow Athlone, Limerick, Carmagnole
> This mighty Work for William is Design'd
> The Scourge of France, and Darling of Mankind'

Source:     *BM Catalogue,* vol. II, no. 1267.

*L' Epiphane du Noveau Antichrist. 1689*

**101**

## 101  *L'Epiphane du Noveau Antichrist*
### *(Epiphany of the New Antichrist)*

BY ROMEYN DE HOOGHE (1645-1708)
BRITISH MUSEUM, LONDON

Print 39 x 35 cms; Dutch text.

This Dutch broadside shows (1) James II wearing a Jesuit cap, with holy water and a rosary at his girdle, pulling a rope to keep the sails of a windmill in motion. The windmill, which has an orb (b) surrounded by the mitres of the seven bishops arrested by James in June 1688, is attached to a pole held by (2) Louis XIV, who is in armour. Between them is the dauphin (a). On one side stands (4) Cardinal Furstenberg holding a standard inscribed *L'Electoral Imaginaire,* a reference to his failure to become Archbishop Elector of Cologne. Behind him is Father Petre, and in front (6) James's queen and the Prince of Wales (c) playing with his windmill toy. To the right of the picture are (3) the Pope holding a cardinal's hat for Petre and (7) the emperor Leopold, 'destroyer of the Turks', with a cap of liberty on the point of his lance. In the distance Catholic churches are being destroyed, rebels are being executed and the French sun is sinking.

*Panurge secondé par Arlequin Deodaat.*
*a la Croisade d'jrlande. 1689.*

Hanard de bon aventure. fec. et exc.

**102**

The feast of the Epiphany in the Christian calendar (6 January) celebrates the showing of the infant Christ to the three wise men.

This is one of the anti-French and anti-Jacobite caricatures for which de Hooghe is said to have been rewarded by William III.

Source: *BM Catalogue*, vol. 1, no. 1167.

## 102 *Panurge secondé par Arlequin Deodaat ala Croisade d'Irelande 1689*
*(Panurge supported by Arlequin Deodaat setting out on the Irish crusade)*

ANONYMOUS, BY OR IN THE STYLE OF ROMEYN DE HOOGHE
BRITISH MUSEUM, LONDON

Print 46 x 38 cms; Dutch text.

This Dutch broadside depicts (1) 'Panurge' (James II, with a pilgrim's hat and Red Indian leggings to show that he is a homeless wanderer) saying goodbye to his queen, who with her right hand is fondling the face of his friend (2)

Arlequin sur l'Hippogryphe ala Croisade Lojoliste

Armée van de Heylige Lingue voor der Jesuiten Monarchy.

**103**

'Arlequin Deodaat' (Louis XIV), who fills James's purse with gold. Behind Louis is (3) Father Petre with the Prince of Wales and his windmill toy. The armoured figure on horseback is the dauphin before whom, mounted on a cock, is Cardinal Furstenberg (Louis's nominee for the archbishopric of Cologne). In the boat 'Jonge Bastert Panurges' (Panurge's young bastard, namely James Fitzjames, Duke of Berwick) is drinking.

Mary of Modena's dowry on her marriage to James (then Duke of York) was paid by Louis; this was the origin of the sexual scandal hinted at in the picture.

Panurge was the licentious, cowardly and debt-ridden companion of Pantagruel in Rabelais's *History of Gargantua and Pantagruel*. Arlequin (Harlequin in English) was one of the stock characters of Italian comedy. 'Deodaat' is a Dutch translation of 'Dieudonne' - the God-given - as Louis was described at his birth.

Source:     *BM Catalogue,* vol. 1, no. 1194.

## 103 *Arlequin sur l'Hippogryphe ala Croisade Lojoliste*
### *(Harlequin on the Wild Ass to the Jesuit crusade)*

BY OR IN THE STYLE OF ROMEYN DE HOOGHE
BRITISH MUSEUM, LONDON

Print 38.4 x 33.6 cms; Dutch text.

This complicated broadside depicts Arlequin (Louis XIV) with a wooden leg and Panurge (James II), both wearing the one Jesuit hat, mounted on a wild ass. The beast also carries a ciborium and stoup of holy water, and the shield of the Fifth Monarchy of the Jesuits with the monogram 1HS and the letters L for Loyola (founder of the Jesuits) and J for Jesuit. Father Petre (3) rides a lobster, carries the new-born Antichrist (the Pretender with his windmill) and has a papal crown behind him. The bishop of Strasbourg, fallen from a tortoise, lies in the Rhine, nearly losing his cardinal's hat. The young man (2), creeping in a box on a toad's back, is presumably the dauphin. Behind him, fighting orders of monks carry banners honouring those who have murdered kings and plotted massacres.

**104**

To their right (11) is the peculiar grave of the Jesuits in England, namely the gallows.

Source:     *BM Catalogue*, vol. 1, no. 1205.

## 104  *Hy Holt  Hy Holt*
### *(He runs! He runs!)*

BY AN UNKNOWN ARTIST
BRITISH MUSEUM, LONDON

Print 17.5 x 23.7 cms; Dutch text.

This mezzotint illustrating the probable failure of James II's cause in Ireland is an adaptation of de Hooghe's etching *Arlequin sur l'Hippogryphe ala Croisade Lojoliste* (see no. 103). James (2) and his friend Louis XIV (1) are mounted on the wild ass of 'Jesuit monarchy'. Below, Father Petre (4), carrying a stoup of holy water and holding the Prince of Wales, is mounted on a lobster. They are departing for Ireland, but have been halted by the young man in armour (3), presumably William. James is falling backwards, apparently wounded, while Louis urges him to have courage. The figure (5) at bottom right is the bishop of Strasbourg, a city seized by Louis in 1681 during a time of peace. He has fallen off a tortoise into the river Rhine and is trying to hold on to his cardinal's hat.

Source:     *BM Catalogue*, vol. II, no. 1236.

105

## 105 *Pantagruel Agonisant*

BY ROMEYN DE HOOGHE (1645-1708), UNDER THE PSEUDONYM J. MARLAIS
BRITISH MUSEUM, LONDON

Print 35 x 26.7 cms; Dutch and French text.

This etching represents a bedchamber where Pantagruel (Louis XIV) is dying.
The heart-shaped jewel on his breast is engraved with an orb of sovereignty, to
indicate his lust for power, and surmounted by a crescent, a reference to his
scandalous alliance with the Turks. Round him are gathered the Devil (1), his
mistresses and his ministers. 'Le Roy Courier' (James II, with a bugle to indicate
his wandering and unsettled life) sits on a chair; his son 'the Jesuit Prince', with
a little Jesuit's cap and windmill toy, stands at his knees. Father Petre (28) sits
alone telling his beads. In the foreground is a picture of *La mort imaginaire du
Roy Guillaume gravé à Paris 1690*, a mocking reference to the print produced by
the French to mark the (false) news of William's death. 'Pantagruel Agonisant',
in fact, was the Williamite answer to that print. Through the archway to the right
'Tyrconel' (21) and 'Sarsfield' (22) kneel in submission before a resurrected
King William.

Source:     *BM Catalogue*, vol. II, no. 1245.

De onverwagte Tijding uyt Yerlandt, aen den
Koninck van Vranckrijck.

**106**

**106** *De onverwagte Tijding uyt Yerlandt, aen den
Koninck van Vranckrijck*
*(The unexpected News from Ireland, to the King of France)*

BY P-BO-SC [?ROMEYN DE HOOGHE]
BRITISH MUSEUM, LONDON

Print 30.5 x 19.1 cms; Dutch text.

This satirical etching celebrates the supposed effect of the battle of the Boyne on
Louis XIV. Louis lies in bed attended by (4) a Turkish doctor and (6) an Irish
doctor; a heart surmounted by a crescent is embroidered on his garment - a
reference to his reputed alliance with the Sultan against the emperor Leopold.
Two devils (3) lurk behind, ready to carry Louis off. Father Petre (7), in Jesuit's
cap, travelling clothes and riding boots, holds a letter with the bad news of
James's defeat. According to the text the figure (9) is a papal doctor receiving
the letter and concluding from it that King William is dead, which will cheer the
patient up. The figure (11) in the doorway, wearing a Turkish turban, is the
messenger who is maimed and on crutches because he brings bad news.

Source:       *BM Catalogue*, vol. II, no. 1246.

**107a**

## 107a-b *Reported death of William III (1690)*

By an unknown artist
British Museum, London

French prints published in Paris (a) 26.7 x 21 cms (b) 31.8 x 21.5 cms. [a copy]; French text.

While reconnoitring the enemy position on 30 June 1690, the day before the battle of the Boyne, William was slightly injured by a cannon ball aimed at his party by Jacobite gunners. When news reached Paris that he had been killed bonfires were lit and there was great rejoicing. The first of these two prints (a) was produced to celebrate the event. It shows William's body being borne to its grave, followed by male figures representing the Dutch, the Scots, the English and the Irish. In the distance beside a gallows Prince George (Anne's husband), holding a bottle and glass, rejoices because William's death brings his wife one step nearer to the English throne. The names of 'Halifax,' 'Burnet,' 'Sheubury,' 'Dikvelt,' 'Portlant' and 'La Princesse d'Orange' are inscribed below the characters, and ten bitterly anti-Williamite verses above and below. The copy (b) has the names engraved above the heads of the characters ('brunet' for Burnet, 'Shreuburi' for Shrewsbury) and five verses below, as well as a 'Billet d'Enterrement' top left and an 'Epitaphe' top right. The main difference between (b) and the original (a), however, is the addition (to right) of a walled city, 'Londre.' and a picture of Hell with 'Schombert' chained amid devils in the flames and William descending on the back of a dragon.

On their lower margins, both prints have manuscript ironic verses 'faits sur l'entree de Mylord Portland ambassadeur de Guillaume 3e Roy de la Grande Bretagne a Paris le 9e Mars 1698.'

Source:     *BM Catalogue*, vol. II, nos. 1241 and 1242.

**107b**

### 108 *Folies Extravagantes De La France Sur La Mort Imaginaire De Guillaume III*
*(Ridiculous Follies of France on the supposed death of King William III)*

BY AN UNKNOWN ARTIST
BRITISH MUSEUM, LONDON

'Copie sur l'original Gravé a Paris,' print 32.4 x 23.7 cms; French text.

The rejoicings in France following the false report of William's death at the Boyne were a gift to Williamite propagandists. In this print, 'copied from the original engraved in Paris,' the French print is used to make mock of the premature and unseemly celebrations in various parts of France (detailed in the accompanying text), which merely confirmed the status William had attained in the eyes of his enemies.

Source:          *BM Catalogue*, vol. II, no. 1243.

## FOLIES EXTRAVAGANTES DE LA FRANCE
### SVR LA MORT IMAGINAIRE
### DE GUILLAUME III· ROY DE LA GRAND' BRETAGNE, PRINCE D'ORENGE, &c.

Pleurez. Heretiques. pleurez,
Et vous. Potentats conjurez,
Qui vous flattez de mettre un jour la France en poudre
Le Tyran des Anglois GUILLAUME est au cercueil;
Le Ciel a confondu son crime et son orgueil,
LOUIS l'a fait tomber sous sa puissante foudre;
DICKWELT et Shrevsburi Burnet avec Portland,
De ses lâches fureurs Ministres detestables.
Portent son Cadavre sanglant,
Ou les becs des Corbeaux attendent les coupables.

Veritables Anglois, triomphez et riez,
Et vous tous, Princes Alliez,
Esperez de réduire un jour la France en poudre.
Le Heros est vivant qu'on mettoit au Cercueil;
Dieu veut par luy confondre et le crime et l'orgueil,
Et terrasser LOVIS par sa puissante foudre:
Il exterminera ses Flateurs insolens.
Des fureurs du tyran Ministres detestables;
Les Bourreaux traineront leurs Cadavres sanglans,
Ou les becs des Corbeaux attendent les coupables.

108

## 109  *The Protestant Grind-Stone*

BY AN UNKNOWN ARTIST
BRITISH MUSUEM, LONDON

English print 37 x 18.5 cms; English text.

This rare surviving example of an English anti-papal print shows 'King' William
and 'Queen' Mary pressing the Pope's nose against a grindstone, which is turned
by Sancroft, archbishop of Canterbury and Compton, bishop of London. To the
left are a monk, a friar, the devil wearing a Jesuit's cap, a Jesuit and a cardinal,
all lamenting; to the right 'Schomberg', Halifax and Burnet. The presence of
Schomberg may refer to the Williamite campaign of 1689 in Ireland, as well as
to the persecution of the French Protestants (which Pope Innocent XI in fact
condemned). The Scottish cleric Burnet accompanied William on his invasion as
his chaplain and was subsequently made bishop of Salisbury; his *History of his
Own Time* is the major contemporary account of the period from a Williamite
point of view.

The eight lines of verse are typical of the harshly controversial tone of these
propaganda productions:

> 'Old Holy Father, there was once a time
> When Clemency was thought a mortall Crime
> For Hereticks no pitty you could find:
> But, most Severely did their Faces Grind,

115

The Protestant Grind-Stone.

Schomberg

Queen    King

Old Holy Father, there was once a time
When Clemency was thought a mortall Crime
For Heriticks no pitty you could find:
But most Severely did their Faces Grind.

The time's now turn'd, harsh Stripes upon you fall.
Too well deserv'd, and this is done that all
Who see the Whore of Babylon may Say.
Shee's pox't because her nose is worn away.

**109**

The time's now turn'd, harsh Stripes upon you fall,
Too well deserv'd, and this is done that all
Who see the Whore of Babylon may Say.
Shee's pox't because her nose is worn away.'

Source:     *BM Catalogue*, vol. II, no. 1255.

## 110 *The Scientifik three horned Doctor, Father Peters, a great Labourer, in Works of Darkness*

BY AN UNKNOWN ARTIST
BRITISH MUSEUM, LONDON

Dutch copy of a print published in London 41.3 x 27.3 cms; Dutch text.

The title of the Dutch verses printed below this engraving translates as 'The Workshop of Father Peters and the Jesuits in England, revealed through Eusebius and Simplicius.' As a leading force on the Catholic side in the Counter-Reformation, the Jesuits were seen by their opponents as sinister and malign. In the alchemist's den shown here James II's confessor and other Jesuits, with the help of devils, superstitiously consult the stars, make idols, forge chains for oppressed Protestants and sharpen weapons for the propagation of the faith.

Source:     *BM Catalogue*, vol. 1, no. 1209.

*The scientifik three horned Doctor, Father PETERS, a great Labourer, in Works of Darcknefs.*
à Londres chez Paul van Sommerset.

# Het STOOKHUYS van
# PATER PETERS,
## en der Jesuiten in Engeland, ontdekt door
### EUSEBIUS en SIMPLICIUS.

**111**

**111** *De Laaste Afsceydts Dronck van Koninck Jacobus by het verlies van de Zeeslag met de Koninck van Vranckryck na het Clooster*
*(The last Farewell Drink of King James, on losing the sea-fight, with the King of France)*

BY AN UNKNOWN ARTIST
BRITISH MUSEUM, LONDON

Print 42.5 x 35 cms; Dutch text.

This engraving celebrates the end of James II's hopes of invading England in May 1692, when the French invasion fleet was destroyed by the Anglo-Dutch at Barfleur and La Hogue; the two crossed brooms behind the title indicate the sweeping of the sea. Louis XIV, risen from his chair of state, is holding the parting cup and shaking hands with James, in monk's robes, from whose shaven head slips a crown; 'veni, vidi,' ('I came, I saw') on the hem of his robe are not accompanied by 'vici' ('I conquered') - a reference to the fact that James actually watched the battle from a clifftop. Behind him Father Petre looks at the battle through a telescope and pulls at James's robe to tell him he must save himself quickly by retiring to a monastery. To the left James appears again as a cowled monk seated in a low wagon drawn by a cock (France), which is being driven hard by a dog and a lion (Holland); monks come out of the monastery to receive him. In the background his queen (M) and the Pretender (L) are nearing the steps of a mill; the boy runs in order to avoid his false mother and to join his true father, the miller (O). On the horizon Louis's sun emblem is setting in the

**112**

sea; his proud motto 'Nec pluribus impar' (literally 'not unequal to many', meaning 'equal to anyone') has been replaced by 'et Pluribus impar' ('unequal to many').

Source:       *BM Catalogue*, vol. II, no. 1278.

## 112   *The Irish monster (1690)*

BY E. BÄCK
BRITISH MUSEUM, LONDON

Print published in H[amburg]  29 x 18.7 cms; German text.

This engraving with its grotesque monster - part camel, part human, perhaps based on an alpaca exhibited in Europe at the time - is a crude reference to the supposed barbarity of the Irish. Why the creature is being displayed by a Scotsman is not clear.  In the background another is exhibited to a crowd; to the left one devours a man on the ground, to the right one seizes a horseman.  Bones of a horse lie in front.

The inscription in German below, engraved on a separate plate, describes the monster as a man-eater, caught in Ireland near Fermanagh and brought to Dublin; a similar monster was brought before King William in 1690. This one is said to have been more or less tamed - no doubt a reference to the defeat of the Jacobite cause in Ireland. The mixture of fear and ridicule displayed is typical of much of the anti-Irish propaganda of the time in English popular literature.

Source:       *BM Catalogue*, vol. II, no. 1254.

**113**

### 113 *Wirt, Rudolph (called Hospinian)*

*The Jesuits manner of consecrating both the persons and weapons imploy'd for the murdering kings... and princes by them accounted hereticks... Dublin, reprinted by Joseph Ray... for Joseph Howes and William Winter... 1681*

THE QUEEN'S UNIVERSITY, BELFAST

quarto: [1], 6 pp.
Lit:     Wing H2889.

The pamphlet contains the ownership inscription of James Hamilton of Bangor. Hamilton was a first cousin of James Hamilton of Tollymore and, like him, raised a regiment for William. Schomberg, on landing at Bangor in 1689, lodged at Hamilton's house. A number of books from his library are at Castleward, Strangford. The printer Joseph Ray's uncompromising Anglican views led to the temporary confiscation of his press in 1689 by James II's then semi-official government printer, James Malone. However, he himself was the printer of the Williamite government paper, the *Dublin Intelligence,* in 1690.

### 114 *A Full and Impartial Account*

*of all the secret consults, negotiations, stratagems, & intriegues of the Romish party in Ireland, from 1660, to... 1689. For the settlement of Popery in that kingdom. London, printed for Richard Baldwin... MDCXC [1690]*

THE QUEEN'S UNIVERSITY, BELFAST

quarto: [5], 152 pp.

The first edition of this pamphlet was published by Richard Chiswell during the autumn of 1689. This edition must have been published after February 1690, when Chiswell's edition is listed in the *Term Catalogues.*

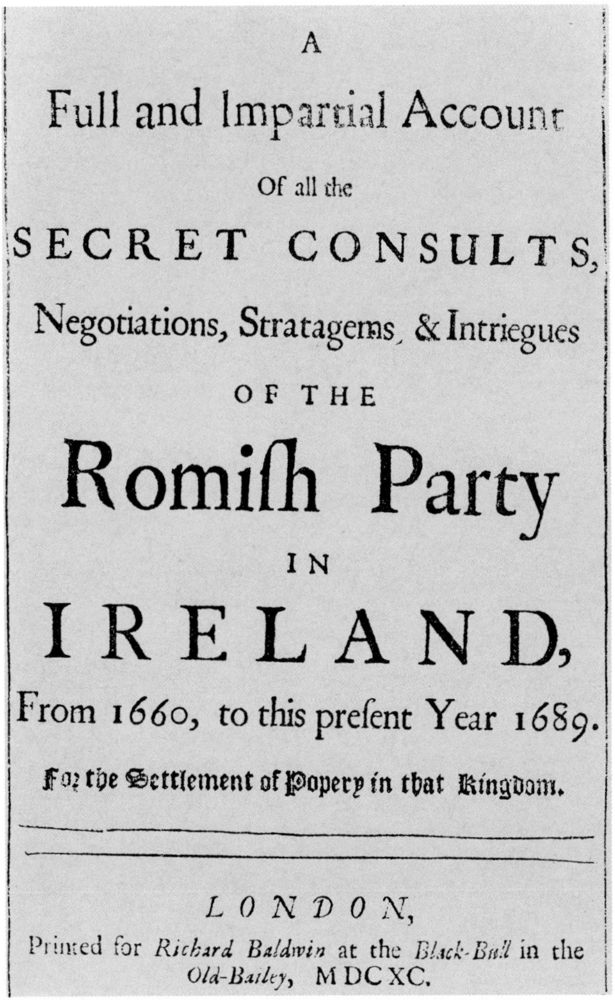

A

# Full and Impartial Account

Of all the

## SECRET CONSULTS,

Negotiations, Stratagems, & Intriegues

OF THE

# Romifh Party

IN

# IRELAND,

From 1660, to this prefent Year 1689.

𝕱𝖔𝖗 𝖙𝖍𝖊 𝕾𝖊𝖙𝖙𝖑𝖊𝖒𝖊𝖓𝖙 𝖔𝖋 𝕻𝖔𝖕𝖊𝖗𝖞 𝖎𝖓 𝖙𝖍𝖆𝖙 𝕶𝖎𝖓𝖌𝖉𝖔𝖒.

*L O N D O N,*

Printed for *Richard Baldwin* at the *Black-Bull* in the *Old-Bailey*, MDCXC.

**114**

**115** *Chevalier, Nicholas (d.1720)*
*Histoire de Guillaume III ... Par Medailles, Inscriptions, Arcs de Triomphe, & autres monuments Publics.*
*(Amsterdam, 1692)*

ULSTER MUSEUM, BELFAST

quarto: 232 pp, illustrated.

This compilation illustrates the career of William from his birth in 1650 to the end of the Jacobite war in Ireland in October 1691, as it was celebrated in medals and public monuments. Each item is illustrated, and described in French, with French translations of the Latin inscriptions. Similar publications in France, of earlier date, had sung the praises of Louis XIV; this did the same for his great opponent. The book, incidentally, contains the first illustrations of James's Irish gun money.

Nicholas Chevalier was a Huguenot pastor from Sedan who fled from France when the Edict of Nantes was revoked in 1685. He settled in the Dutch Netherlands, first at Amsterdam, later at Utrecht. A medallist himself, he produced medals in the latter city. He also worked for William's cousin Frederick I of Prussia. He died in 1720.

Source:     L. Forrer, *Biographical Dictionary of Medallists* (London, 1904).

Within the illustration:

GUILELMO. III.

HISTOIRE
METALIQUE
DE
GUILLAUME
III. ROY
DE LA GRANDE
BRETAIGNE

R de Hooghe inv

**115**

**116**                    **117**

## 116  *Tin-glaze plate*

NETHERLANDS
ULSTER MUSEUM, BELFAST

Earthenware, tin-glazed, painted underglaze in cobalt blue, diameter 24.4 cms.
Double portrait of William and Mary beneath draped curtain with the initials and inscription
'K.W.D.3.M.S.K.I.V.G.B.T.', all within a scroll border.
Donated by Mrs. A. Vromen in 1959 to mark the take-over of the North of Ireland Paper Mill Co.,
Larne by the Dutch company Vromen in 1958.

Many similar pieces exist of Dutch manufacture, bearing similar inscriptions or
as English copies, chiefly of London and Bristol origin, with the initials of the
two monarchs. As this is Dutch and dateable to c. 1688, it probably
commemorates the accession of William and Mary to the throne. Later English
examples were produced until Mary's death in 1694.

Sources:       A.Ray, *English Delftware Pottery* (London, 1966); F. Britton, *English Delftware in
               the Bristol Collection* (London, 1982).

## 117  *A Delft blue dash equestrian charger*

LONDON, C. 1690
ULSTER MUSEUM, BELFAST

Earthenware, tin-glazed, painted in cobalt blue with ochre and antimony yellow 34.5 x 34 cms.
Inscr: 'K W' above the equestrian figure.
Purchased Christie's, 1989.
Prov:    Ex. collections Admiral Sir Lionel Preston; the Hon. Mrs. P.A. Robinson;
         Sotheby's, 15 May 1979 (62). A label on the reverse states 'Moorwood Collection.'

The equestrian portrait of William III in ermine robes holding a sceptre and
riding a prancing stallion is based on a print by Cornelius van Dalen of Charles I
entering Edinburgh in 1641.  The image, however, has been reversed. The print
by van Dalen provided the source for paintings on tin-glazed chargers for at least
four monarchs: Charles I and Charles II, identifiable by the presence of a
moustache; James II and William III, both of whom were clean-shaven.
Fortunately, the UM charger can be identified as representing William from its
inscription. A similar charger is in the Victoria and Albert Museum, London.
    As further evidence of the interchangeability of likenesses, a print of
William III by T. van Merlen was used to represent James Francis Edward
Stuart, the Old Pretender.

Sources:       A. Ray, *English Delftware Pottery* (London, 1966); F. Britton, *English Delftware in
               the Bristol Collection* (London, 1982).

**118**

## 118 *The Boyne cup*

ENGLISH, PROBABLY LAMBETH
ULSTER MUSEUM, BELFAST

Earthenware, tin-glazed, painted in cobalt blue, height 8.9 cms.
Inscr: 'GOD.SEND.Ye.KING.SAVE.TO.IRLND.'
Purchased Sotheby's, 1956.
Exh:    *Drinking Vessels, Vintner's Hall,* June 1933, repr. pl. 18c.
       *English Ceramic Circle,* Victoria and Albert Museum, London 1948 (14), repr. pl. 3.
Lit:     G.E. Howard, *Early English Drug Jars* (London, 1931), no. 65, pl. 19.
       *Illustrated London News*, 18 June 1932.

The piece is typical of a small number of similar tin-glazed vessels dating from the late seventeenth century and is probably Lambeth 1689. The inscription perhaps refers to the projected visits of James in March 1689 or William in June 1690. There is no evidence as yet for either supposition; this is however possibly the first reference to 'the King across the Water'.

## 119 *Joshua stopping the sun in its course*

MEDAL BY J. LUDER (FL. 1680-1710)
PHOTOGRAPH

**119** obv.

**119** rev.

Copper, 50 mm.
Lit:        *Medallic Illustrations* 680-81, no. 59.
Description:   obv. laureate bust of William III, draped over armour.
            legend: GVILIELMVS. III. D. G. MAG. BRIT. FRAN. ET. HIB. REX
            [William III, by grace of God king of Great Britain, France and Ireland].
            REX is much smaller than the rest of the lettering.
         rev. an army, armed with spears and shields, charges left. A figure stands up in
            their midst, pointing at the sun.
            legend: UT ET. IOSUA. CURSUM. SOLIS. RETINET [thus like Joshua
            he holds back the course of the sun]. IOSUA and SOLIS are in much larger
            letters than the rest. At the bottom: 1689.

This medal is a rather poor cast, which appears to have been made either from a struck original or from the wax model for such a medal. The reverse in particular does not lend itself to casting and has failed to come out well. The lettering is ineptly spaced and it is hard to believe that the piece was produced by Luder. The design, however, is interesting and well thought out. The sun was associated with France, the moon with the United Provinces; England could be personified as Joshua, who made both stand still. The message would appear to be that with the addition of English power William would be able to overcome Louis.

## 120 *William III and Louis XIV contrasted, 1691*

MEDAL BY ANON
ULSTER MUSEUM, BELFAST

White metal, 52 mm.

Lit:            *Medallic Illustrations,* 23, no. 191.

Description:    obv.    William in Roman armour, but with long hair, stands facing holding a standard, the bottom of which rests on a globe. There is a christogram and the cap of liberty on the banner. He holds his sword up with his outstretched right hand. To the right of the globe are two harpies fleeing. Piled to the left is a trophy of crowned shields, on which are visible the arms of Scotland, England and Ireland, and British flags, with a trident behind. Above, rays from heaven shine down.

legend: HISARMIS.TRIA REGNA PARAT [by these arms he procures three kingdoms]; (in exergue): GUILELMUS .III LIBERATOR. FLORENS [William III, the flourishing liberator].

                    rev.    Louis XIV, also in Roman armour, wearing a mantle covered in *fleurs de lis,* leans on a sword made of coins, the point of which is on a burning bomb. To the left is a view of a burning fortified town under bombardment, with besiegers' trenches disappearing off behind Louis. To the right five women walk off; above them is a coach, the horses of which are being whipped, which also goes to the right.

legend: UNAM.SIC OCCUPAT.URBEM [thus he seizes one city]; (in exergue): LUDOVICUS.XIIII OPPRESSOR.DECREPITUS [Louis XIV, the decrepit oppressor].

For a discussion of William in this guise see medal no. 244b. This medal is very obviously aimed at a Continental audience: it is unlikely that the boast that William had seized the United Kingdom by force would have been appreciated in England. William, although twelve years younger than Louis, predeceased him. Louis's forces captured Mons in 1691, and the gist of the message on the reverse is that he had obtained the victory by a combination of brutish force and bribery. The coach and ladies, possibly a reference to Louis's personal morals, are presumably returning to Versailles.

The metal of this medal is worth comment. White metal is a generic term for a number of alloys made up of zinc, lead and tin. When fresh it has a bright sparkle, which made it a popular medium for medals, particularly in the nineteenth century. It is likely that this specimen is a later striking from the original dies, as medals of this period are almost always found struck primarily in silver and less regularly in gold and copper.

## 121 *The triumphal entry of William III into The Hague, 1691*

MEDAL BY J. SMELTZING (FL. 1685, D. 1695)
ULSTER MUSEUM, BELFAST

Silver, 51 mm.

Lit:            *Medallic Illustrations,* 12, no. 174.

Description:    obv.    ornate triumphal arch with three passages, with an equestrian statue over the middle dome; through the arch can be seen the palace.

legend: HIC HEROUM HOMOS [this in honour of heroes]; (in exergue): P.F.I.GULIELMO.III.TRIUMP.P.P.GUB.P.C.I.P.RESTAUR.BEL.FED. LIB.A.SERV.S.PA.C.H. REDUC.D.31.IAN.1691 [this stands for: to William III, pious, prosperous, illustrious, triumphant, the father of his country, the perpetual governor of the confederated Low Countries, the restorer of the Belgic Confederacy, the deliverer of England, preserver of Scotland, pacifier of Ireland, on his return, 31 January 1691].

                    rev.    a number of men in a rowing boat, which is flying a standard; to the right a rock which is labelled ORANIE POLD [Orange Polder] and a man on a horse in the sea firing a pistol; behind and to the right a ship fires guns, with a number of ships lined along the horizon.

legend: (on a ribbon above): SERVANDUM SERVATUS [having been saved he is to be preserved] (in exergue): DIE TOT:NOCTEQ;IN SCHAP; FLUCT:APUL:IN HOLL:D:31 IAN:1691 [tossed for a day and a night in a small boat he arrived in Holland on 31 January 1691].

**121** obv.

**121** rev.

When William considered it safe to leave Britain, with Mary remaining behind as regent, his return to the Netherlands was a literal triumph. Three celebratory

KOMSTE VAN
KONING WILLEM
IN HOLLAND.

In den Haegh
by Arnout Leers 1691.

122

arches were erected at The Hague, that shown on this medal being the third. Smeltzing has managed to capture a considerable amount of detail, to produce a feeling of genuine depth in spite of the very low relief, particularly in showing the palace through the arch. However, the almost-contemporary engravings from N. Chevalier's *Histoire Métalique de Guillaume III* (Amsterdam, 1692) give a better impression of the extravagance of the structure. It is perhaps worthy of note that the central arch has a shield with the Belgic lion and the two side passages are surmounted by British coats of arms.

William had a very difficult and dangerous passage, taking three days to cross the North Sea. Finally the fleet lay becalmed, beset by fog in freezing conditions. Against advice he disembarked into a small boat, which took the day and night mentioned in the legend. When in the breakers, the boat was finally guided in by the lighting of a bonfire and the firing of guns.

A relatively large number of medals were issued in connection with the celebrations. We know very little about the mechanism by which medals were commissioned, made and distributed, but this medallic enthusiasm suggests that the occasion and the thrilling story of the landing were considered a likely source of sales.

## 122 *Title page of Komste Van Koning Willem in Holland*
### *(Arrival of King William in Holland) (1691)*

BY ROMEYN DE HOOGHE (1645-1708)
ULSTER MUSEUM, BELFAST

Print 33.5 x 22 cms.

The *Komste*, published by Arnout Leers at The Hague in 1691, with Dutch text and illustrations by de Hooghe (except for the frontispiece), is a lavishly-produced volume celebrating the triumphant return to Holland of the Stadtholder King. It was William's first visit to his native land since his departure in 1688 and he was received rapturously at The Hague.

This engraving is a fine example of de Hooghe's propagandist work, presenting William as a classical hero amid allegorical figures.

## 123 *Inhaling Van S.K. Maj. aende Westeynder brug door de E.A. Magistraet van'S Gravenhage/ Reception De Sa Majesté Au Pont Du Westende*
### *(His Majesty's Reception at the Westende Bridge by the magistrates of The Hague)*

BY ROMEYN DE HOOGHE (1645-1708)
ULSTER MUSEUM, BELFAST

Engraving 33.5 x 44.5 cms.
From *Komste van Koning Willem in Holland.*

**123**

**124** *Vreugde - En Eereteekenen Voor Het Stadthuis*
*Van 'S Gravenhage/Illuminations Et Autres Marques*
*D'Honneur De La Maison De Ville*
*(Illuminations at the Town Hall of The Hague)*

BY ROMEYN DE HOOGHE (1645-1708)
ULSTER MUSEUM, BELFAST

Engraving 33.5 x 44.5 cms.
From *Komste van Koning Willem in Holland.*

124

125

**125** *Eerepoort Op De Plaats/Arc De Triomphe Sur La Place*
*(Triumphal arch at the Market Place)*

BY ROMEYN DE HOOGE (1645-1708)
ULSTER MUSEUM, BELFAST

Engraving 34 x 45 cms.
From *Komste van Koning Willem in Holland*.

**126**

**126** *Vuurwerk In De Vyer/Feu D'Artifice Au Vyver*
*(Fireworks in the Vyver gardens)*

BY ROMEYN DE HOOGHE (1645-1708)
ULSTER MUSEUM, BELFAST

Engraving 33.5 x 44.5 cms.
From *Komste van Koning Willem in Holland.*

# 5. 'Brass Money'

James II arrived in Ireland in March 1689 determined to recover the thrones he had lost. To succeed he needed money as well as men. His Irish viceroy Tyrconnell could provide him with a large army of Catholic soldiers, but money was another matter. Ireland was not a wealthy country and much of its wealth was in the hands of Protestants, hostile to him, who had fled to England with their money and goods or had concealed what they could not carry. James therefore depended on Louis XIV for subsidies. He also needed to raise money in Ireland, and to provide his Irish subjects with coins for everyday commerce.

Fortunately for James there was a mint in Dublin. In the absence of gold and silver this was used to produce emergency coins of gun-metal and pewter. These were really promissory notes in metal, which would be redeemable in gold or silver when James came into his own again.

The 'brass money' worked quite well for a time, but the arrival in 1690 of thousands of French troops who were paid in silver undermined its value in trade. Later in the same year, James's defeat at the Boyne and the Jacobite retreat behind the Shannon finished it off in the greater part of the country. It continued to be used in the areas under Jacobite control, however. In the last stages of the war coins known as 'Hibernias' - so called because they used the figure of Hibernia on an Irish coin for the first time - were minted at Limerick and circulated there during the siege of 1691.

## 127 *James II silver halfcrown, 1685*

ENGLAND
NATIONAL MUSEUM OF IRELAND, DUBLIN

Obv:  draped and laureate bust of James II.
      legend: IACOBVS . II  DEI . GRATIA [James II, by grace of God].
Rev:  four crowned shields with the arms of England,  Scotland, France and Ireland arranged
      around a representation of the breast star of the Order of the Garter.
      legend: REX.16  85.MAG.  BR.FRA.  ET.HIB [King of Great Britain, France and
      Ireland, 1685].
Edge: DECVS.ET.TVTAMEN ANNO REGNI PRIMO [A decoration  and a protection, first
      year of the reign].

The regular milled (that is, made by mechanical press) coinage of England
started in 1662 with an issue of crowns, followed the next year by halfcrowns
and shillings.  These coins were not only a technical departure but also radically
altered the style of coinage, and in particular the way the king was depicted.
Charles II's earlier coins show him crowned, wearing contemporary dress. The
new design by John Roettier, however, reveals a more modern image of
kingship.  Charles now has a sterner, more mature face; the hair, although long
in the previous style, is now more formally curled and is held by a laurel wreath;
instead of a collar with fussy detail the bust finishes in classical drapery. Above
all, the size of the bust has grown to dominate the obverse side of the coin, both
breaking through the inner circle to interrupt the legend and taking advantage of
the higher relief allowed by the new process to use more plastic modelling.

The reverse is similarly transformed; previously a single shield quartered
with the arms of the countries ruled or claimed was placed over a cross fourchée.
On this coin, the inner circle is interrupted and the design makes use of the
circular shape of the flan instead of being imposed upon it.

James's coins followed the style of his brother's very closely; all were
engraved by the Roettier family under the supervision of John. James, however,
does not quite manage the style of Charles, in portraiture as in life, and the
flamboyant inter-linked Cs of the earlier coins have no equivalent on the larger
denominations.

The use of lettering on the edge was another innovation made possible by
the screw press. The old hand-made coins were irregular in shape and size,
making the removal of slivers of silver from the edge ('clipping') easy. These
fragments could then be melted down for a profit. On the new coins lettering was
preferred to simple graining, which forgers might have been able to reproduce.

## 128 *James II silver halfcrown, 1688*

ENGLAND
NATIONAL MUSEUM OF IRELAND, DUBLIN

Obv:  draped and laureate bust of James II.
      legend: IACOBVS. II  DEI . GRATIA [James II, etc.].
Rev:  four crowned shields with  the  arms  of England, Scotland,France and Ireland arranged in
      cruciform fashion around a representation of the breast star of the Order of the Garter.
      legend: REX.1688.MAG  BR.FRA.  ET.HIB [King of Great Britain, etc.].
Edge: DECVS.ET.TVTAMEN ANNO REGNI QVARTO [A decoration  and a protection,
      fourth year of the reign].

There is a very slight difference between the bust in this coin and the previous
one, but the main interest of the piece is in the possibility that it was struck in the
reign of William and Mary. The mint was ordered to continue striking coins
using the dies of the previous monarch, even when the new sovereigns had
entered London.  Maintaining the flow of commerce, at a time when there were
difficulties over the price and amount of silver available, was obviously more
important than making the political point.

**129** rev.

## 129 *James II copper halfpenny, 1685*

IRELAND
ULSTER MUSEUM, BELFAST

Obv:  laureate and draped bust of James II.
      legend: IACOBVS.II. DEI.GRATIA [James II, etc.].
Rev:  crowned harp, the front post of which is in the form of a Maid of Erin.
      legend: REX MAG.BR.FRA.ET.HIB. [King of Great Britain, etc.]. the date 16 85 at either
      side of the band of the crown.

In Ireland there had been a trial emission of small copper pennies and halfpennies in 1601-2, but the experiment, caught up with a more general debasement, had not been followed up. James I had tried to cope with the pressing need for small change by selling a licence to make copper farthings, but these were never popular and ceased during the English Civil War.

Under the Commonwealth, traders had started to issue tokens on a large scale (in England mostly for a farthing, in Ireland the same size was usually a penny) to facilitate trade. Ultimately the only way of suppressing the tokens effectively and reasserting royal authority was to produce large copper halfpennies, which first appeared in England in 1672.

Charles II did not introduce this new type of coinage into Ireland until 1680, when, following the former practice, a patent was granted to Sir Thomas Armstrong and Colonel George Legg for the issue of halfpennies. These appeared up to 1685, when the patent was transferred to Sir John Knox, Lord Mayor of Dublin who, having paid £1,500 for the privilege, was perhaps a little relieved that James II renewed the grant when his brother died the same year.

**130** rev.

## 130 *James II copper halfpenny, 1688*

IRELAND
ULSTER MUSEUM, BELFAST

Obv:  laureate and draped bust of James II.
      legend: IACOBVS.II DEI.GRATIA [James II,etc.].
Rev:  crowned harp, the front post of which is in the form of a Maid of Erin.
      legend: REX MAG.BR.FRA.ET.HIB. [King of Great Britain, etc.], the date 16 88 at either
      side of the band of the crown.

At some time the patent for the right to make halfpennies for Ireland passed from Knox to a Colonel Roger Moore. The terms of the patent became irrelevant with the issue of the brass money (described below), and so it was revoked on 18 June 1689, the day before an order was made for the seizure of all the coining equipment. It follows that the same machinery (and probably many of the same workmen) made these halfpennies as the huge amounts of brass or gun money which were to appear in 1689. It seems that after his victory William III renewed Moore's patent.

**131(a)** obv.        **131(a)** rev.

## 131a *James II brass money sixpence, June 1689*

IRELAND
ULSTER MUSEUM, BELFAST

Obv:  laureate and draped bust of James II.
      legend: IACOBVS.II.DEI.GRATIA [James II, etc.].
Rev:  central royal crown, through which run crossed sceptres; above 'VI'; below 'Jvne.'
      legend: REX. 1689.MAG.BR.FRA.ET.HIB. [King of Great Britain, etc.].

The following extract is from a proclamation issued on 18 June 1689, which introduced the new coinage of brass or gun money.

> 'Whereas, for remedy for the present scarcity of money in this our kingdom, and that our standing forces may be better paid and subsisted, and that our subjects of this realm may be the better enabled to pay and discharge the taxes, excise customs, rents and other debts and duties, which are or shall be hereafter payable to us; we have ordered a certain quantity of copper and brass money to be coyned to pass currant in this our kingdom during our pleasure, in sixpenny pieces;... We do, by this our royal proclamation, promise and engage to all our subjects here, that as soon as the said money shall be decried and made null, that we shall

thereupon receive from all and every our subjects within this kingdom such proportion of the said money as shall be, and remain in their respective hands at the time the said shall be so decried and made null; and at the same time either allow for the same the value thereof, at the rates aforesaid, out of what rent, duties or debts, they respectively shall owe to us, or to make them full satisfaction for the same according to the rates aforesaid, in gold or silver of the currant coyne of this kingdom' (J. Simon, *An Essay towards an Historical Account of Irish Coins*, Dublin, 1749, pp. 148-50).

At this time money was thought of as being in gold or silver and people were prejudiced against token coinages in base metal. There were always shortages of coin in Ireland: these sixpences were obviously intended to cope with a need for small change. They were struck at a mint in Capel Street, Dublin, which had been set up to strike copper halfpennies.

**131(b) obv.**     **131(b) rev.**

## 131b *James II brass money shilling, July 1689*

IRELAND
ULSTER MUSEUM, BELFAST

Obv:    laureate bust of James II.
       legend: IACOBVS.II. DEI.GRATIA [James II, etc.].
Rev:    central royal crown, through which run crossed sceptres; above 'XII'; below 'July.'
       legend: REX. 1689.MAG.BR.FRA.ET.HIB. [King of Great Britain, etc.]. (XII represents twelve in Roman numerals, the number of pennies in a shilling).

It must have become apparent very quickly that the financial problems facing James required more than the production of small change. A further proclamation was issued, dated 27 June 1689, making shillings and halfcrowns legal tender, as well as removing some of the exceptions imposed in the order of 18 June.

**131(c) obv.**

**131(c) rev.**

## 131c *James II brass money halfcrown, July 1689*

IRELAND
ULSTER MUSEUM, BELFAST

Obv:    laureate and draped bust of James II.
       legend: IACOBVS.II. DEI.GRATIA [James II, etc.].
Rev:    central royal crown, through which run crossed sceptres; above 'XXX'; below 'July.'
       legend: REX. 1689.MAG.BR.FRA.ET.HIB. [King of Great Britain, etc.]. (XXX represents 30 in Roman numerals, the number of pennies in two shillings and sixpence).

Brass money coins were issued in every denomination in every month until April 1690, when all except the sixpence were reduced in size. There is considerable variety in the way in which the month was expressed; it seems probable that some sort of mint code ('privy marking') was being used to keep track of production. A recent note by Fr G. Rice, 'The Gun Money of James II', *Spink Numismatics Circular,* vol. XCVII (September 1989), pp. 224-6, discusses the possibility of distinguishing another form of privy marking which might have been used to differentiate between the products of the two presses.

## 131d *James II brass money halfcrown, July 1689*

IRELAND
ULSTER MUSEUM, BELFAST

Obv:    laureate and draped bust of James II.
       legend: IACOBVS.II. DEI.GRATIA [James II, etc.].
Rev:    central royal crown, through which run crossed sceptres; above 'XXX'; below 'July.'
       legend: REX. 1689.MAG.BR.FRA.ET.HIB. [King of Great Britain, etc.].

## 131e *James II brass money halfcrown, March 1689*

IRELAND
ULSTER MUSEUM, BELFAST

Obv:    laureate and draped bust of James II.
       legend: IACOBVS.II. DEI.GRATIA [James II,etc.].

**131(e) rev.**

Rev: central royal crown, through which run crossed sceptres; above 'XXX'; below 'Mar.'
legend: REX. 1689.MAG.BR.FRA.ET.HIB. [King of Great Britain, etc.].

## 131f *James II brass money halfcrown, March 1690*

IRELAND
ULSTER MUSEUM, BELFAST

Obv: laureate and draped bust of James II.
legend: IACOBVS.II. DEI.GRATIA [James II,etc.].
Rev: central royal crown, through which run crossed sceptres; above 'XXX'; below 'Mar.'
legend: REX. 1689.MAG.BR.FRA.ET.HIB. [King of Great Britain, etc.].

At this time the British Isles were still using the Julian calendar and starting the new year on 25 March, instead of 1 January, which explains why some of the brass money coins have these puzzling dates. The change to the Gregorian calendar was made in September 1752, when eleven days were apparently lost because of the accumulated inaccuracies of the old system.

**131(g) obv.**

**131(g) rev.**

## 131g *James II brass money halfcrown, April 1690*

IRELAND
ULSTER MUSEUM, BELFAST

Obv: laureate and draped bust of James II.
legend: IACOBVS.II. DEI.GRATIA [James II, etc.].
Rev: central royal crown, through which run crossed sceptres; above 'XXX'; below 'Apr.'
legend: REX. 1689.MAG.BR.FRA.ET.HIB. [King of Great Britain, etc.].

## 131h *James brass money halfcrown, May 1690*

IRELAND
ULSTER MUSEUM, BELFAST

Obv: laureate and draped bust of James II.
legend: IACOBVS.II. DEI.GRATIA [James II, etc.].
Rev: central royal crown, through which run crossed sceptres; above 'XXX'; below 'May.'
legend: REX. 1689.MAG.BR.FRA.ET.HIB. [King of Great Britain, etc.].

**131(h) rev.**

## 131i *James II brass money halfcrown, April 1690*

IRELAND
NATIONAL MUSEUM OF IRELAND, DUBLIN

Obv: laureate and draped bust of James II.
legend: IACOBVS.II. DEI.GRATIA [James II,etc.].
Rev: central royal crown, through which run crossed sceptres; above 'XXX'; below 'Apr.'
legend: REX. 1689.MAG.BR.FRA.ET.HIB. [King of Great Britain, etc.].

## 131j *James II brass money halfcrown, May 1690*

IRELAND
ULSTER MUSEUM, BELFAST

Obv: laureate and draped bust of James II.
legend: IACOBVS.II. DEI.GRATIA [James II,etc.].
Rev: central royal crown, through which run crossed sceptres; above 'XXX'; below 'May.'
legend: REX. 1689.MAG.BR.FRA.ET.HIB. [King of Great Britain, etc.].

A proclamation was issued, dated 21 April 1690, reducing the size of the brass money halfcrowns and shillings. The old, large halfcrowns were over-struck to make crowns and the new shillings were roughly the size of the sixpence.

The situation was complicated by the existence of two mints at this time, the original and more productive one being in Dublin and a second in Limerick. All the small halfcrowns, dated April 1690, were made in Dublin and all the large halfcrowns, dated May 1690, in Limerick.

**131(k) obv.**

**131(k) rev.**

**131(l) rev.**

**131(m) obv.**

**131(m) rev.**

**131(n) obv.**

**131(n) rev.**

### 131k *James II brass money shilling, April 1690*

IRELAND
ULSTER MUSEUM, BELFAST

Obv:   laureate and draped bust of James II.
      legend: IACOBVS.II.  DEI.GRATIA [James II,etc.].
Rev:   central royal crown, through which run crossed sceptres; above 'XII'; below 'Apr.'
      legend: REX.  1689.MAG.BR.FRA.ET.HIB. [King of Great Britain, etc.].

## 131l *James II brass money shilling, April 1689*

IRELAND
ULSTER MUSEUM, BELFAST

Obv:   laureate and draped bust of James II.
      legend: IACOBVS.II.  DEI.GRATIA [James II,etc.].
Rev:   central royal crown, through which run crossed sceptres; above 'XII'; below 'Apr.'
      legend: REX.  1689.MAG.BR.FRA.ET.HIB. [King of Great Britain, etc.].

Compare the size of this coin with the previous one. The change is explained under 131j.

## 131m *James II brass money shilling, September 1690*

IRELAND
ULSTER MUSEUM, BELFAST

Obv:   laureate bust of James II.
      legend: IACOBVCS.II.  DEI.GRATIA [James II,etc.].
Rev    :central royal crown, through which run crossed sceptres; above 'XII'; below 'Sepr.'
      legend: REX.  1689.MAG.BR.FRA.ET.HIB. [King of Great Britain, etc.].

These coins were probably the last of the brass money to be made. The capture of Dublin brought operations at the mint there to an end, but Limerick remained in Jacobite hands until October 1691. It seems that there was enough of James's coin in the area under his control, and consequently little need to strike more. William issued a proclamation, dated 10 July 1690, reducing the value of a brass money crown to a penny, the small shillings and sixpences to farthings and the other sizes by similar amounts, related to their value as scrap. The emergency coinages were wholly demonetised in February 1690/1.

## 131n *James II brass money crown (five-shilling piece), 1690*

IRELAND
ULSTER MUSEUM, BELFAST

Obv:   James in armour, on horse prancing left.
      legend: IAC.II.DEI.GRA.MAG.BRI.FRA.ET.HIB.REX [James II, by grace of God, king of Great Britain, France and Ireland].
Rev:   Crowned shields with arms of England, Scotland, France and Ireland arranged in a cross about a central crown.
      legend: CHRIS TO. VICT ORE. TRI. VMPHO [I triumph in  Christ's victory]; across upper field: ANO DOM [in the year of the Lord]; across lower field: 1690; contraction marks over 'Ano Dom'.

The silver crown (or five shilling piece) was introduced in 1551, with an obverse depicting the king on horseback.  This remained the mark of the denomination until 1662, when the new milled coinage of Charles II replaced it with a conventional bust on the obverse and an arrangement of shields on the reverse, similar to that used here. Crowns (and halfcrowns with the same obverse) of Charles I, minted during the English Civil War, would still have been familiar at this date. The portrayal of James is closest to that of his father, down to details like the flying sash, emphasising the similarity of their travails.

    Proclamations dated 15 June 1690 recalled 'all the halfcrown pieces of copper and brass money which appear by the stamp on them to have been coyned within this our kingdom, before the month of May last ...' (Simon, pp. 161-63) (i.e. the large halfcrowns) and made the crowns legal tender. This was an admission that the white metal crowns authorised by a proclamation of 21 April 1690 were not to be proceeded with.

## 132a *James II brass money crown (five-shilling piece), 1690, struck in gold*

IRELAND
NATIONAL MUSEUM OF IRELAND, DUBLIN

Obv: James in armour, on horse prancing left.
legend: IAC.II.DEI.GRA.MAG.BRI.FRA.ET.HIB.REX [James II, King of Great Britain, France and Ireland].

Rev: Crowned shields with arms of England, Scotland, France and Ireland, arranged in a cross about a central crown.
legend: CHRIS TO.VICT ORE.TRI.UMPHO [I triumph etc.]; across upper field: ANO DOM [in the year of the Lord]; across lower field: 1690; contraction marks over 'Ano Dom'.

Numbers of brass money coins are known struck in gold, silver and tin. Conventionally these have been described as proofs. In the seventeenth century they were usually presentation pieces, struck with special care, often in a precious metal which might not have been used for currency specimens of the same issue. The arguments advanced by M. Dolley and G. Rice in 'The Mint of Limerick under James II' (Numismatic Society of Ireland *Occasional Paper* no. 32 in *Small Change*, Dublin, 1988) are quite technical, but confirm the suspicion that the whole class of brass money coins in the wrong metal are of a different category. A close examination of the contemporary literature and of the provenances of surviving coins suggests that all were produced in the early eighteenth century, certainly after the mint ceased to make coins for circulation.

The mint in Dublin was taken over intact by the Williamite forces, with a substantial sum in brass money in stock, as well as dies and the coining press. The coins had a contemporary notoriety and wealthy collectors, as well as simple souvenir hunters, may have been attracted by the idea of precious metal specimens. This would have been simple to accomplish, given the availability of dies, and some coins are known struck over other pieces, such as guineas, which date from after 1690.

132(b) obv.

132(b) rev.

## 132b *James II brass money crown (five-shilling piece), 1690, struck in silver*

IRELAND
ULSTER MUSEUM, BELFAST

Obv: James in armour, on horse prancing left.
legend: IAC.II.DEI.GRA.MAG.BRI.FRA.ET.HIB.REX [James II, etc.].

Rev: Crowned shields with arms of England, Scotland, France and Ireland arranged in a cross about a central crown.
legend: CHRIS TO. VICT ORE.TRI. UMPHO [I triumph etc.]; across upper field: ANO DOM [in the year of the Lord]; across lower field: 1690; contraction marks over 'Ano Dom'.

Silver specimens like this are obviously much commoner than those struck in gold. The dies used for these 'proofs' are unusual, in particular 'U' instead of 'V' is used in 'Triumpho' on the reverse.

132(c) obv.

132(c) rev.

## 132c *James II brass money crown (five-shilling piece), 1690, struck in copper*

IRELAND
ULSTER MUSEUM, BELFAST

Obv: James in armour, on horse prancing left.
legend: IAC.II.DEI.GRA.MAG.BRI.FRA.ET.HIB.REX [James II, etc.].

Rev: Crowned shields with arms of England, Scotland, France and Ireland arranged in a cross about a central crown.
legend: CHRIS TO. VICT ORE. TRI.UMPHO [I triumph etc,]; across upper field: ANO DOM [in the year of the Lord]; across lower field: 1690; contraction marks over 'Ano Dom'.

This coin is distinguished from normal currency specimens by a number of factors, as well as those mentioned under 132b. The edge is plain and the coin has much higher relief and greater detail than usual, having been struck on a new plain flan rather than on top of an existing halfcrown.

**132d** *James II brass money shilling, May 1690, struck in gold*

IRELAND
NATIONAL MUSEUM OF IRELAND, DUBLIN

Obv:    laureate bust of James II.
       legend: IACOBVS.II. DEI.GRATIA [James II, etc.].
Rev:    central royal crown, through which run crossed sceptres; above 'XII'; below 'May'.
       legend: REX. 1690.MAG.BR.FRA.ET.HIB. [King of Great Britain, etc.].

**132e** *James II brass money shilling, May 1690, struck in silver*

IRELAND
ULSTER MUSEUM, BELFAST

Obv:    laureate bust of James II.
       legend: IACOBVS.II. DEI.GRATIA [James II, etc.].
Rev:    central royal crown, through which run crossed sceptres; above 'XII'; below 'May'.
       legend: REX. 1690.MAG.BR.FRA.ET.HIB. [King of Great Britain, etc.].

**132f** *James II brass money halfcrown, April 1690, struck in silver*

IRELAND
ULSTER MUSEUM, BELFAST; NATIONAL MUSEUM OF IRELAND, DUBLIN

Obv:    laureate bust of James II.
       legend: IACOBVS.II. DEI.GRATIA [James II, etc.].
Rev:    central royal crown, through which run crossed sceptres; above 'XX'; below 'Apr'.
       legend: REX. 1689.MAG.BR.FRA.ET.HIB. [King of Great Britain, etc.].

**132g** *James II brass money sixpence, February 1689, struck in silver*

IRELAND
ULSTER MUSEUM, BELFAST

Obv:    laureate and draped bust of James II.
       legend: IACOBVS.II.DEI.GRATIA [James II, etc.].
Rev:    central royal crown, through which run crossed sceptres; above 'VI'; below 'Feb'.
       legend: REX. 1689.MAG.BR.FRA.ET.HIB. [King of Great Britain, etc.].

**132h** *James II brass money shilling, April 1690, struck in silver*

IRELAND
ULSTER MUSEUM, BELFAST

Obv:    laureate bust of James II.
       legend: IACOBVS.II. DEI.GRATIA [Jame II, etc.].
Rev:    central royal crown, through which run crossed sceptres; above 'XII'; below 'Apr.'
       legend: REX. 1690.MAG.BR.FRA.ET.HIB. [King of Great Britain, etc.].

**132i** *James II brass money shilling, May 1690, struck in silver*

IRELAND
ULSTER MUSEUM. BELFAST

Obv:    laureate bust of James II.
       legend: IACOBVS.II. DEI.GRATIA [James II, etc.].
Rev:    central royal crown, through which run crossed sceptres; above 'XII'; below 'May.'
       legend: REX. 1690.MAG.BR.FRA.ET.HIB. [King of Great Britain, etc.].

**133(a) obv.**    **133(a) rev.**

### 133a *James II pewter halfpenny, 1689*

IRELAND
NATIONAL MUSEUM OF IRELAND, DUBLIN

Obv:    laureate bust of James II.
        legend: IACOBVS.II DEI.GRATIA [James II, etc.].
Rev:    crowned harp.
        legend: REX. 1689 .MAG.BR.FRA.ET.HIB. [King of Great Britain, etc., 1689].

The bust on this coin shows James with much shorter hair and an altogether less regal appearance. The Royal Mint had found difficultly in working copper and the blanks had had to be imported from Sweden when Charles II introduced the copper halfpenny to the English series. There was a strong lobby from Cornish tin interests urging that their metal should be used for the coinage. Farthings in this metal appeared in 1684. All James's English petty coinage was made in this, so it was not surprising that when an effort was made to supply low value coins this metal should be chosen, especially as it would be readily distinguishable from the brass coins of higher value. It has been suggested that these coins should perhaps be regarded as tin, but the order sent to the mint specifically calls for 'white mix'd metall' and pewter would have been readily available from domestic plates and vessels. An order was sent to the mint, dated 1 March 1689/ 90, signed by Richard Nagle on behalf of James for 'coyne of two sorts to pass currant in this our kingdom of Ireland; the one the biggness of a shilling to be made of white mix'd mettall..., and... haveing a piece of princes mettall fix'd in the middle;... which piece is to pass for a penny; and the other piece about the biggness of a six pence to be made of like mettall and stampt of both sides.... and to pass for a half-penny...' (Simon,pp.155-56). There is a certain lack of contact with reality shown here. It is debateable whether the mint's scarce resources, already under pressure producing brass money, should have been diverted in this way, but it was certainly true that the inclusion of the plug of prince's metal (a type of bronze added to prevent forgery) was an unnecessary and wasteful complication.

A proclamation was issued, dated 28 March 1689-90, making the pewter money legal tender (Simon, pp.156-57), (the mint had obviously responded with exemplary speed in making the dies). Production figures for the James press at the Dublin mint survive for the relevant period and show that pennies and halfpennies were struck at the rate of 110,612 pence and 101,914 halfpennies in the period 29 March to 5 April, and 7,612 pennies in the week 5 to 12 April. In spite of these figures, only two of the 1689 halfpennies are recorded in public collections, with both types dated 1690 being much commoner. The surviving mint records are fragmentary, however, and relate only to the James press, which was bigger and more likely to have been used for the heavy work of striking brass coins.

**133(b) obv.**

**133(b) rev.**

### 133b *James II pewter penny, 1689*

IRELAND
ULSTER MUSEUM, BELFAST; NATIONAL MUSEUM OF IRELAND, DUBLIN

Obv:    laureate bust of James II.
        legend: IACOBVS.II DEI.GRATIA [James II, etc.].
Rev:    crowned harp.
        legend: REX. 1689 .MAG.BR.FRA.ET.HIB. [King of Great Britain, etc.].

Unlike the halfpenny, which uses a slightly awkward bust, perhaps by a different hand from that which produced the dies for most of the other coins, the penny uses a head which is the same as, or very similar to, that on the brass money shillings. This coin is known from only three specimens.

### 133c *James II pewter halfpenny, 1690*

IRELAND
ULSTER MUSEUM, BELFAST; NATIONAL MUSEUM OF IRELAND, DUBLIN

Obv:    laureate bust of James II.
        legend: IACOBVS. II DEI.GRATIA [James II, etc.].
Rev:    crowned harp.
        legend: REX. 1689 .MAG .BR.FRA.ET.HIB . [King of Great Britain, etc.].

**133(d) obv.**    **133(d) rev.**

### 133d *James II silver striking of pewter halfpenny, 1690*

IRELAND
ULSTER MUSEUM, BELFAST

Obv:    laureate bust of James II.
        legend: IACOBVS.II DEI.GRATIA [James II, etc.].
Rev:    crowned harp.
        legend: REX. 1690 .MAG.BR.FRA.ET.HIB. [King of Great Britain, etc., 1690].

Silver strikings of this coin are much commoner survivals than those made in pewter (no. 133c). These have been described as proofs, and in some senses this may be a not inaccurate description. In modern times a proof is a special striking, carefully made, usually with a special finish, but in the past they were presentation pieces, often sold as a prerogative of the engraver or mint master. The piece shown here with the obverse seems to have been struck over a French twelfth écu of 1685, and French coins seem to have provided most of the flans used. A possible explanation is that when normal production ceased, the dies were used to make souvenirs. At this time small French coins would have been readily available.

### 133e *James II pewter halfpenny, 1690*

IRELAND
ULSTER MUSEUM, BELFAST

Obv:    laureate bust of James II, with fleuron below.
        legend: IACOBVS.II. DEI.GRATIA [James II, etc.].
Rev:    crowned harp.
        legend: REX. 1690 .MAG.BR.FRA.ET.HIB. [King of Great Britain, etc., 1690].

The main difference between this and the previous type is the addition of the leaf beneath the bust and the manner in which the date is split by the crown, making a more balanced reverse.

**133(f) obv.**    **133(f) rev.**

### 133f *James II pewter penny, 1690*

IRELAND
ULSTER MUSEUM, BELFAST; NATIONAL MUSEUM OF IRELAND, DUBLIN

Obv:    laureate bust of James II.
        legend: IACOBVS.II DEI.GRATIA [James II, etc.].
Rev:    crowned harp.
        legend: REX. 1689 .MAG.BR.FRA.ET.HIB. [King of Great Britain, etc., 1689].

This coin seems to represent merely a date change, rather than an alteration of the type, and is slightly less rare than the 1689 coin (no. 133b).

**133(g) obv.**    **133(g) rev.**

### 133g *James II pewter penny, 1690*

IRELAND
ULSTER MUSEUM, BELFAST

Obv:    laureate bust of James II, with the denomination D.
        legend: IACOBVS.II DEI.GRATIA [James II, etc.].
Rev:    crowned harp.
        legend: REX. MAG.BR.FRA.ET.HIB. [King of Great Britain, etc., 1690], the date 16 90 either side of the lower part of the harp.

It is unclear why it was thought necessary to put the denomination on this piece; it was not the usual practice at this date, except in cases where confusion over metal or size might arise. The penny mark looks very much like an afterthought, but the earlier type, using the same head as on the brass money, would seem more likely to have caused difficulties.

**133(i) obv.**

**133(i) rev.**

**133(j) obv.**

**133(j) rev.**

### 133h *James II pewter groat, 1689*

IRELAND
NATIONAL MUSEUM OF IRELAND, DUBLIN

Obv:    draped and laureate bust of James II.
        legend: IACOBVS.II. DEI.GRATIA [James II, etc.].
Rev:    crowned harp with a Roman two either side.
        legend: REX.1689.MAG.BR.FRA.ET.HIB. [King of Great Britain, etc., 1689].

This coin is a pattern. It is extremely scarce and no documentation seems to survive regarding it. The obverse appears to be the same as that used on the sixpence dies.

### 133i *James II pewter crown, 1690*

IRELAND
NATIONAL MUSEUM OF IRELAND, DUBLIN

Obv:    James in armour, holding up a sword and riding a  horse prancing left.
        legend: IAC.II.DEI.GRA.MAG.BRI.FRA.ET.HIB.REX [James II, by grace of God king of Great Britain, France and Ireland].
Rev:    Crowned shields with the arms of England, Scotland, France and Ireland arranged in a cross about a central crown.
        legend: CHRIS TO.VICT ORE.TRI UMPHO [I triumph  etc.]; across the lower field: 1690.
Edge:   MELORIS . TESSERA . FATI . ANNO . REGNI . SEXTO . [A better token issued in the sixth year of the reign].

This is another extremely scarce coin. A proclamation was issued, dated 21 April 1690, describing these coins and making them legal tender. Export and import were forbidden, to reduce the risk of forgery. The added complication of the edge inscription, which would have slowed production considerably, is further confirmation of an awareness of the damage large-scale illicit minting might inflict. It is also the case that since the normal higher-value milled silver coins had edge inscriptions, primarily to prevent the clipping which had been so prevalent when they had still been made by hand, the use of similar devices on the pewter may have been intended to reinforce their legitimacy.

There is no mention of these coins in the surviving mint account, and in any case a decision must have been made not to proceed with them, as the proclamation about the brass money crowns is dated 15 June. The same design (and, in at least one case, the same die) was used, perhaps indicating that the additional complication of striking in a different metal was just too much as pressure grew.

The brass plug is positioned to give a golden appearance to the central crown.  A similar device was used on the St Patrick's 'halfpennies' of the 1670s. It is highly probable that most of the specimens surviving today derive from the five thousand coins which remained in the mint when the Williamite forces captured it.

### 133j *James II pewter money crown, 1690, struck in silver*

IRELAND
NATIONAL MUSEUM OF IRELAND, DUBLIN

Obv:    James in armour, holding up a sword and riding a horse prancing left.
        legend: IAC.II.DEI.GRA.BRI.FRA.ET.HIB.REX [James II, etc.].
Rev:    Crowned shields with the arms of England,  Scotland,France and Ireland arranged in a cross about a central crown.
        legend: CHRIS TO.VICT ORE.TRI UMPHO [I triumph  etc.];  across the lower field: 1690.
Edge:   MELORIS . TESSERA . FATI . ANNO . REGNI . SEXTO . [A better token etc.].

Silver strikings are commoner than coins struck in the proper metal and are, of course, difficult to distinguish from silver strikings of the brass money, except for the edge marking. It seems likely that this coin is simply a later utilisation of the dies to make a reproduction in precious metal.

**134(a) obv.**

**134(a) rev.**

### 134a *James II brass halfpenny issued at Limerick, 1691*

IRELAND
ULSTER MUSEUM, BELFAST

Obv: laureate and draped bust of James II.
 legend: IACOBVS.II.DEI.GRATIA. [James II, etc.].
Rev: seated female, representing Hibernia, leaning on a harp with her left hand and holding up a shamrock with her right.
 legend: HIBERNIA [reversed Ns]. 1691.

These coins were issued at some time during the siege of Limerick, perhaps at the end of March 1691. Very little is known about them; even the face-value is to some extent conjecture. They were made by over-striking large brass money shillings and are the first coins to use Hibernia to represent Ireland, earlier issues having utilised the harp alone. The design follows that used on English half pennies first issued in 1672, which introduced Britannia on coins, following a series of Roman archetypes. It may be significant that Britannia rests on a shield and is armed with a spear, although she does hold up an olive branch. Hibernia's harp is depicted quite realistically, especially when compared to the way in which it is shown on other seventeenth century Irish coins, even James II's pewter money.

The device which Hibernia holds up seems to be a shamrock leaf. The origins of the association of this plant with Ireland and St Patrick are quite obscure, but the saint can be seen displaying it on the St Patrick 'halfpennies' issued in Dublin c. 1672.

The iconography of these coins is quite striking. All James's other coins are careful to give him his full titles, even the obsolete and potentially embarrassing (given the source of most of his material support) claim to France. Here the grace of God seems to have no temporal manifestation; there is no claim even to be king of Ireland, although there is a space on the reverse crying out for the addition of 'Rex'. Some have seen these coins, known as 'Hibernias', as an assertion of Irish identity. In the circumstances, abandoned by James and his foreign supporters, the Jacobites within the beleaguered walls of Limerick may indeed have had such feelings.

**134(b) obv.** **134(b) rev.**

### 134b *James II brass farthing issued at Limerick, 1691*

IRELAND
ULSTER MUSEUM, BELFAST

Obv: laureate and draped bust of James II.
 legend: IACOBVS.II.DEI.GRATIA. [James II, etc.].
Rev: seated female, representing Hibernia, leaning on a harp with her left hand and holding up a shamrock with her right.
 legend: HIBERNIA [reversed Ns]. .1691.

Issued at the same time as the halfpennies, this denomination was over-struck on brass money small shillings or sixpences. Most have the same error of a reversed 'N' as the bigger coins, but a few have the letter the right way round.

### 134c *James II brass halfpenny issued at Limerick, 1691*

IRELAND
ULSTER MUSEUM, BELFAST

Obv: laureate and draped bust of James II.
 legend: IACOBVS.II.DEI.GRATIA. [James II, etc.].
Rev: seated female, representing Hibernia, leaning on a harp with her left hand and holding up a shamrock with her right.
 legend: HIBERNIA [reversed Ns]. .1691.

The under-type can be clearly seen, which perhaps indicates that the coin-making press in Limerick was quite small, possibly the 'Duchess' machine mentioned in documents as having been originally in Dublin. The amount of pressure required totally to obliterate the design on the coin which was being used to provide a flan must have been quite large, especially given the varying hardness of the brasses used. The possibility that conditions did not permit them to be annealed before reworking cannot be discounted.

## 134d *James II brass farthing issued at Limerick, 1691*

IRELAND
ULSTER MUSEUM, BELFAST

Obv: laureate and draped bust of James II.
legend: IACOBVS.II.DEI.GRATIA. [James II, etc.].

Rev: seated female, representing Hibernia, leaning on a harp with her left hand and holding up a shamrock with her right.
legend: HIBERNIA [reversed Ns]. .1691.

The under-type can be clearly seen.

## 135a *Cork token*

ULSTER MUSEUM, BELFAST

Uniface: plain brass disc stamped with a die c.11 mm in diameter; within a border of beads a facing leopard's head, below CORKE, above crossed palms. On this specimen the reverse is engraved 11 1/2.

This coin is something of a mystery. It was originally suggested that it was part of the issues put out by some southern towns during the 1640s. These are in themselves subject to a reconsideration, but in any case this particular type is known to have been struck on trade tokens of William Ballard of Cork, dated 1677. Day ('Proceedings', *Journal of the Royal Society of Antiquaries of Ireland* vol. XV (1879-82), pp. 632-4) suggested that they might have been made when the city was being besieged by Marlborough. This appears highly unlikely, since the siege was short. Day notices at least three different dies used on only eight examples, suggesting that a quantity was made, yet brass money is likely to have been available in sufficient quantity to cope with the defenders' needs in the short term.

In the absence of direct documentary evidence, one may look for conditions in the city after the siege that were likely to generate an emergency issue. Corporation records resume in 1690 and are full of references to shortages of money, if not of actual coin. Caulfield (*The Council Book of the Corporation of the City of Corke,* Guilford, 1876, p. xxv.) transcribes a document, dated 4 August 1691, authorising a warrant for £800 paid by Carlton, Collector of their Majesties Customs, when the frigate *Breda* blew up with the cash for the forces the previous year. One is also tempted to see significance in the fact that William Ballard was the first Mayor under the new regime and that he, with David Crone and others, had advanced £750 sterling to Colonel Hasting 'for the subsistence of his regiment in the garrison' and that Ballard was still owed £58 6s 1d for his expenses as mayor as late as 1693 (Caulfield, *Council Book of Corke*, p. 223). The Corporation was in desperate need of cash, not only for its normal business, but also to make good the damage from the war, and several times pledged the town seal as a guarantee for loans against future revenue. Four different types of token associated with the civic authorities, including one of the mayor in 1658, appeared during the 1650s. These may have provided a precedent. Given the lavish design and production of Ballard's tokens, it seems unlikely that the counter-stamping was an attempt by him to revalue, or otherwise alter, his own tokens at the time of their currency.

The engraved numbers on the reverse of this specimen are also a mystery: they do not relate to the weight, which is around 2dwt 16grs (4.155 grams), but are, as far as can be judged from such a small sample, of contemporary style.

## 135b *Token of William Ballard, Cork, 1677*

NATIONAL MUSEUM OF IRELAND, DUBLIN

Obv: CORKE with '1677' above and a knot below.
legend: *WILLIAM*BALLARD*HIS*PENNY (opposite 'Corke', at a break in the inner circle) IN.

Rev: a bust in a tree, with three crowns above; to the left of the trunk a pikeman, to the right an armed horseman.

Edge: TO PASS IN THIS CITY AND COVNTIE.

As well as providing the flan for some examples of no. 135a, this coin is interesting in itself. In the absence of royal authority, from the 1650s onwards traders and others issued over 800 different varieties of tokens in Ireland. These were a form of metallic promissory note. Most were for a penny, and continued in existence (in spite of several attempts at suppression), until the threat of firm legal action and the arrival of much larger regal halfpennies in 1680 finally put an end to them.

The design of Ballard's token appears to make reference to Charles II's escape after Worcester by hiding in an oak tree. The three crowns were the arms of Ireland before Henry VIII supplanted them with the harp; soldiers at the base of the tree may be intended to represent the searching forces of the Commonwealth. This expression of loyalty to the crown sheds an interesting light on the attitudes of prosperous Protestants, given Ballard's subsequent career (see no. 135a). This token is one of only two seventeenth century tokens (out of nearly 14,000 from the British Isles) to have an edge inscription, the other being from Kinsale.

## 136a *Louis XIV silver coin of 3 sols and 6 deniers, 1675*

FRANCE
ULSTER MUSEUM, BELFAST

Obv:   draped bust of Louis XIV, with two small laurel branches over.
        legend: LVDOVICVS. .XIIII.D.GRA. [Louis XIV, by grace of God].
Rev:   four *fleurs de lis* arranged base to base around an 'A', with a small crown above.
        legend: FRAN.ET.NAVARRA.REX.1675 [king of France and Navarre, 1675].

Even towards the end of the seventeenth century the French coinage still exhibited elements of the chaos from which it emerged, with some feudal lords retaining the right to strike low value coins. No single system of denominations existed. This piece started out as being worth 4 sols tournois, which was the equivalent of a fifteenth of an écu worth 60 sols. Its value was reduced to 3 sols 9 deniers on 1 April 1679 and to 3 sols 6 deniers on 8 May. It was replaced by a new coin in 1691, being taken in by the mints at 3 sols 7 deniers. The central 'A' was the mark of the Paris mint and it was also struck at Vimy.

A number of French coins were among the range of foreign pieces which were allowed to pass as legal tender in Ireland, but these were of relatively high value. A proclamation was issued, dated 4 May 1689, making the 'French three pence halfpenny' legal tender (Simon, p. 149). This was a slight over-valuation; the coin was issued at a weight of 1.809 grams in 798.3% silver, which in England should have been worth about threepencefarthing, but one can assume that few reached the official standard by the time they got to Ireland. As Simon remarked, the coin was a useful size for paying soldiers, although its value must have been enhanced as the brass money went into circulation.

## 136b *Louis XIV, silver coin of 3 sols and 6 deniers, 1674*

FRANCE
ULSTER MUSEUM, BELFAST

Obv:   draped bust of Louis XIV.
        legend: LVDOVICVS. .XIIII.D.GRA. [Louis XIV, etc.].
Rev:   four *fleurs de lis* arranged base to base around a 'D', with a small crown above.
        legend: FRAN.ET.NAVARRA.REX.1674 [king of France etc.].

In this case the letter 'D' indicates that the coin was made at the Vimy mint. This was the first year of issue; production stopped in 1679.

**137(a) obv.**      **137(a) rev.**

## 137a *Louis XIV, gold louis d'or, 1653*

FRANCE
NATIONAL MUSEUM OF IRELAND, DUBLIN

Obv:   laureate bust of Louis XIV.
        legend: LVD.XIIII.D.G. (rosette and lozenge) FR.ET.NAV.REX [Louis XIV, by grace of God king of France and Navarre]; at truncation of bust: .1653.
Rev:   four sets of pairs of 'Ls' back to back and crowned, arranged to form a square round an 'A' within a circle; *fleurs de lis* in the angles.
        legend: .CHRS. .REGN. .VINC. .IMP. [Christ rules, conquers and commands].

This portrait, showing Louis as a boy, was not up-dated on the coinage until 1658. The central 'A' on the reverse is the mark of the Paris mint.

The louis d'or, worth ten livres, was introduced in 1640 and to some extent provided a pattern for the guinea in England, introduced in 1663. Both were machine-struck, they had an identical fineness (916 2/3 parts per thousand) and were of roughly similar weight, with the English coin being just under two grams heavier.

A wide mixture of foreign coins circulated in Ireland in the seventeenth century; even before 1689 this included a variety of French pieces. Gold was always scarce and the bulk of it which circulated in Ireland seems to have been Spanish, as was the silver. The French 'lewis' generally went under the name of the pistole, the name used for the Spanish two escudos of the same weight. Both were legal tender, but had to be weighed to make sure they were at or above the official standard. It is probable that a cross-section of the circulating medium in France came in with the French troops, as part of the money Louis provided for James, but this has left little trace on the physical record in Ireland.

## 137b *Louis XIV, gold louis d'or, 1653*

FRANCE
NATIONAL MUSEUM OF IRELAND, DUBLIN

Obv:    laureate bust of Louis XIV.
        legend: LVD.XIIII.D.G. (rosette and lozenge) FR.ET.NAV.REX [Louis XIV, by grace of
        God etc.]; at truncation of bust: .1653.
Rev:    four sets of pairs of 'Ls' back to back and crowned, arranged to form a square round a 'D'
        within a circle; *fleurs de lis* in the angles.
        legend: .CHRS. .REGN. .VINC. .IMP. [Christ rules, etc.].

'D' is the mint-mark of Lyon.

## 138 *William and Mary silver halfcrown, 1689*

ENGLAND
NATIONAL MUSEUM OF IRELAND, DUBLIN

**138** obv.

**138** rev.

Obv:    conjoined busts of William and Mary, both draped, he laureate.
        legend: GVLIELMVS.ET.MARIA.DEI.GRATIA [William and Mary, by grace of God].
Rev:    crowned shield with the arms of England, Scotland, France and Ireland, with the lion of
        Nassau on an escutcheon in the middle.
        legend: REX.ET.REGINA.1689.MAG.BR.FR.ET.HIB. [King and Queen of Great Britain,
        France and Ireland, 1689].
Edge:   DECVS ET TVTAMEN, ANNO REGNI PRIMO [a decoration and a protection, first
        year of reign].

For the first months of the reign, other pressing concerns brought a reliance upon a continued issue of James's coins and the importation of Dutch pieces. When coins did start to appear in the names of the new monarchs, only guineas, half-guineas, halfcrowns, fourpences, threepences, twopences and silver pennies were issued. It does not seem, therefore, that any great importance was put on using this method to spread the royal image and authority.

The shield used here must have been regarded as being unsatisfactory, since it was changed at some point in the year for another with the same basic design but with the first and second quarters of the shield showing the arms of England and France quarterly.

The dies were once again the work of John Roettier and his family, although they were adherents of the Stuarts, having been installed in the mint at an inflated salary by Charles II, in return for favours when he was in exile. Norbert Roettier fled to France in 1695, and there were further accusations against John in 1697, ending with his dismissal.

**139** obv.

**139** rev.

**141** rev.

## 139 *William and Mary silver crown, 1691*

ENGLAND
NATIONAL MUSEUM OF IRELAND, DUBLIN

Obv:  conjoined busts of William and Mary both draped, he laureate.
legend: GVLIELMVS.ET.MARIA.DEI.GRATIA [William and Mary, etc.].
Rev:  crowned shields with the arms of England, Scotland, France and Ireland arranged in cruciform fashion around the lion of Nassau, W and M monograms in each corner and the digits of the date 1692 below each, starting at 10 o'clock.
legend: REX.ET.REGINA.MAG.BR.FR.ET.HIB. [King and Queen of Great Britain, etc., 1689].
Edge:  DECVS ET TVTAMEN, ANNO REGNI TERTIO [a decoration and a protection, third year of reign].

This, the first crown of the reign, uses a new and perhaps more successful reverse, closer to that of the previous two monarchs. The happy coincidence of the shape of the initials may have led to their being used with particular frequency as the royal badge. The frequent recurrence of them in the refurbished Hampton Court indicates their popularity with William and Mary.

## 140 *William III silver crown, 1695*

ENGLAND
ULSTER MUSEUM, BELFAST

Obv:  draped and laureate bust of William III wearing armour.
legend: GVLIELMVS. III.DEI.GRA. [William III, by grace of God].
Rev:  crowned shields with the arms of England, Scotland, France and Ireland arranged in cruciform fashion around the lion of Nassau, the date split either side of the top shield.
legend: REX .MAG. BR.FRA. ET.HIB [King of Great Britain, France and Ireland].
Edge:  DECVS ET TVTAMEN ANNO REGNI SEPTIMO [A decoration and a protection, seventh year of the reign].

Mary died in December 1694, leaving William as sole monarch. While he appears to have worn armour on coins of the joint reign, his breastplate becomes decidedly more obvious on later portraits, when he was ruling alone. The style of these coins is also rather plainer: not only are the imposed initials omitted, but the date is prosaically arranged around twelve o'clock on the reverse, and the size and boldness of the lettering is reduced. It may be that the changes reflect the planned Great Recoinage which started in 1696, making silver coins dated 1696 and 1697 common even today.

## 141 *William and Mary copper halfpenny, 1692*

IRELAND
ULSTER MUSEUM, BELFAST

Obv:  conjoined busts of William and Mary.
legend: GVLIELMVS.ET.MARIA.DEI.GRATIA [William and Mary, etc.].
Rev:  crowned harp, the front post of which is a Maid of Erin.
legend: REX.ET.REGINA. MAG.BR.FR.ET.HIB. [King and Queen of Great Britain, etc.]; the date of 16 92 either side of the band of the crown.

The brass money ceased to have any legal status in February 1690/1, but it was not until near the end of 1692 that new copper halfpennies were again put into circulation. It seems that the patent granted to Colonel Moore in the previous reign was renewed.

**142**

**142** *Silver paperweight incorporating a gun money coin of 1689*

<small>NATIONAL ARMY MUSEUM, LONDON</small>

Height 7 cms, length 10.5 cms, width 6.5 cms.
Exh: *1688 Glorious Revolution?* National Army Museum 1988 (148).

The Jacobite coin was found on the battlefield of Wandewash, India in 1760. Presumably it was carried to India by a soldier in an Irish regiment in the French service. At Wandewash the defeated French were led by Count Lally (1702-66), son of a Jacobite exile from Galway, who was subsequently executed in Paris for surrendering India to the British. The British forces were led by Eyre Coote (1726-83), who was born in Co. Limerick and came from a well-known Irish Protestant family.

# 6. Schomberg and the War in Ireland in 1689

Following the successful defence of Londonderry and Enniskillen by William's supporters, which led to the withdrawal of most of the Jacobite forces from Ulster (except for garrisons in Carrickfergus and Charlemont), Schomberg was despatched from Chester with a large force - consisting mostly of newly raised English regiments, with a stiffening of Dutch and Huguenots - to reconquer Ireland.  Landing unopposed near Bangor in Co. Down in mid-August 1689, he occupied Belfast and Lisburn and attacked Carrickfergus, whose garrison surrendered after a short siege.  He then advanced south towards Dublin, passing through Newry - which the Jacobites had burned - to Dundalk; artillery and stores went by sea.

At Dundalk he camped to await the fleet's arrival, thus losing the chance to engage the Irish army when it was still weak.  James soon had many more soldiers than Schomberg and was able to confront him at Dundalk and offer battle. In dreadful weather, badly supplied and without adequate shelter, the English army fell victim to sickness, which carried off thousands. When James, unable to tempt the Williamites out of their trenches, drew back towards Dublin, Schomberg retreated north early in November and went into winter quarters.  The whole campaign had been a disaster, made worse by Sarsfield's capture of the town of Sligo in the far west. The only gain for the Williamites was that they now had a firm grip on Ulster.

## 143 *Frederick Herman, Duke of Schomberg (1615-90) (c.1675)*

ATTRIBUTED TO SIR GODFREY KNELLER (1646-1723)
THE TENTH DUKE OF LEEDS'S WILL TRUST

Oil on canvas 130 x 102 cms.
Exh: *1688 Glorious Revolution*? National Army Museum 1988 (103), repr. p. 26.

Born at Heidelberg in December 1615, Frederick Herman was the son of Hans Meinhard von Schonberg and Anne Sutton, daughter of the ninth Lord Dudley. He began his military career at the age of seventeen and, like most professional soldiers of the period, sought employment where he could find it: between 1633 and 1650 he served in the Dutch army, then the Swedish, then the French, before returning to the Dutch. From 1661 to 1668 he commanded French and British troops in Portugal and in 1673 was employed by the English to fight the Dutch; the rest of his career between 1652 and 1685 was spent in the service of France. Louis XIV rewarded him well, granting him a dukedom in 1674 and making him a marshal of France the following year.

After the revocation of the Edict of Nantes in October 1685 he left France and went to Portugal, but was allowed to retain his French property and pensions as a special concession. His departure from France was on principle; as a Calvinist, he could no longer endure the persecution of the Huguenots, to whom he was bound by religion. In 1687 he entered the service of the Elector Frederick William of Brandenburg, who showered him with gifts, appointing him a privy councillor and commander-in-chief of his army. (On his way to Berlin he met William at The Hague when, in all probabilty, his role in a possible Dutch intervention in England was discussed). His part in the invasion of England was considered further when William met the new Elector, Frederick III, in September 1688; besides providing the Prince of Orange with troops, Frederick consented to Schomberg's joining William as his second-in-command. In the same month Schomberg led Brandenburg troops into Cologne to forestall French attempts to interfere in a dispute about the vacant archbishopric. As a result of this obvious alliance with the politics of Protestant Europe, his French property was confiscated and his pensions stopped. In November 1688 he accompanied William to England.

The following spring he was rewarded munificently by king and parliament. On 3 April he received the order of the Garter, the next day he was naturalised, and later in the month he was appointed master-general of the ordnance. In May he was created Baron of Teyes, Earl of Brentford, Marquis of Harwich and Duke of Schomberg. To compensate him for his losses in France (which had been substantial), parliament made him a gift of £100,000. In mid-July he was appointed commander-in-chief of the forces in Ireland and on 12 August 1689 sailed from Hoylake near Chester with twelve regiments of infantry (the cavalry and the rest of the foot were to follow). He landed unopposed near Bangor, Co. Down, took possession of Belfast and Carrickfergus (the latter had been held by the Jacobites) and marched to Dundalk via Lisburn, Dromore and Newry, arriving there in early September.

At Dundalk he hoped to pick up the provisions and transport which he had ordered to be shipped into Carlingford Lough. When he reached the town, however, the fleet had not yet arrived, supplies of bread and beer quickly ran out and many of his men fell ill. Rather than march further south, where he would have found better ground, he chose to encamp about a mile north of Dundalk, in a low marshy area. Here he was to remain for about two months, a period which was to be filled with disaster both for the health of his men and for his personal standing with William.

Jacobite suspicions that all was not well within the Williamite camp grew as Schomberg settled in at Dundalk, conclusions which proved correct when deserters told of sickness among the Williamite troops and shortage of provisions. Heartened by this news, James decided to advance from his camp at Drogheda to Ardee (halfway between Drogheda and Dundalk). Schomberg, loath to take the offensive, dug trenches to defend his position. James meanwhile moved closer, until he was within half a mile of the Williamite army. This was a considerable encouragement for the Jacobites who, 'transported with courage by the presence and great example of their king at the head of them could not forbear by shouting and other demonstrations of joy to dare and challenge the invaders, who nevertheless could not be provoked nor invited by any means out of their fortifications' (Simms, p. 128). William wrote from England urging Schomberg to attack. The aged commander, however, continued to do nothing, giving as reasons the poor quality of his troops and weaponry, the superior strength of James's army and the bad condition of the roads. In fact, age appeared to have caught up with him; tired and unable to exert his authority, he had grown over-cautious and unwilling to take a risk.

Conditions in the Dundalk camp were appalling: fever and flux [a form of dysentery] decimated the troops; accommodation was wretched and medical supplies were inadequate. Soldiers seemed loath to part with their dead comrades: 'whilst they had them in their huts they either served to lay between them and the cold wind or at least were serviceable to sit or lie on' (Simms, p. 130). All told, 7,000 men perished in the camp; many more were to die in the hospital in Belfast during the course of the winter.

Both armies remained at close range for over two weeks until, on 6 October, James withdrew to Ardee. Shortly afterwards Schomberg also withdrew and established his winter headquarters at Lisburn. His troops were dispatched to various parts of Ulster, which with the exception of Charlemont was now firmly under Williamite control.

Schomberg took Charlemont in May 1690. A month later William arrived to take charge of operations in Ireland. Disillusioned with Schomberg, he treated the old man coldly and made him feel his subordinate position. At the Boyne, on noticing the Huguenots falling back before the French cavalry, Schomberg rushed forward to encourage them, crying 'Allons Messieurs, voila vos persecuteurs' [Come on, gentlemen, there are your persecutors]. With that, he was surrounded by a number of Tyrconnell's horse and was killed by two sabre wounds to the head and a carbine shot in the neck from behind. *(A Jacobite Narrative* states that one Bryen O'Tool fired the shot). He was subsequently buried under the altar in St Patrick's Cathedral, Dublin. His last resting place remained unregarded until 1731, when Dean Swift and the cathedral chapter placed a memorial tablet close to the spot.

The portrait shows Schomberg as a vigorous man of sixty. Kneller painted him again about 1689 in an equestrian pose; versions of this are owned by Lord Yarborough and the Marquis of Lothian. An engraving after the equestrian portrait was executed by John Smith c.1689.

Sources:     *DNB*; J.G.Simms, *Jacobite Ireland 1685-91* (London, 1969); H. and B. van der Zee, *William and Mary* (London, 1973); John Childs, 'A Patriot For Whom? 'For God and for Honour': Marshal Schomberg,' *History Today,* vol. 38, July 1988.

**143**

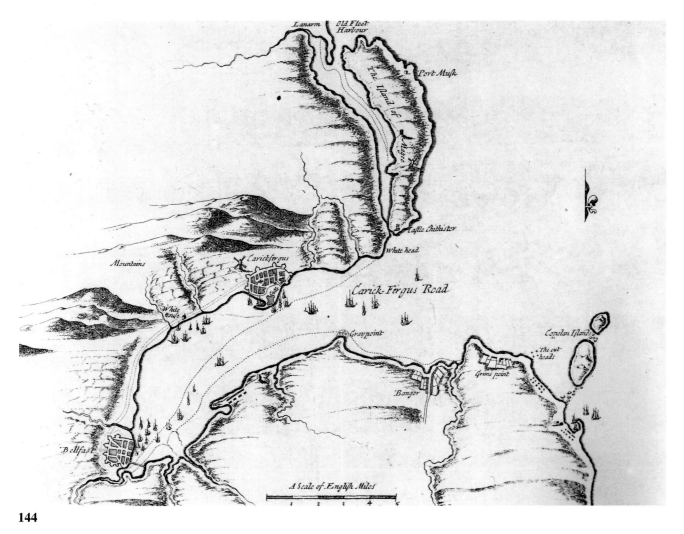

144

**144** *Belfast Lough in 1689*
*(to illustrate the landing of Schomberg )*

FROM STORY'S *CONTINUATION* (1693)
REPRODUCTION

**145** *A Full And True Account Of The Besieging And
Taking Of Carrickfergus*
*by the Duke of Schomberg... In a Letter from Chester of August
the 31st. (London, 1689)*

PUBLIC RECORD OFFICE OF NORTHERN IRELAND

quarto: 2 pp.

When Schomberg landed near Bangor, Co. Down in mid-August 1689 the
Jacobites soon withdrew from most of Ulster, leaving only garrisons in
Carrickfergus and Charlemont. Schomberg occupied Belfast and then besieged
Carrickfergus, whose strong Norman castle and town walls were held by some
2,000 troops under the command of the MacCarthy More and Cormac O'Neill.

After a siege of less than a week the Jacobite commander sued for terms.
The garrison were allowed to march out - 'Colours flying, Arms, and Drums
beating', as reported here - to join their comrades at Charlemont. 'But such was
the ill nature of the Rabble', we are told, 'that they fell upon them in their
March, and dis-arm'd them.' In fact Schomberg was obliged to intervene
personally, pistol in hand, to prevent their being murdered. The effects of the
siege on the town were evidently severe :'The Town has been so miserably
defaced by the continual playing of the Bombs for Five Days together, that it
looks like a dismal heap of ruine.'

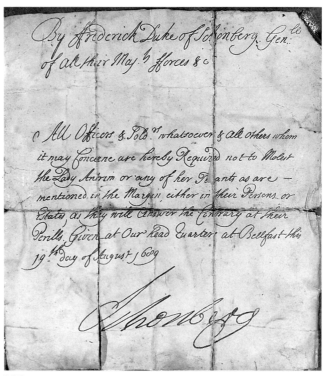

**146**

## 146 *Letter of protection from Frederick Duke of Schomberg to Lady Antrim, 19 August 1689*

<small>Viscount Dunluce</small>

Alexander MacDonnell, third Earl of Antrim, was James II's leading supporter in Ulster. The withdrawal of the Jacobite army from the north, following the unsuccessful siege of Derry, left his estates at the mercy of local Williamites until Lady Antrim obtained official protection.

> [By ffrederick Duke of Schonberg, Genll of all their Maj.'s fforces &c
> All Officers & Sold.rs whatsoever & all others whom it may Concerne
> are hereby Required not to Molest the Lady Antrim or any of her
> Tenants as are mentioned in the Margin, either in their Persons or
> Estates, as they will Answer the Contrary at their Perills. Given at Our
> head Quarters at Belfast this 19th day of August 1689 Schonberg]

'Schonberg', as used here by the general himself, is the proper German form of his name.

## 147 *Dutch camp scene, c. 1660*

<small>By Jan de Visscher, after Philips Wouwermans (1619-68)</small>
<small>National Army Museum, London</small>

Engraving 34 x 39 cms; published c. l660.
Exh: *l688 Glorious Revolution?* National Army Museum 1988(137).

Ill-disciplined, irregularly paid and poorly supplied, seventeenth-century armies were also accompanied on campaign by large numbers of non-combatants. Though military administrations became more sophisticated in the later part of the century, this Dutch camp scene is probably typical of most armies of the period. At their worst, unpaid and undisciplined and let loose upon the civilian population, they were the ruin of any area that had the misfortune to lie in their path. By contrast, a well-paid army spent money wherever it passed, to the advantage of at least some parts of the local economy. In areas such as the Netherlands, which were the scene of frequent military operations at this time, commanders usually avoided pillage because they might depend upon such resources for their own winter quarters.

147

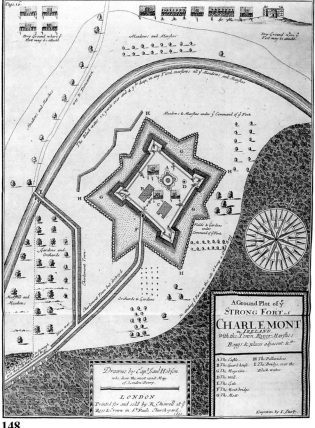

148

157

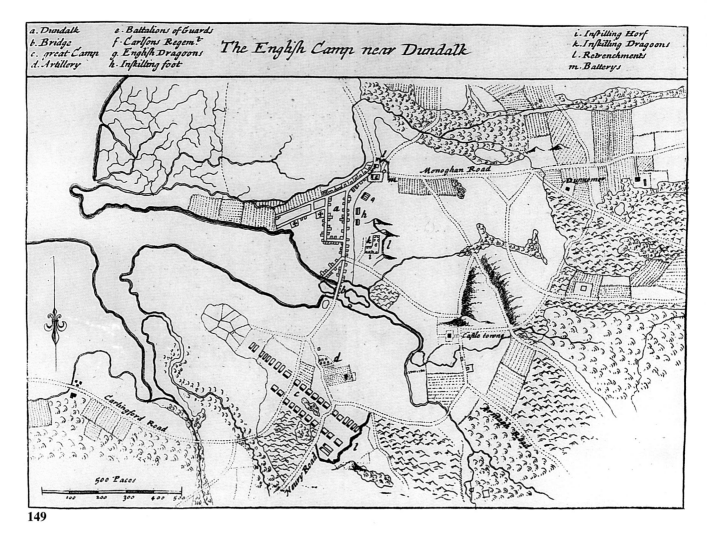

a. *Dundalk*  e. *Battalions of Guards*
b. *Bridge*  f. *Carsons Regem.ᵗ*
c. *great Camp*  g. *English Dragoons*
d. *Artillery*  h. *Inskilling foot*

*The English Camp near Dundalk*

i. *Inskilling Horf*
k. *Inskilling Dragoons*
l. *Retrenchments*
m. *Batterys*

*Monoghan Road*

*Dunover*

*Castle towne*

*Carlingford Road*

*Navy Road*

*500 Paces*

*100   200   300   400   500*

**149**

**148** *'A Ground Plot of ye Strong Fort of Charlemont in Ireland'*

BY SAMUEL HOBSON, FROM STORY'S *CONTINUATION* (1693)
REPRODUCTION

**149** *'The English Camp near Dundalk,' 1689*

FROM STORY'S *CONTINUATION* (1693)
REPRODUCTION

**150** *A Letter From Duke Schomberge's*
*camp, giving an account of the condition of the English and Irish army. And a true account of all the Papists in Ireland... and the several parties amongst them... Dundalke November 4. 1689... London, printed for Tho. Parkhurst: and published by Randal Taylor... 1689*

THE QUEEN'S UNIVERSITY, BELFAST

quarto:  [1]. 9 pp.
Lit:  Wing L1461.

According to the printer and bookseller John Dunton, Thomas Parkhurst was the most 'eminent Presbyterian bookseller in the Three Kingdoms.'

**151**

**151** *A Relation of what most*
*remarkably happened during the last campaign in Ireland, betwixt*
*His Majesties army royal, and the forces of the Prince of Orange,*
*sent to joyn the rebels, under the command of the Count de*
*Schomberg... Dublin, printed for... James Malone... 1689*

THE QUEEN'S UNIVERSITY, BELFAST

quarto: 15pp.
Lit:     Wing R896.

Alderman James Malone was a Dublin printer and bookseller who served as a
captain in James II's army. He was the publisher of the official Jacobite paper,
the *Dublin gazette* 1689-90 and, jointly with his son, was appointed King's
Printer in Ireland in 1690.

William brought his King's Printer, Edward Jones, to Ireland with him in
1690, together with a press on which to print government proclamations.  Jones
may have produced such items in Belfast and Londonderry in the same year.
None exist, however, and surviving correspondence makes it doubtful that much
could have been done on a peripatetic press. The printers complained, 'one day's
sudden motion will more disturb and disorder their utensils than in three days
can be rectified' and they pointed out that they could work only in a house rather
than in a moving camp.  (Christopher Carleton to [? Sir Robert Southwell] 25
June 1690).

After the battle of the Boyne Jones eventually set up his press in King's
Hospital, the Blew Coat school at Oxmantown, in the northern suburbs of
Dublin. The boys had been turned out of the school by Tyrconnell in November
1689 and James had allocated the premises as a hospital for his wounded French
troops. When Jones was assigned quarters for his press in 1690, following the
hasty departure of the French, the school was being used as a corn store for the
Williamite army.

**152**               **153**

Tyrconnell would certainly have found himself seriously handicapped without a press when he moved his centre of government to Limerick in 1690. If anything was printed there, none of it survives.

## 152 *'Tyrconnel, Vice-Roy in Ireland'*

FROM *HIBERNIA VINDICATA* (HAMBURG, 1691)
BY DIEDERICH LEMKUS
REPRODUCTION

*Hibernia Vindicata* was a German book published in Hamburg shortly after the surrender of Limerick. William III's successful conclusion of the war in Ireland was regarded on the Continent as a defeat for Louis XIV, hence the interest among the Protestant states of Germany. The same Hamburg publisher had produced the German version of Walker's story of the siege of Derry in 1689.

The scene of rape and pillage in the background was probably copied from one of the propaganda prints of the period.

Lemkus (or Lembkes) was a German engraver who worked in Hamburg during the late seventeenth century. His ouput included pictures of monuments and local notables (he became one himself, as a burgher of the city).

## 153 *'Fridericus Hertzog von Schomberg'*

FROM *HIBERNIA VINDICATA* (HAMBURG, 1691)
BY DIEDERICH LEMKUS
REPRODUCTION

While the engraving of Tyrconnell may be fanciful, this one is quite a good portrait of Schomberg, evidently copied from one of the numerous pictures of the famous soldier. The background shows the Williamite army crossing the Boyne and the fighting around the village of Oldbridge, where Schomberg was killed. It is copied from one of the numerous Dutch engravings of the scene.

IRELAND
1689-1691

LONDONDERRY
*SIEGE*

CARRICKFERGUS
*Siege*

Bangor

Belfast

‡ CHARLEMONT
*Siege*

‡ ENNISKILLEN
*Siege*

Sligo

L.Erne

**NEWTOWNBUTLER**

Dundalk

Drogheda

R. Boyne

**BOYNE**

Dublin

**AUGHRIM**   ‡ ATHLONE
*Siege*

Galway

R. Shannon

LIMERICK
*SIEGE*

Wexford

Waterford

CORK
*Siege*

KINSALE
*Siege*

BANTRY BAY
*Sea Battle*
*May 1689*

| | BATTLE |
|---|---|
| *SIEGE* | MAJOR |
| *Siege* | MINOR |

161

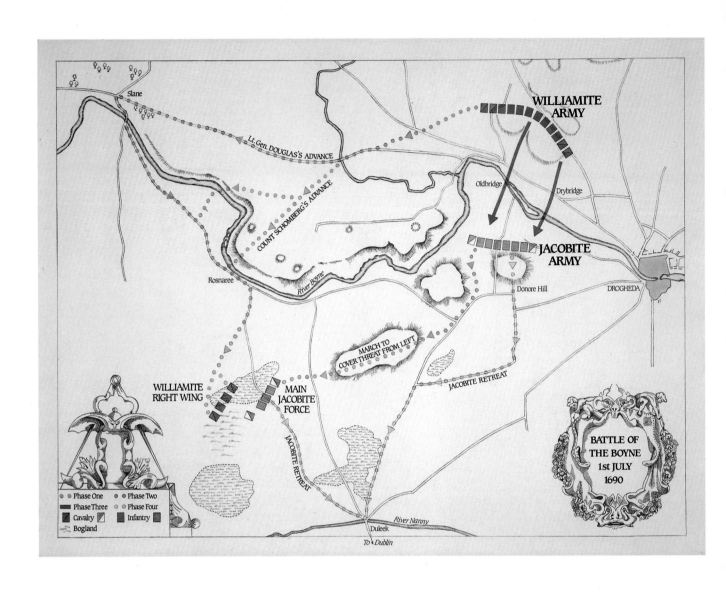

WILLIAMITE
ARMY

Oldbridge    Drybridge

Slane

Lt. Gen. DOUGLAS'S ADVANCE

COUNT SCHOMBERG'S ADVANCE

JACOBITE
ARMY

Rosnaree

River Boyne

Donore Hill

DROGHEDA

MARCH TO
COVER THREAT FROM LEFT

JACOBITE RETREAT

WILLIAMITE
RIGHT WING

MAIN
JACOBITE
FORCE

BATTLE OF
THE BOYNE
1st JULY
1690

JACOBITE RETREAT

○ ○ Phase One   ○ ○ Phase Two
▬▬ Phase Three   ○ ○ Phase Four
◪ Cavalry   ◪ Infantry
Bogland

River Nanny

Duleek

To Dublin

162

# 7. 1690

The campaigning season in 1690 opened with Dublin and most of the country still firmly under the control of the Jacobites. In March they were reinforced by more than 6,000 seasoned French troops under the command of the comte de Lauzun (though the French insisted on taking an equal number of Irishmen in exchange). Following Schomberg's failure the previous year, for which the aged duke was never forgiven, William decided to lead a second and more formidable expedition in person.

He landed at Carrickfergus on 14 June to an enthusiastic reception from the Protestant inhabitants of the north. By the end of the month his cosmopolitan army, amounting to about 36,000 men with a large train of artillery and ample supplies, had reached the river Boyne. Here James, despite considerably smaller numbers (he had about 25,000), less well equipped and ill supplied with cannon, took his stand rather than abandon Dublin and retreat to the line of the Shannon. The battle fought on 1 July (the date by the old calendar; it would have been eleven days later by the present one) was not a great affair from the point of view of casualties (about 1,000 Jacobites and half as many Williamites); Jacobite writers called it a mere skirmish. There was some hard fighting, nevertheless, especially by the Irish cavalry, before James's men broke and fled, and the victory was rightly seen in Europe as a real defeat for Louis XIV as well as James. Dublin was abandoned, and the remnant of the Jacobite army made its way towards Limerick. A Williamite army of 10,000, sent west to secure the Shannon crossing at Athlone, was successfully defied by the Jacobite governor, who broke down the bridge.

William entered Dublin four days after his victory at the Boyne, by which time James was on his way to France. There was little resistance as he advanced towards Limerick, where the Irish army had gathered to make a last stand (Lauzun and his troops had embarked for home at Galway). The assaults on Limerick were beaten back in desperate hand-to-hand fighting in which the Williamites suffered heavy casualties. The loss of his siege guns en route to the city, destroyed in a daring cavalry raid by Sarsfield, bad weather and the need to return to England made William abandon the siege. He was greatly disappointed that the Irish business would require another major effort. Late in the year, Marlborough captured Cork and Kinsale in a short but very successful campaign, thus closing the ports most convenient for the French.

**154**

**154** *Antonin Nompar de Caumont, Comte (later Duc) de Lauzun (1632-1723)*

ATTRIBUTED TO PIERRE MIGNARD (1612-95)
MUSÉES D'ART ET D'HISTORIE DE LA ROCHELLE
REPRODUCTION

Lauzun, a recklessly ambitious courtier whom Louis XIV had once imprisoned for ten years (and whom he twice sent to the Bastille for shorter periods), was in England in 1688 at the time of the Revolution. (He knew James, having served with him in Flanders when the latter was Duke of York). In December 1688 he escorted the Queen and the infant Prince of Wales safely to France shortly before James himself fled. In gratitude James awarded him the Garter.

In 1689 he sought the command of the French expedition to Ireland but Conrad von Rosen, a German who had been in French service for forty years, was preferred. At James's insistence, however, he replaced Rosen the following year, landing at Kinsale in March 1690 with some 6,000 officers and men. The appointment was met with gloom in Ireland, for Lauzun's military experience was minimal (he had never held a high command). Furthermore, he was hated by Louvois, the French Minister of War, who had not been consulted about his appointment and who was therefore unlikely to co-operate with him.

**155**

The prospect of Lauzun as commander also upset the French officers already in Ireland, for he had a reputation as an intriguer and trouble-maker. The French ambassador d'Avaux disliked him too and was relieved to be recalled to France shortly after he arrived. James's choice of him, in fact, convinced Louvois of James's general incompetence and incapacity to lead. In the event, however, Lauzun proved to be a better general than expected, showing valour in battle and trying hard to bring order to the army. He commanded at the Boyne, when the French took little part in the battle itself but covered the Jacobite retreat afterwards. Despite performing better militarily than had been expected, his character and attitude to the Irish did little to endear him to them: according to an officer in the Irish Brigade 'M. de Lauzun was more fitted to play at gallantries, more capable of unravelling petty court intrigues than of distinguishing himself at the head of a brigade; in addition he was quick, proud and so self-sufficient that he treated us as foreigners in our own country' (*The Irish Sword,* p. 69). He and his army left from Galway in September 1690. On his return to France he again fell from favour with Louis XIV, because of his lack of success in Ireland (though he was created a duke in 1692). He remained in favour at the Jacobite court, however: it was he who brought Mary Beatrice news of the Jacobite defeat at Sheriffmuir in November 1715. He died on 19 November 1723.

The portrait shows him wearing the Greater George and Garter mantle. The inscription to the left, above the coat of arms, reads 'Antonien Nompar de Caumont, [comte de Lauzun], duc de Lauzun and duc de St. Fargeau, Captain of the Old Company of One Hundred Gentlemen of the King's Household, Captain of the First Company of Life Guards; Governor General of the province of Berry and of the towns of Bourges and Issadoun; chief and Colonel General of the French Dragoons; Knight of the Illustrious Order of the Garter of Great Britain.' Pierre Mignard, to whom the painting is attributed, worked in Rome between 1636 and 1657, when he was summoned back to France by Louis XIV. He achieved considerable success both as a portrait painter and as a decorator of private houses and churches. On the death of his great rival Charles Lebrun in 1690, he was appointed First Painter on the king's orders and also, by his command, director and chancellor of the Academy of Painting and Sculpture.

Sources:    R.J. Hayes, 'Reflections of an Irish Brigade officer,' *The Irish Sword,* vol.1, (1949-53); J.G. Simms, *Jacobite Ireland 1685-91* (London, 1969); John Miller, *James II: a Study in Kingship* (Hove, 1978).

## 155 *Coat and vest of a French general officer or marshal, c. 1690-1710*

NATIONAL ARMY MUSEUM, LONDON

Exh:    *1688: Glorious Revolution?* National Army Museum 1988 (157).

The uniform is that of a high-ranking officer in the French army of the 1690s or early 1700s, probably a mounted officer. The exact origin is unknown, but the likelihood is that the uniform came to England as a result of Marlborough's victories in the War of the Spanish Succession. Nine senior French officers were killed at Blenheim in 1704 and sixteen were captured and taken to England as prisoners; Lt Col. Thomas Bellew. who commanded Meredith's Regiment of Foot (later the 37th Regiment) at Blenheim, and whose family once owned the uniform, may have brought it back with him.

## 156 *Chart of the river Dee at Chester*
*Inset in 'Carte Generale des Costes d'Irlande, et des Costes Occidentales d'Angleterre avec une Partie de celles d'Ecosse,' from Le Neptune François (1693) (no. 252)*

PROFESSOR R.S.J. CLARKE
REPRODUCTION

Chester was the chief port for Ireland in the late seventeenth century and the main assembly point for the military expeditions of Schomberg in 1689 and William in 1690. The troops were embarked at the mouth of the river, at Hoylake ('Hich Lake' on this French chart).

**156**

**157** *Portrait of an unknown gentleman, thought to be*
*Ferdinand Wilhelm, Duke of Würtemberg-Neustadt*
*(1659-1701)*

BY AN UNKNOWN ARTIST
WEIKERSHEIM CASTLE, WEIKERSHEIM
REPRODUCTION

Ferdinand Wilhelm, Duke of Würtemberg-Neustadt, a German aristrocrat, joined
the Danish army at an early age and after distinguishing himself in the war
between Denmark and Sweden was appointed lieutenant-general at the tender
age of twenty-three. After serving in Hungary against the Turks he was made
commander-in-chief of the army corps sent by Christian V of Denmark to fight
on the Williamite side. The Danish corps subsequently took part in all the major
engagements of the Irish campaign, from the Boyne to Aughrim and Limerick.

Though the Danish force was under the command of Schomberg (or
whoever else was in command of the British army at the time), discipline was
left to Würtemberg, who was present at all councils of war. Throughout the
campaign he went to great lengths to keep the Danish king fully informed of the
military operations in which his troops were involved. Most of the Danish
officers were French or German; few were Danes. The other ranks included
many non-Danes. According to Molesworth, William's envoy at the Danish
court, the Danish infantrymen were 'for the most part strangers of all countries

**157**

Foto Braun, Weikersheim

whom choice or fortune brings there: Germans, Poles, Courlanders, Dutch, Swedes, Scotch, Irish, and now and then an English seaman whom they make drunk after a long voyage' (Danaher and Simms, p. 11). The force was well armed and had been equipped with the latest flintlock muskets for the Irish campaign; also bayonets instead of pikes.

Würtemberg spent January and February 1690 in London, discussing the campaign and its administrative and financial details with William. On 13 March following he arrived in Belfast, and subsequently established his headquarters at Galgorm Castle near Ballymena. During the winter of 1690-91 he made Waterford his base. Throughout the campaign he acquitted himself ably and was thought highly of by Schomberg, who described him as having a 'spirit gentle, patient and desirous of doing well' (Danaher and Simms, p. 18). He never ceased to ensure that he and his troops were given their due respect, perhaps a reflection of the considerable jealousy which existed between the Danish and English commanders. This reached a climax in September 1690, before the attack on Cork, when he and Marlborough quarrelled over who should have command. In the end a compromise was reached; each commanded on alternate days.

Würtemberg's military prowess and brave spirit were greatly admired in many quarters. At the siege of Athlone, during which his grenadiers carried him across the river on their shoulders (he had crossed the Boyne in similar fashion), his valour helped towards the operation's ultimate success. Praise for his attitude and conduct was frequent throughout the entire Irish campaign and was reported by William to Christian V in March 1692.

After the close of the war in Ireland Würtemberg continued to serve William in the Low Countries, and after the peace of Rijswijk was appointed governor of Dutch Flanders. He saw active service again in 1698 and 1700. He died in 1701, from complications of a head wound he had received in 1685.

Sources:    K. Danaher and J.G. Simms, eds., *The Danish Force in Ireland 1690-1691* (Dublin, 1962); J.G. Simms, *Jacobite Ireland 1685-91* (London, 1969).

**158** obv.

**158** rev.

## 158 *Danish auxiliaries in Ireland, 1691*

MEDAL BY ANON
PHOTOGRAPH

Lead, 38 mm.

Lit:        *Medallic Illustrations* 49-50, no. 240.
Description:   obv. a palm tree from which two shields hang.
                legend: on the left shield: DA NORVM FOR TIBVS
                AVSIS [by the courageous sally of the Danes]; on the right
                shield: VI RIBVS VNI TIS [by the united (military)
                forces].
            rev. a female representing Hibernia stands with her right hand
                outstretched, on which stands a winged Victory, holding
                out a laurel wreath. Hibernia rests her left hand on a harp.
                There are rosettes at the beginning and end of the legend.
                legend: RELEVATA [delivered]; in exergue: .1691.

This medal was produced by the Danes to mark the return of their troops. The palm tree is a symbol of victory. The use of a tiny crowning victory on coins goes back to ancient Greece.

## 159 *The Landing of King William of Glorious Memory at Carrickfergus, 1690*

BY WILLIAM VAN DER HAGEN (D.1745)
ULSTER MUSEUM, BELFAST

Oil on canvas 183 x 131.5 cms.

Inscr:   'The Landing of King William of Glorious Memory at Carrickfergus 1690' along top.
Purchased from Rupert Preston Gallery, London 1967.

Prov:   Leonard Partridge, London; bought by Morton Lee, Chichester Antiques, Ltd. Sold to
        Hawker Siddeley Holdings Ltd., 1948-9; bought by Preston Gallery 1966. The painting may
        have been at Curraghmore, seat of the Marquis of Waterford, in 1913; Strickland's
        *Dictionary of Irish Artists* records a painting of the subject, by Johann van der Hagen
        (perhaps a cartoon for Baillie's tapestry) as being there. However, there is no record of the
        painting at Curraghmore (letter from the Marquis of Waterford, 4 October 1973). Attributed
        to William van de Velde in 1948; attributed to William van der Hagen by 1966.

Exh:    *Netherland Seventeenth Century Seascape Paintings from Vroom to Van de Velde*, Rupert
        Preston Gallery, London 1967 (9).
        *Glorious Revolution. The World of William and Mary,* Nieuwe Kerk, Amsterdam, June-
        September 1988 (254), repr. pl. 48.

Lit:    Rupert Preston, *The 17th Century Marine Painters of the Netherlands* (Leigh-on-Sea, 1974),
        p. 25, repr. fig. 36.
        Christopher Wright, *Old Master Paintings in Britain* (London, 1976), pp. 86, 232.

The painting may be a cartoon for an unexecuted tapestry by Robert Baillie, intended for the Irish House of Lords. In 1727 Baillie presented a petition to the Irish Parliament suggesting he make a series of tapestries commemorating the Glorious Revolution, for the new Parliament House on College Green, the foundation stone of which was laid early in 1729. He proposed six tapestries, to show the following:

> The valiant Defence of Londonderry, from the Opening of the Trenches
> to the raising of the Siege, by the Arrival of the English Army.
> The Landing of King William and his Army at Carrickfergus.
> The glorious Battle and Victory of the Boyne, with the Rout of the
> Irish Army.
> The splendid and joyful Entry of King William into Dublin.
> The Battle of Aughrim.
> The taking of Cork and Kinsale by the late victorious Duke
> of Marlborough.

The suggestion was accepted, and in May 1728 Ballie received an order to supply the tapestries. In the same year he commissioned van der Hagen to design them and take 'prospects' of the various places to be represented in the series. This painting was probably intended as a design for the tapestry showing William III landing at Carrickfergus. By 1731, however, Baillie's contract had been changed and only two tapestries were eventually produced: the defence of Londonderry and the battle of the Boyne. Both were placed in the Irish House of Lords on 10 September 1733. They can still be seen in the House of Lords chamber in the building, which was purchased by the Bank of Ireland in 1802. A landscape of

**159**

**159a**

Londonderry, also by van der Hagen and owned by Derry City Council, is close to the background of the Londonderry tapestry and may have been used towards its design.

The Dutch artist William van der Hagen, whose Christian name Strickland erroneously gives as Johann, came to Ireland probably during the 1720s. In addition to being the first important name in Irish landscape painting he was well known as a scene painter and decorative artist, carrying out work in a number of Irish houses, including Curraghmore.

Though he worked in various parts of Ireland he seems not to have visited Carrickfergus, judging from the inaccuracy of detail in the picture: instead of showing the keep in its rightful position, central in the castle, he has transposed it to the end of the rock. He is, however, correct in his inclusion of latrine shoots (the arched details) on the keep; these features can still be seen today. From this it would appear that he saw an accurate drawing or model of the keep but, as he did not see the castle, produced a somewhat muddled depiction of it. His source is unfortunately unknown.

The painting has considerable propagandist overtones. The scene shows Sir Cloudisley Shovell's flagship, the *Monck*, in the foreground, depicted inaccurately however; the *Monck* was a third-rate warship of about seventy guns and not the first-rate vessel of about one hundred guns shown here. Van der Hagen has exaggerated the guns and ports of the *Monck* and has made the ship appear much grander than it actually would have been, for dramatic effect. The vessel to the right of the *Monck* is probably the yacht *Mary,* which carried William; it too has been exaggerated in size, probably to emphasize the importance of the occasion. The small barge leaving the *Mary* is Shovell's and is taking William ashore. There are discrepancies in the flags depicted which indicate that they post-date Admiral Russell's *Permanent Instructions* of the late seventeenth century, which revised signalling methods. The painting is an attractive but decidedly unrealistic image of William's landing at Carrickfergus.

Sources:     A.K. Longfield, 'History of Tapestry-making in Ireland in the 17th and 18th Centuries,' *Journal of the Royal Society of Antiquaries of Ireland,* vol. LXVIII, part I, June 1938; C.P. Curran, 'The Architecture of the Bank of Ireland. Part I. The Parliament House 1728 - 1800,'*Irish Georgian Society*, vol. XX, nos. 1 and 2, January - June 1977; advice on castle from T.E. McNeill, Q.U.B.; information on ships from Dr. R. McCaughey.

**159a** *The valiant Defence of Londonderry, from the Opening of the Trenches to the raising of the Siege, by the Arrival of the English Army*

TAPESTRY BY ROBERT BAILLIE, DESIGNED BY WILLIAM VAN DER HAGEN
BANK OF IRELAND, DUBLIN
REPRODUCTION

**160**

## 160 *William III landing at Carrickfergus, 14 June 1690*

INSET IN THE CHART OF BELFAST LOUGH BY CAPTAIN GREENVILE COLLINS,
PUBLISHED IN 1693 (NO. 254)
ULSTER MUSEUM, BELFAST
REPRODUCTION

Collins actually took part in the event depicted, as captain of the yacht *Mary* (A)
which had conveyed William from Hoylake. (See no. 253 for information
on Collins).

## 161 *William called to Ireland, 1690*

MEDAL BY J. LUDER (FL. 1680-1710)
HUNTERIAN MUSEUM, GLASGOW

**161** obv.

Silver, 57 mm.
Lit:            *Medallic Illustrations*, 705-06, no. 114.
Description:    obv. bust of William draped over ornate armour.
                     legend: GVILMVS.III.D.G.MAG.BRIT.FRAN.ET.HIB.REX [William III,
                     by grace of God king of Great Britain, France and Ireland].
                rev. to the left, on a rock are two females, the one in the foreground wearing a
                     crown and holding out her arms in supplication, the other raising her arms
                     in the air. The sea is at their feet. Neptune rises from it with his trident,
                     waving an arm in the air; a plume of smoke (or spray) is on his left. In the
                     sky Jupiter sits in a cloud, holding a bundle of thunderbolts; below him
                     Phaeton in his chariot goes to the right.
                     legend: NISI TU QUIS TEMPERET IGNES [no one but you can quell
                     the flames].

The symbolism of Phaeton has already been discussed under no. 61. One may
assume that the crowned female represents Hibernia; the other however remains
obscure. The historical background of the symbolism was the fact that the aged
Duke of Schomberg had got bogged down in Ireland and that William, having
spent time consolidating his position in England and worried about a possible
direct attack from Louis, was now in a position to take control himself. Great
things were obviously expected.

**161** rev.

The grand rendition of William on the obverse contrasts with the almost
naive figures on the reverse. Although Luder has made quite a good job of
placing the design within the circular format, it almost seems as if the concept
was graphic rather than intended for medallic rendition.

## 162a *William arrives in Ireland*

MEDAL BY J. SMELTZING (FL. 1685, D. 1695)
HUNTERIAN MUSEUM, GLASGOW

Silver, 49 mm.
Lit:            *Medallic Illustrations*, 707, no. 117.
Description:    obv. bust of William III, draped and laureate.
                     legend: GUIELM:III.D.G.BRIT: REX,ARAUS:PR:BELG:GUB:
                     [William III, by grace of God king of Britain, prince of Orange, governor
                     of Belgica].

rev. an eagle, carrying branches of bay and orange in its beak and a sceptre in its talon, flies over the sea; to the right are a large number of ships; to the left is a harbour and shore on which is growing a broken-down tree.

legend: ALIS NON ARMIS [by wings not arms]; in exergue: TRAIECTUS IN HIBERNI: LOND: 4/14 IUN:1690 [the crossing to Ireland, 4/14 June 1690].

The message of the reverse seems to be that William was relying more on speed than on force to recapture Ireland; his fleet set sail from Chester on 1 June and arrived at Carrickfergus on 4 June. The date is expressed in terms of both the Julian and Gregorian calendars, emphasising the importance of the European over the insular audience. As well as being associated with victory, bay was a protection against lightning; this may be why the eagle is shown carrying it. The depiction of the shore is intended to illustrate the devastation of Ireland.

## 162b *William arrives in Ireland*

MEDAL BY ANON
HUNTERIAN MUSEUM, GLASGOW

Silver, 52 mm.
Lit:            *Medallic Illustrations*, 706, no. 115.
Description:   obv.  bust of William III, draped over armour and wearing a steel cap.
                     legend: GVILIELMVS.III.D.G.MAG.BRIT.FRAN.ET.HIB.
                     RIX.BELG.GUB [William III, by grace of God king of Great Britain,
                     France and Ireland, governor of the Low Countries].
               rev.   a unicorn leaps from left to right, over marshy ground, on which are three
                     frogs sitting up on their hind legs; behind is the sea with a number of
                     ships.
                     legend: NON . METAM . ABIECTA.MORANTUR [not held back by the
                     fear of the cowardly; 'abiectus' can also have the sense of 'lowly' or
                     'common']; in exergue: TRAIECTUS.IN.HIBERNIAM MDCLXXXX
                     (the crossing into Ireland, 1690].

**162(b)** obv.

**162(b)** rev.

The unicorn is a beast capable of carrying a huge burden of symbolism; here it is probably sufficient to note that as well as being one of the English royal beasts it is also associated with courage, strength and purity.

William's departure for Ireland was delayed by a series of domestic circumstances: not only was there the possibility of an invasion or rising in England, there were also political troubles in Holland, to where he was being urged to return. Here he is shown rising above all these petty troubles to get on with more important business.

## 163 *'The Military Duties Of The Cavalry, Containing the way of exercising the Horse, According to the practice of this present time,' translated by 'A.L.,' (London, 1678)*

NATIONAL ARMY MUSEUM, LONDON

Exh:   *1688: Glorious Revolution?* National Army Museum 1988 (24).

Originally written in French by the Sieur de la Fontain, this drill book is illustrated with prints showing battles of foot against foot and cavalry against cavalry.

## 164 *'Military Discipline; Or The Art of War Shewing Directions for the Postures In Exercising Of The Pike and Muskett The Dragoons, Granadeers, and Horse,' by Capt J.S.,' (London, 1689)*

NATIONAL ARMY MUSEUM, LONDON

Exh:   *1688: Glorious Revolution?* National Army Museum 1988 (26).

Illustrated with twenty-one plates, this drill book updated those of the Civil War period. By 1689 the introduction of bayonets had reduced the numbers of pikemen. The 'granadeers' were a new kind of soldier (see no. 220).

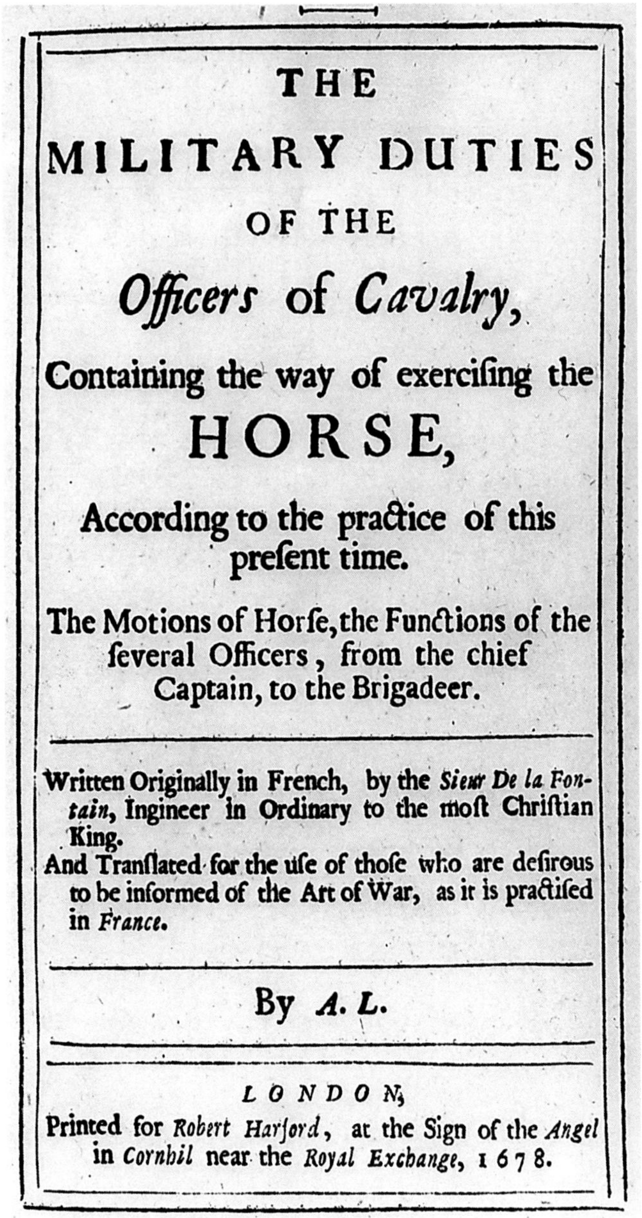

## THE
## MILITARY DUTIES
### OF THE
### *Officers* of *Cavalry*,

Containing the way of exercifing the
## HORSE,

According to the practice of this
prefent time.

The Motions of Horfe, the Functions of the
feveral Officers, from the chief
Captain, to the Brigadeer.

---

Written Originally in French, by the *Sieur De la Fon-*
*tain*, Ingineer in Ordinary to the moft Chriftian
King.
And Tranflated for the ufe of thofe who are defirous
to be informed of the Art of War, as it is practifed
in *France.*

---

## By *A. L.*

---

*L O N D O N,*
Printed for *Robert Harford*, at the Sign of the *Angel*
in *Cornhil* near the *Royal Exchange,* 1 6 7 8.

---

163

## 165 *The battle of the Boyne*

BY JAN WYCK (C.1640-1702)
NATIONAL ARMY MUSEUM, LONDON

Oil on canvas  78 x 110 cms.

Exh:      1688 *Glorious Revolution?*  National Army Museum 1988 (107), repr. p. 67.

Following the failure of Schomberg in 1689, William III came in person to
Ireland in June 1690 with a large and well-equipped army composed of Dutch,
Germans, Huguenot French and many other nationalities as well as English and
Scottish. When joined by Schomberg and regiments from Londonderry and
Enniskillen he had a force of about 35,000. James II's army numbered about
25,000 including 6,000 French under Lauzun, but he had few cannon and many
of his infantry were ill-trained and poorly equipped. Against the advice of both
Tyrconnell and Lauzun, James decided to block William's advance towards
Dublin at the river Boyne near Drogheda.

The battle fought at the Boyne on 1 July (by the old calendar then used in
the British Isles, 12 July by the present one) was not a great affair in military
terms: about 1,000 Jacobites and 500 Williamites were killed (of whom
Schomberg was one). Most of the Jacobite army, and a large part of the

*Title Page*

Military Diſcipline;

OR THE

# ART of WAR.

SHEWING

Directions for the Poſtures

IN

EXERCISING

OF THE

## PIKE and MUSKET

THE

Dragoons, Granadeers, and Horſe;

The Art of Doubling, wheeling, Forming and Drawing up a Battalion or Army into any Figure, &c.

The Method of conducting Armies in Champaign, Hilly or Woody Countries : Of Encampings, Beſiegings, giving of Battel, with all ſorts of Inſtructions and other Obſervations belonging to the whole Art of War: as now practiced.

All repreſented in Twenty two ſeveral Copper Plates, with variety of ſeveral Proſpects and other Deſigns, for the Practice and Exerciſe of Arms.

The ſecond Edition with many Additions and Corrections.

Improved and Deſigned by Capt. *J. S.*

Publiſhed and Sold by *Robert Morden*, at the *Atlas* near the *Royal Exchange* in *Cornhil*. 1689.

**164**

Williamite one, saw little action and most of the Jacobites got away afterwards. By threatening to outflank the Jacobite left, William pinned down many of James's best troops for most of the day while the main Williamite force crossed the river near Oldbridge and overcame stiff resistance - including repeated charges by the Irish cavalry - to defeat the Jacobite centre and right and cause a general retreat. Though not by any means the end of the war, the battle of the Boyne nevertheless caused James II to quit Ireland and gave William Dublin and most of the country. In Europe it was celebrated as an important victory for the anti-French alliance. Contrary to popular belief, Te Deums were not sung in Rome, but there was official rejoicing in Vienna by William's ally the Catholic emperor Leopold.

The painting shows William, mounted on a white horse, and his officers in the right foreground. In the middle background to the right, the Williamite forces can be seen crossing the Boyne at Oldbridge, where the main engagement took place. In the middle and left background the Jacobites can be seen retreating over the hills towards Duleek.

A much larger version of the painting, also by Wyck and dated 1693, is in the NGI; there is another in Slane Castle.

165

**166** *The victory of King William III at the battle of the Boyne, 1 July 1690*

By Dirck Maas (1659-1717)
National Gallery of Ireland, Dublin

Etching  53 x 105.5 cms (plate cut).
Lit:     Adrian Le Harivel, ed., *National Gallery of Ireland Illustrated Summary Catalogue of Prints and Sculpture* (Dublin, 1988), p. 358, repr.

Dirck (also known as Theodor) Maas worked for William III and accompanied him to the Boyne, where he recorded his impressions of the battle in a drawing now in Windsor Castle. This etching, with annotations in both English and French, is after the drawing.  Some time later Maas executed an oil painting based on the drawing but with a number of alterations, for the Duke of Portland. The picture, signed 'Dirck Maas 1690,' is still at Welbeck Abbey, seat of the duke.  Another painting of the same subject, attributed to Maas, is at Petworth.

    The etching is a highly valuable record of the battle, being an eye-witness representation of the events of the day. The movements of both sides can be easily followed from Maas's notes. Wyck's subsequent depictions of the battle were influenced by the etching.

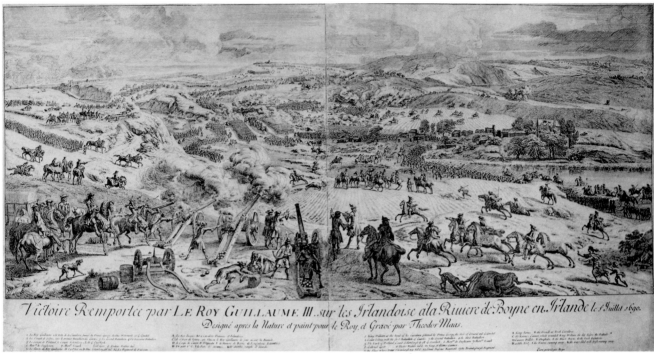

166

## 167 *KingWilliam III (1650-1702)*

ATTRIBUTED TO JAN WYCK (C. 1640-1702)
ULSTER MUSEUM, BELFAST

Oil on canvas 98 x 77.3 cms.
Purchased from K.N. Goodbody, Burton, Cheshire 1969.
Prov:    Ex. collection Mr. Hugh Armytage-Moore, Rowallane House, Co. Down.
Exh:    *County Down Loan Exhibition of Old Masters*, B.M.A.G., March-April 1948 (27).
        *The Huguenots and Ulster 1685-1985*, Lisburn Museum, October 1985-April 1986 (5), repr.
        on cover and in catalogue (unpaginated).
        *Glorious Revolution. The World of William & Mary*, Nieuwe Kerk, Amsterdam, June-
        September 1988 (225).
Repr:    Peter Berresford Ellis, *The Boyne Water* (Belfast, 1989), on cover.

The Dutch artist Jan Wyck came to England with his father Thomas, also an
artist, after the Restoration. He specialised in battle scenes, notably the Boyne, of
which there are numerous examples. He also painted a number of portraits of
William on horseback, with various backgrounds: unidentifiable battle scenes,
military encampments and the landing at Torbay. Examples are to be found in
the NMM and at Blenheim, among others. The image of William on a rearing
charger (usually white), sword held aloft, became a popular icon for Irish
Protestants during the eighteenth century and is still frequently illustrated in
Northern Ireland on Orange banners, gable ends and souvenirs.

## 168 *A cavalry skirmish*

BY JAN WYCK (C.1640-1702)
ULSTER MUSEUM, BELFAST

Oil on canvas 96 x 131.5 cms.
Inscr:    'J. Wyck' b.l.
Purchased at Boyd-Rochfort Sale, Osborne, King and Megran, Belfast 1958.
Prov:    Formerly in the collection of Captain Harold Boyd-Rochfort, Ennel Lodge, Mullingar,
        Co. Westmeath; purchased by the first Earl of Belvedere c.1750.
Exh:    *1966 Golden Jubilee of the Easter Rising,* NGI, April 1966 (5).
Lit:    Christopher Wright, *Old Master Paintings in Britain* (London, 1976), pp. 221, 232.

Although traditionally said to represent Schomberg's death at the battle of the
Boyne, the picture contains no evidence to support this claim; it has accordingly
been re-catalogued as representing a cavalry skirmish. Schomberg was seventy-
five when killed, but his supposed figure, falling backwards off a white horse,

167

**168**

appears considerably younger than this. Other factors too militate against a positive identification: Schomberg was killed by two sabre wounds to the head and a carbine shot in the neck, close by a tree and some huts (according to the Maas engraving). There is no sign of similar wounds on the figure in the picture, or of similar surroundings. Furthermore, the figures in the painting are too generalised to be of any help in identifying the battle portrayed. The picture is, however, a spirited and dramatic depiction of a cavalry skirmish of the same period as the Boyne.

Sources:      Advice from Malcolm Rogers, NPG (letter of 2 January 1976) and A.E. Haswell Miller (letter of 13 January 1976).

## 169 *Hans Willem Bentinck, first Earl of Portland (1649-1709)*

BY AN UNKNOWN ARTIST, AFTER HYACINTH RIGAUD (1659-1743)
NATIONAL TRUST

Oil on canvas 133.5 x 100.5 cms (sight).

Bentinck, who came from a Dutch noble family, joined William's household as a page in 1664 and quickly became one of his closest friends. The depth of his devotion to the Prince was seen in 1675 when William fell ill with smallpox, the disease which had killed both his parents. According to medical belief of the day, the disease could only be stopped if a young man of the same age shared the patient's bed and exposed himself to the infection. Bentinck volunteered, and by the warmth of his body caused William to sweat so heavily that the smallpox broke out. Thereafter he caught the disease himself and was in a dangerous condition for some time. Ever by his master's side, he subsequently accompanied William on his campaign against the French in the Spanish Netherlands and in 1677 was sent to England to negotiate the Prince's marriage to Mary Stuart, daughter of the Duke of York and Charles II's niece. He returned to England in 1683 and 1685 on diplomatic missions, and during the preliminaries to the Revolution of 1688 was involved in negotiations with the princes of northern Germany (especially Frederick III of Brandenburg) to secure their support.

Bentinck accompanied William to England in November 1688 and remained with him as confidant and adviser. As one of a number of Dutch nobles and officers with whom the king surrounded himself during his first year in England, he was easily the most hated man at court. The English resented William's obvious preference for his countrymen - especially Bentinck, whom they nicknamed 'the Wooden Man' on account of his stiff and unbending

**169**

manner. A popular lampoon of the day attacked his jealous and possessive attitude towards the king:

> Make room crys Sir Thomas Duppa [William's gentleman usher]
> Then Benting up-locks
> His King in a box
> And you see him no more till supper (van der Zee, p. 286)

Shortly before the coronation he was created Earl of Portland and was appointed groom of the park, first gentleman of the bedchamber and a privy councillor. As the king's favourite he soon became one of the wealthiest men in England but, spurning splendour, went around dressed like a servant - a situation which further alienated him from the English at court.

Although most of his work for William was in the diplomatic field, he commanded a regiment of horse at the Boyne and also at Aughrim. He later fought in Flanders and held the rank of lieutenant-general in the English army. During the l690s he was with William in his campaigns in Flanders and served as one of his most trusted confidential diplomats. In March l697 he was installed a K.G; the following month his son, Viscount Woodstock, was given the Earl of Clancarty's forfeited estate of 135,820 acres in Ireland. (The grant had actually been given to Portland but was subsequently transferred to his son, partly because of opposition from the Commons, which objected to William's large grants to his favourites). In June l697 he was appointed one of the generals of the English horse.

In January l698 he was sent as ambassador to France, partly because he was the best person for the position but also because his hitherto close relationship with the king had become fraught and strained and a temporary separation was considered advisable. Behind the discord lay his jealousy and resentment at William's attachment to the Earl of Albemarle, who had been growing more important and intimate with the king since l691. William's feelings for his favourites were deep and intense and may have had homosexual overtones, an allegation put about not only by his enemies but by common gossip in England, at The Hague and in the army. In l697 Portland had warned him about such rumours in regard to his relationship with Albemarle. William was thunderstruck at 'such horrible calumnies' but refused to dismiss his young favourite, saying, 'It

**170**

seems to me very extraordinary that it should be impossible to have esteem and regard for a young man without it being criminal' (van der Zee, p. 419). Portland, hating his rival and intensely hurt at his own eclipse, had to face up to the inevitable by 1698: that Albemarle was as important to the king (in an emotional sense) as he himself had been for many years. Threats to resign, unless Albemarle went, proved useless.

Portland remained in France until June 1698, undertaking delicate negotiations with Louis regarding the Spanish succession. On his return he again talked of retiring, but instead accompanied William to Holland in July. Spurning a reconciliation with the king, however, he resigned his positions in the royal household in May of the following year. He continued nevertheless with his diplomatic affairs after his retirement to Windsor. In 1701 he was threatened with impeachment for his part in the Second Partition Treaty, which had been negotiated without consultation in parliament; proceedings against him were later dismissed by the House of Lords. Despite the ill-feeling of their latter years together, he was with the king when he died on 8 March 1702 (OS); William's last gesture was to take his hand and press it to his heart. He spent his last years in various diplomatic ventures and died in November 1709. He left a large family, having married three times, his second wife being a sister of Elizabeth Villiers, Countess of Orkney, at one time William's mistress (see no. 300).

Rigaud worked almost exclusively as a court painter from 1689 and painted virtually everyone of distinction at Versailles. His sitters included most members of the French royal family, eminent generals and visiting princes and diplomats.The original of this portrait of Portland (at Welbeck Abbey) was painted in 1698, when the sitter was in Paris as ambassador extraordinary. Other versions of the painting include those in the NPG, Stratfield Saye (Duke of Wellington) and at the Hoo (Viscount Hampden). The picture is typical of Rigaud's military portraits in that it presents the sitter in modern armour, three-quarter length, against a landscape background.

Sources:    J. T. Gilbert, ed., *A Jacobite Narrative of the War in Ireland 1688-1691* (Dublin, 1892, reprinted Shannon, 1971); *DNB*; J.G. Simms, *The Williamite Confiscation in Ireland 1690-1703* (London, 1956); D. Piper, *Catalogue of the Seventeenth Century Portraits in the National Portrait Gallery 1625-1714* (Cambridge, 1963); H. and B. van der Zee, *William and Mary* (London, 1973).

**171**

**170** *Thomas, Lord Coningsby (1656-1729) seated in a romanticised landscape, with a view of the north prospect of Hampton Court, Herefordshire in the background (1692)*

BY THOMAS BATE (FL. C. 1692)
ULSTER MUSEUM, BELFAST

Oil on canvas 78.8 x 88.9 cms, oval, contemporary frame.
Inscr:     'T. Bate fecit '92' b.l.
Purchased from Christopher Gibbs, London 1973, with the aid of a grant from the Friends of
the National Collections of Ireland.
Prov:     Painted for Thomas, Lord Coningsby; from the collection of the Earl of Essex; from the
          collection of Richard Arkwright; from the Burrell collection; from the collection of
          Viscount Hereford; Christopher Gibbs; thence to Ulster Museum.
Exh:      *A Country House Portrayed, Hampton Court, Herefordshire, 1699-1840*, Sabin Galleries,
          London, February-March 1973 (4), repr.
Lit:      John Cornforth, 'Hampton Court, Herefordshire-II,' *Country Life,* 1 March 1973, repr. p.
          518.
          Bruce Arnold, *A Concise History of Irish Art* (London, 1977), revised ed., p. 54, repr. pl. 42.
          Anne Crookshank and The Knight of Glin, *The Painters of Ireland* (London, 1978), p. 31,
          repr. pl. 4.
Repr:     *Burlington Magazine,* March 1973, p. 191, pl. 26.
          Brian de Breffny, ed., *Ireland: A Cultural Encyclopaedia* (London, 1983), p. 178.

Thomas Lord Coningsby was the son of Humphrey Coningsby and Lettice
Loftus, eldest daughter of Sir Arthur Loftus of Rathfarnham, Co. Dublin. As an
ardent supporter of the Revolution of 1688, he 'throughout his life resolutely
resisted, sometimes with more zeal than discretion, the aims of the Jacobite
faction' (*DNB*). He served with William during his Irish campaign, tending the
king when he was injured on 30 June (OS) and fighting alongside him at the
Boyne the following day. The handkerchief which he used to bind the king's
wound was preserved at his family seat, Hampton Court, Herefordshire, for
many years; its present whereabouts are unfortunately unknown.

In 1690 Coningsby was appointed joint receiver and paymaster-general of
the Williamite forces in Ireland, and from 1690 to 1692 served as one of the lords
justices who governed the country in the absence of the king. In this capacity he

was involved in arranging the treaty of Limerick. For his services he received a grant of '5966 Acres, with several Chiefries, Tythes, and many Houses in the City of *Dublin,* with 1000 l. Mortgage; Consideration, Services done' *(Report of the Commissioners of Forfeitures).* He was subsequently accused by his political opponents of using his position in Ireland to embezzle stores and steal land belonging to Irish Jacobites. Despite these accusations, however, he remained in the king's favour and in 1692 was created Baron Coningsby of Clanbrassil. Two years later he was officially pardoned for any misdeeds he might have committed.

The accusations against him were in fact quite substantial. According to the forfeiture commissioners, during the period after the Boyne 'Plunder ... was so general, that some men in considerable Employments were not free from it; which seems to us a great reason why this matter has not been more narrowly searched into. Particularly, the Lord *Coningsby* seized a great many Black Cattle, to the number of 300, or thereabouts, besides Horses, which were left in the Park after the Battle of the *Boyne,* and which we do not find were ever accounted for to His Majesty: He also seized all the Plate and Goods in the House of Sir Michael *Creagh,* Lord Mayor of Dublin for the Year 1689, which are generally thought to amount to a great Value: But this last is said to be by Grant from His Majesty.' Furthermore, 'There were several Rich Goods and other Houshold-stuff delivered by the Commissioners of the Revenue to the then Lords Justices, the Lord *Sidney* and Lord *Coningsby,* which we do not find were ever returned, accounted for to His Majesty, or left in the Castle [ie., Dublin Castle] at their departure from the Government.'

Coningsby served as MP for Leominster, Herefordshire, from 1679 to 1710 and from 1715 to 1719. In 1714 he was appointed lord lieutenant of Herefordshire and Radnorshire, and the following year was granted a baronetcy. In 1719 he was created Earl Coningsby. A quarrelsome and highly unstable character, he was involved in numerous lawsuits during the later years of his life, and in 1721 was imprisoned in the Tower of London for libelling the Lord Chancellor. He died on 1 May 1729.

The painting shows him wearing a colourful version of Roman military dress, seated in front of his family home. The picture is the only known work by Thomas Bate, an obscure artist who was apparently well-known for painting on glass and lived mostly in Ireland.

Sources: *Report of The Commissioners Appointed by Parliament To Enquire into the Irish Forfeitures* (London, 1700); J. Williams, *The Leominster Guide* (1808); *DNB*; P. Berresford Ellis, *The Boyne Water* (London, 1976).

## 171 *Sir Robert Southwell (1635-1702)*

BY JOHN SMITH, AFTER SIR GODFREY KNELLER (1646-1723)
NATIONAL GALLERY OF IRELAND, DUBLIN

Mezzotint 34.7 x 25.2 cms (plate 34.2 x 24.7), published 1704.
Lit: Adrian Le Harivel, ed., *National Gallery of Ireland Illustrated Summary Catalogue of Prints and Sculpture* (Dublin, 1988), p. 321, repr.

Sir Robert Southwell, son of Robert Southwell of Kinsale, Co.Cork, received his early schooling in Ireland. In 1650 he went to England, where he acquired a legal training at Oxford and Lincoln's Inn. After completing his education by Continental travel he returned to England and in 1664 was made a clerk to the privy council. The following year he received a knighthood and was appointed deputy vice-admiral of the province of Munster, succeeding his father as vice-admiral on the latter's death in 1677. Between 1665 and 1672 he was twice sent to Portugal on diplomatic missions and spent some months in Brussels as envoy extraordinary. He was MP for Penrhyn in 1673 and for Lostwithiel in 1685. In the interim he purchased an estate at King's Weston, was envoy extraordinary to the Elector of Brandenburg and chose to retire to his country seat.

William III made him a customs commissioner and subsequently appointed him principal secretary of state for Ireland, in which capacity he accompanied the king on his Irish campaign in 1690. He was responsible for the drafting of the Finglas declaration of 7 July (OS), in the aftermath of the Boyne, which promised a pardon to poor labourers, soldiers and tradesmen who surrendered by 1 August. The declaration was intended to separate the lowly rank and file of Jacobite supporters from the higher echelons, who would be left

**172**

to suffer the consequences of war. As Southwell explained, the plan was 'to invite in all of the meaner sort ... but not to be meddling with the landed men till it appears into what posture they throw themselves or into what corners they retire' (Simms, p. 160). The declaration, it was hoped, would draw in 'the bulk of the nation and the rest will afterwards look the more abject' (as above, p. 161). The attempt to divide the common people from the landed classes was a total failure, however; the promise of protection in return for surrender was broken by plundering Williamite troops. Jacobite officers, furthermore, mistrusted the terms of the declaration. Although Jacobite opinion tended to the view that William excluded the landed classes from his mercy because of pressure from his chief officers and consideration of the English interest in Ireland, this appears not to have been the case: William believed the Jacobite cause to be lost and did not therefore see any need to offer more tolerable terms. (In the event, the declaration served to stiffen Jacobite resistance).

Irish affairs preoccupied Southwell a great deal, even before he became principal secretary of state for Ireland (a position he held until his death in 1702). After James's accession in 1685 the maintenance of the Restoration settlement, which had placed Protestants in possession of four-fifths of the land of Ireland, became a major topic in his correspondence with his close friend and kinsman Sir William Petty. Attacked by Tyrconnell and the Catholics, the settlement was the most contentious question of James's reign; as Southwell aptly said of it, 'the settlement like St. Sebastian is stuck full of arrows' (Moody, Martin and Byrne, p. 481).

In addition to his diplomatic career, Southwell wrote a number of political pamphlets and a biography of James, first Duke of Ormonde (which he never finished, because of old age). Elected a Fellow of the Royal Society in 1662, he served as its President from 1690 to 1695. He died at King's Weston on 11 September 1702.

The engraving is after a three-quarter length oil painting by Kneller in the Royal Society. The Southwell family were among Kneller's earliest English patrons.

Sources:  *DNB*; J.G. Simms, *Jacobite Ireland 1685-91* (London, 1969); T.W. Moody, F.X. Martin, F.J. Byrne, eds., *A New History of Ireland III 1534-1691* (Oxford, 1976).

## 172 *Count Meinhard Schomberg, Baron Tara, Earl of Bangor and Duke of Leinster (1641-1719)*

BY JOHN SMITH, AFTER SIR GODFREY KNELLER (1646-1723)
NATIONAL GALLERY OF IRELAND, DUBLIN

Mezzotint 34 x 29 cms (plate), published 1693.

Lit:     Adrian Le Harivel, ed., *National Gallery of Ireland Illustrated Summary Catalogue of Prints and Sculpture* (Dublin 1988), p. 322, repr.

Count Meinhard Schomberg, third son of Frederick Herman, Duke of Schomberg, was born at Cologne on 30 June 1641. He served in Portugal with his father between 1660 and 1668, and after his return from France became a French citizen. He reached the rank of marechal-de-camp in the wars against Holland. After the revocation of the Edict of Nantes in 1685 he served against the Turks in Hungary and subsequently entered the service of the Elector Frederick William of Brandenburg (uncle and erstwhile guardian of William III), who appointed him general of cavalry and colonel of a corps of dragoons.

About March 1689 he came to England and was sent to Ireland by William, to deliver despatches to Schomberg. He thereafter went to Berlin to obtain dismission from the Elector's service and susbsequently returned to England, where he was appointed general of horse on 19 April 1690. He accompanied William to Ireland in June and played a leading role at the battle of the Boyne, being in command of the right wing which crossed the Boyne at Rosnaree. He took part in the first siege of Limerick in August 1690 (where his horse was shot from under him) and returned to England with William in September. He was generally expected to be given command of the Irish campaign during the summer of 1691 but was passed over in favour of Ginkel.

In March 1692 he was created Baron of Tara, Earl of Bangor and Duke of Leinster and was appointed lieutenant-general of the British forces during William's absence abroad. In May of that year he joined William in Holland, after the proposed expedition against the key French naval bases of St Malo, Brest and Rochefort had been abandoned. In October 1693 he succeeded to the English dukedom of Schomberg, on the death of his brother Charles. On the accession of Queen Anne he became a favourite and was made a Knight of the Garter in 1703. He died on 5 July 1719 and was buried in Westminster Abbey. He appears to have been an irascible and argumentative character; acccording to the *DNB*, he 'quarrelled with everybody except the enemy' during his brief command of the British forces in Lisbon in 1704 and was 'one of the hottest, fiery men in England, which was the reason King William would never give him any command where there was action.'

Kneller also painted Count Schomberg's father, Frederick, first Duke of Schomberg.

Sources:     *DNB*; K. Danaher and J.G. Simms, eds., *The Danish Force in Ireland 1690-91* (Dublin 1962); J.G. Simms, *Jacobite Ireland 1685-91* (London, 1969).

## 173 *Sir Neil O'Neill, second baronet of Killelagh (?1658-90)*

BY GARRET MORPHEY (FL. 1680-1716)
THE LORD O'NEILL

Oil on canvas 127.6 x 100.8 cms.

Prov:     Formerly at Malahide Castle, Co. Dublin.

Lit:     Anne Crookshank and The Knight of Glin, *Irish Portraits 1660-1860*, exhibition catalogue, NGI August-October 1969, NPG October 1969 - January 1970, UM January-March 1970, p.30. Anne Crookshank and The Knight of Glin, *The Painters of Ireland* (London, 1978), p.24.

The portrait shows O'Neill in armour with a military engagement in the background, probably the battle of the Boyne. An ardent Jacobite, he raised a regiment of dragoons in 1687 at his own expense and fought with considerable bravery at the Boyne (see no. 67). James II, in his memoirs, described O'Neill's stand against the much larger Williamite right wing at the ford of Rosnaree: 'Sir Neal O'Neal's dragoons did their part very well, and disputed the passage with the enemie almost an hour, till their cannon came up, and then retired in good

173

174

order, with the loss of only five or six common men, their colonel [O'Neill] shot through the thigh, and an officer or two wounded' (O'Laverty, p. 320). O'Neill died of his wound in Waterford on 8 July and was succeeded by his brother Sir Daniel, third and last baronet.

Morphey, whose origins are obscure, was the first Irish-born painter of stature. He appears to have visited Holland during the 1680s, as his work shows the influence of the Dutch portrait painters Gaspar and Constantine Netscher. Between 1686 and 1688 he was working in York, according to the Portland papers, which referred to him as 'one Morphew, a Roman Catholic painter, drinking confusion to those who did not read his Majesty's Declaration, [possibly James's Second Declaration of Indulgence of 7 May 1688] was attacked and beaten by one of the King's officers quartering in those parts' (Crookshank and Glin). In late 1688 or 1689 he returned to Ireland, where he painted a number of leading Jacobites. After 1690 his sitters included Williamite supporters and their families. His position in Irish art is an important one, as he raised its quality and standard to a more professional level.

Sources:  J.D'Alton, *King James's Irish Army List (1689)* (Dublin, 1855); Rev. J. O'Laverty, *Diocese of Down and Connor* (Dublin, 1880), vol. II; J.G. Simms, *Jacobite Ireland 1685-91* (London, 1969); Crookshank and Glin, as above.

## 174 *Colonel Thomas Butler of Kilcash (d. 1738) (c.1718-20)*

BY JAMES LATHAM (1696-1747)
KILKENNY CASTLE

Oil on canvas 135.5 x 106.5 cms.
Lit:  Anne Crookshank, 'James Latham 1696-1747,' *The GPA Irish Arts Review Yearbook*, 1988, pp. 60,61,64,65,69, no.8, repr. p.60.

Thomas Butler, son of Walter Butler of Garryricken, inherited Kilcash from his grandfather Richard Butler, youngest brother of James, first Duke of Ormonde. A convinced Jacobite, he served as colonel of a regiment of foot which he raised himself, and was captured by the Danes at the taking of Cork in late September 1690. Würtemberg, the Danish commander, who had got to know him some years before in Hungary and esteemed him greatly, wrote to him in January 1691 urging him to change sides. 'The affection I have for all your family and for yourself in particular obliges me to inform you of the good intentions King William has for your country. They are the freedom of your religion and the security of your estates, together with the continuance of the rank or employment of those who would like to carry on a military career ... And for yourself in particular, I shall do my best to have you given the rank of brigadier. Think about this and do not be a puppet of France, which only seeks to sacrifice you to its own interest' (Danaher and Simms, p.99).

Butler's reply, while acknowledging William's good intentions, was disparaging of the king's recently-adopted countrymen: 'We are quite unable to endure the yoke of the English, who after his [William's] death will not fail to break their word, so hostile are they to this nation ... I pray Your Highness to keep some kind feeling for me and not to think that it is from any friendship for France or interest in her that we are unable to agree, but on account of the people, who will not, I hope, be wanting in the foresight to consider their own interests' (Danaher and Simms). Butler subsequently fought at Aughrim and was captured again.

A cousin of the second Duke of Ormonde, who supported William but was later attainted for his part in the 1715 rebellion, Butler became head of the important and influential Butler family in Ireland in 1716 (his brother the Earl of Arran remained in London). He had three sons and five daughters by his marriage, in 1696, to Lady Margaret Burke, eldest daughter of the Earl of Clanrickard and widow of Bryan Magennis, Viscount Iveagh. He died in 1738.

James Latham, the most distinguished Irish portrait painter of the first half of the eighteenth century, spent 1724-25 in Antwerp and may also have visited Paris, judging from the French influence in his work. His Irish sitters included a number of Huguenots, members of the establishment and leading Catholic families. The portrait of Thomas Butler shows a tower in the left background, which has been identified from Grose's *Antiquities of Ireland* as being part of the fortifications of Kilkenny Castle. The fact that Butler chose to be portrayed wearing armour, in front of the castle, is perhaps indicative of his desire to be seen as head of the Butler family (his military career was long over by this time; furthermore, he did not live in the castle). Latham also painted a portrait of Thomas's brother Christopher, Catholic archbishop of Cashel; this likewise is in Kilkenny Castle (see no. 332).

Sources:     M. Archdall, *The Peerage of Ireland* (Dublin, 1789); J. D'Alton, *King James's Irish Army List (1689)* (Dublin, 1855); K. Danaher and J.G. Simms, eds., *The Danish Force in Ireland 1690-91* (Dublin, 1962); Crookshank, as above; additional information on the portrait supplied by Jane Fenlon.

## 175  *Sir John Bellew, first Baron Bellew of Duleek (d. 1693)*

BY GASPAR SMITZ (D. C. 1707)
PRIVATE COLLECTION

Oil on canvas 124.7 x 101.2 cms (sight).
Inscr: 'G.S. 16' b.r.

John Bellew, son of Sir Christopher Bellew of Bellewstown, Co. Louth, had his property sequestrated by Cromwell but recovered it in October 1660 under Charles II's Act of Settlement.  Knighted by Charles II, he was created Baron Bellew of Duleek in 1686 in recognition of his fidelity to James II. He served on the Irish privy council and sat in James's Irish parliament in 1689. James also appointed him lord lieutenant and governor of Co. Louth.

During 1690 and 1691 he commanded a Jacobite infantry regiment and fought at the Boyne and at Aughrim, where he was badly wounded and captured. According to the inscription on his tomb in Duleek church, he was shot in the belly and 'as soon as he found himself able to undertake a journey, he went with his lady to London.'  There he died on 12 Janury 1693 and was buried in St Margaret's, Westminster, whence his remains were removed to Duleek the following April. He was succeeded by his son Walter, who died in 1694 shortly after his release from prison, where he had been incarcerated since his capture at the battle of Aughrim. The title and estates then passed to Walter's brother Richard, who had been outlawed but had afterwards conformed to the

**175**

established church. Richard's outlawry was reversed in 1697 under the terms of the treaty of Limerick. The family estates, which had been confiscated and granted to Viscount Sydney, were recovered eventually. The title became extinct in 1770 with the death of the fourth baron, Richard's son John.

Smitz, a Dutch artist, moved to England shortly after the Restoration and settled in Dublin probably during the early 1670s, where his patrons included the Nugent family, Earls of Westmeath. Besides painting portraits and still life, he worked as a picture restorer and may perhaps have been an artist's colourman; he may also have taught Garret Morphey, whose early style is very similar to his own. The portrait of Bellew, with its tight face painting and rather dry manner, is typical of Smitz. The battle scene in the background may perhaps be Aughrim. Bellew also sat to Morphey.

Sources:     John D'Alton, *King James's Irish Army List (1689)* (London, 1861);G.E.C., *The Complete Peerage* (London, 1912) J.G. Simms, *The Williamite Confiscation in Ireland 1690-1703* (London, 1956);

## 176a-d *Jacobite regimental colours*

ULSTER MUSEUM, BELFAST

Reconstructed from contemporary descriptions; made by Bridgett Bros., Belfast.

### (a) *The Royal Regiment of Foot Guards of Ireland.*

Raised in 1662 as part of the Irish army and remodelled as a Catholic unit by Tyrconnell, the Guards wore the red uniforms of the royal infantry regiments. Their colours in June 1690 were described as 'the royal colours of England, St George's cross, and the arms of the four kingdoms.'

### (b) *The Earl of Antrim's Regiment.*

Raised in 1689 by the Catholic magnate Alexander, third Earl of Antrim, this regiment's colours showed 'a red cross in a green field, in each quarter of the field a hand proper emerging from clouds holding a cross of Jerusalem gold; in the centre of the colours the Irish harp with a crown imperial with the motto *In hoc signo vinces*' (In this sign you will conquer).

**176 (a)**

**176 (b)**

**176 (c)**

**176 (d)**

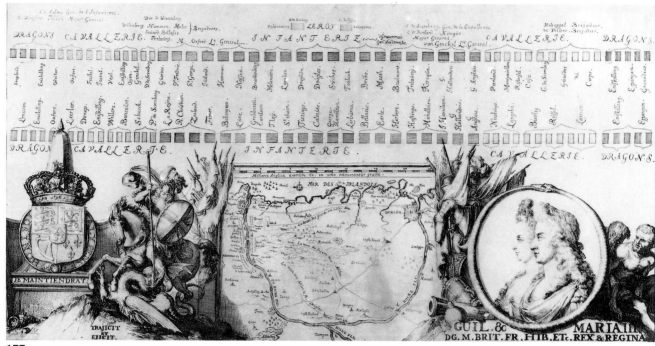

**177**

### (c) *Lord Bellew's Regiment.*

Like Antrim's a new formation, this regiment had colours described as 'bendy black and tawny or filamot [the colour of a dead leaf]. On the top, next the spear, a crown imperial, and round it this motto *Tout d'en Haut* (All from above). In the centre the Irish harp and crown imperial.'

### (d) *Gordon O'Neill's Regiment*

Also a new formation, this regiment carried colours described as 'white, in the centre a bloody hand, round it this motto *Pro Rege et Patria pugno* (I fight for King and Country)'.

The English Jacobite John Stevens, who served as a junior officer in the regiment of the Lord Grand Prior (Berwick's younger brother), describes in his journal some of the colours carried at a muster of James's forces at Dundalk on 19 June 1690. The journal, edited by R.H. Murray, was published in London in 1912. The late Professor G.A. Hayes-McCoy reconstructed the flags described by Stevens, in his *History of Irish Flags* (Dublin, 1979).

## 177 *Williamite order of battle at the Boyne*

ANONYMOUS, PROBABLY DUTCH, C.1690
ULSTER MUSEUM, BELFAST

Engraving 26 x 56 cms; untitled, French text.

The upper part of the engraving correctly shows the positions of the various regiments - identified in most cases by the names of their colonels - in two lines, with dragoons and cavalry at each end and infantry in the centre. The lower part of the engraving has in the centre a map showing the river Boyne, with the positions of the two armies and the routes taken after the battle by the Jacobite fugitives and by the Williamites under Douglas towards Athlone. The Boyne is shown flowing from the west to divide into two branches, one of which flows north into the sea at Drogheda, the other - in defiance of nature - going south to enter the sea at Dublin. On either side of the maps are decorations in the style of Romeyn de Hooghe: to left, the royal arms of England with William III's motto JE MAINTIENDRAY, St George on horseback slaying the dragon and the legend TRAJICIT ET EJICIT (he crosses over and expels); to right, a double portrait in profile of William and Mary with the legend GUIL. E MARIA III DG. M. BRIT. FR. HIB. ETc. REX & REGINA (William and Mary III by grace of God king and queen of Great Britain, France, Ireland etc.).

**178 rev.**

**179 obv.**

**180 obv.**

**180 rev.**

## 178-179 *The battle of the Boyne, 1690*

MEDAL BY R. ARONDEAUX (FL. 1680-1710)
ULSTER MUSEUM, BELFAST (GOLD); NATIONAL MUSEUM OF IRELAND,
DUBLIN (SILVER)

Gold and silver, 49.5 mm.
Lit:         *Medallic Illustrations*, 716-17, no. 136.
Description:  obv. bust of William III draped and in armour.
                  legend: GVILH. III.D.G.MAG BRI.FRAN.ET HIB.REX. [William III,
                  king of Great Britain, France and Ireland].
              rev. William in armour, on a horse up to its belly in water, waving a sword and
                  leading some soldiers towards a bank on which can be seen two cannons
                  and some tiny fighting infantry. Two horsemen are about to come out of
                  the water and a figure on foot throws his hands in the air whilst up to his
                  waist in water. The exergue line forms the river.
                  legend, above ET VULNERA ET INVIA SPERNIT [he spurns wounds
                  and impassable places]; in exergue EIICIT IACOBUM RES: TITUIT
                  HIBERNIAM MDCXC [he throws James out and restores Ireland, 1690].

The reverse design is a striking and unusual solution to the recurring problem of presenting battle action on a medal. The idealised and very grand portrait on the obverse may be contrasted with the way in which William is shown on the reverse. There is a cast copy of this medal, with different obverse legend. The slight differences from the struck original emphasise Arondeaux's skill.

## 180 *The death of Marshal Schomberg, 1 July 1690*

MEDAL BY P.H. MULLER (1653-1718)
ULSTER MUSEUM, BELFAST; NATIONAL MUSEUM OF IRELAND, DUBLIN

Silver, 49 mm.
Lit:         *Medallic Illustrations,* 717-18, no. 140.
Description:  obv. Schomberg, three-quarters facing, in contemporary armour, wearing
                  cravat.
                  legend: FRIDERICUS MARESCHALCUS SCHOMBERG
              rev. a bulky bearded figure in Roman armour, wearing a cloak, representing
                  Hercules, stands facing, resting left hand on a shield with a christogram.
                  Beside this rises a series of shields, with sprigs of laurel. They bear the
                  arms of, in ascending order, Ireland, Spain, Scotland, Austria and France.
                  At his feet are a spilled cornucopia of money, a crown and a snake striking
                  at the large shield. Hercules plants an olive tree with his right hand.
                  legend, above, PLANTAVIT UBIQ UE FERACEM [everywhere he has
                  planted a fruitful club]; in exergue, CONTINVATIS TRIVMPHIS
                  OBDVRATA IN DEVM FIDE IN HIBER.MILITANTI [To him who
                  served in Ireland with continuing success and an enduring faith in God].
              edge. PRO RELIGIONE ET LIBERTATE MORI VIVERE EST [to die
                  for religion and liberty is to live].

When Hercules had finished his labours, he planted his club in the ground, where it grew into an olive tree, symbolising peace. The spilled coins and the crown are being ignored in a selfless gesture. The snake may represent discord, evil or envy.

Facing portraits are extremely difficult to bring off on coins or medals and Muller has had some success on this piece, especially on the reverse. There are a number of seventeenth century German thalers with this type of design. Muller was born in Augsburg and produced a series of medals at Nuremberg, including this one, which also appears struck in wood.

**181 obv.**

**181 rev.**

**182 obv.**

**182 rev.**

## 181 *The flight of James II from Ireland, 1690*

MEDAL BY J. SMELTZING (FL. 1685, D. 1695)
NATIONAL MUSEUM OF IRELAND, DUBLIN; ULSTER MUSEUM, BELFAST,
ELECTROTYPE

Silver, 48 mm.

Lit: *Medallic Illustrations,* 719-20, no. 142.

Description: obv. bust of James II, draped, with the end of his hair in a bag, tied with ribbon.
legend: IACOBVS II BRITAN: REX FUGITIV. [James II, king of Britain, who fled].

rev. a leaping stag, with wings on its hooves, looking back. A background of a harbour with a tower; to the right a broken tree and one growing.
legend, above PEDIBUS TIMOR ADDIDIT ALAS [fear added wings to his feet]; in exergue FUGIT EX HIBERNIA D. 12. IULI. 1690 [he fled from Ireland, 12 July 1690].

The extravagant hair styles or wigs of the period meant that often hair was wrapped in a bag to make travelling easier. The obverse die was used for two other medals, the first issued in January 1689 after James fled from England and the second when the administration was offered to William. The portrait seems almost to flatter James and the bag for his wig, which carries the force of the political comment (that he fled), is by no means obtrusive.

Equally, on the reverse, the stag appears a noble beast and the wings quite an elegant addition. The broken tree depicted is allied to the illustration on the backs of the two medals referred to above, one of which shows a column struck by divine lightning, the other a shattered oak tree beside a flourishing orange bush.

## 182 *The entry of William III to Dublin, 6 July 1690*

MEDAL BY J. LUDER (FL. 1680-1710)
ULSTER MUSEUM, BELFAST

Silver, 58 mm.

Lit: *Medallic Illustrations,* 721, no. 145.

Description: obv. William III on rearing horse points with his sword. Below is a schematic river and, behind, an incline with many small, fighting men. Amongst these are labelled (from right to left) 'IACOB' on a horse, with crown falling off his head as he flees, 'LAUSUN', and 'WALKER' (who has fallen). In front of William, at the bottom of the bank and rather larger, lies the dead 'SCHOMBERG'. Two cannons point down from a bluff to the left.
legend, above, APPARUIT ET DISSIPAVIT [he appeared and dispersed them]; in exergue LIBERATA HIBERNIA MDCLXXXX [Ireland freed, 1690].

rev. at the right, William in Roman armour, his left hand almost in a burning altar, holding out with his right a cap of liberty over a kneeling Hibernia, who supports herself with a hand on a shield bearing a harp. To the left James and a soldier are fleeing behind a bank, on which lie a broken anchor, sceptre, sword and broken yoke.
legend, above FOCUS. SERVAVIT. ET. ARAS [he has watched over our hearths and altars]; in exergue EXPULS. GAL. ET REBEL. DUBLIN. TRIUMPHANS INTRAVIT [the French and rebels having been expelled, he entered Dublin in triumph].

This medal is a contemporary cast off a struck original, and as such is rather thinner and lighter than the prototype. Such casts are often more common than their archetypes and suggest a strong market for some of these propaganda pieces. Detail tends to be lost, however, and the tiny lettering on the side here called the obverse, particularly 'Schomberg', is not very legible. It is of some interest that the portrait of William at the battle is not far from those familiar from more modern depictions. As might be guessed, the obverse is used as the reverse for one of the Boyne medals and the reverse used with another obverse for a different piece celebrating the entry into Dublin. This example is pierced, indicating that it has been worn at some stage in the past.

**183**

**183** *Doot van den Hartog van Schombergh en Doctor Walker/Le Duc de Schomberg et le Docteur Walker tuez au passagie de Boine*
*(The Duke of Schomberg and Doctor Walker killed at the crossing of the Boyne)*

Engraving published in Amsterdam by Adriaan Schoonebeek
Ulster Museum, Belfast
Reproduction

Schomberg (centre left) is shown being shot in the neck from behind, as he actually was shot in hand-to-hand fighting on the southern bank of the river near the village of Oldbridge. Walker, the hero of Derry, is shown being carried off right.

**184** *Guilielmo III. In Hibernia. De Rebell. Et. Gallis. Fortiss. Triumphanti.*
*(To William III, triumphant in Ireland over the rebellion and the mighty French)*

By Romeyn de Hooghe (1645-1708)
N.A. Whittley

Double print 50 x 60 cms.

The lower part of this engraving is separately titled, in Dutch and French, OVERWINNING VAN KON. WILLEM DE III. door het volkomen Slaan van Jacob de II. in Ierland. den 11 July l690./ VICTOIRE REMPORTEE PAR LE ROY GUILLAUME III. par la defaite entiere de l'Armee de Jaques II. en Irlande. le 11e de Juillet l690. It depicts the fighting at Oldbridge in which

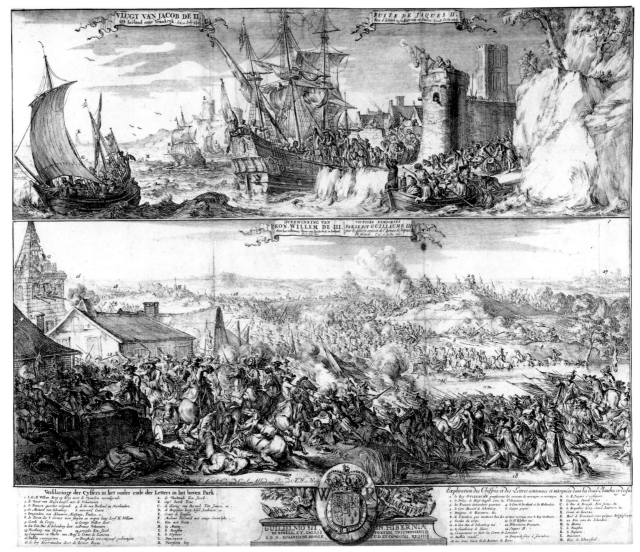

Schomberg and Walker (both identified in the key below) were killed.

The upper part is also separately titled, in Dutch and French, VLUGT VAN JACOB DE II. nyt Ierland naar Vrankrijk. den 12 July 1690/ FUITE DE JAQUES II. hors d'Irlande et sa Retraite en France. le12 de Juillet 1690.

It depicts James, the Duke of Berwick and other Jacobites and French officers going on board ship, apparently at Waterford. Duncannon Fort is in the background. In fact, James departed not from Waterford but from Duncannon, in a French privateer from St Malo (called the *Lauzun*) which took him to Kinsale; there he transferred to a French warship for the voyage to Brest, which was reached on 10/20 July.

## 185 ' *Prospect' of Duncannon Fort, Co.Wexford, 1685*

By Thomas Phillips (c.1635-93)
National Library of Ireland, Dublin

Watercolour on paper 36.4 x 113.5 cms.

Duncannon, at the mouth of Waterford Harbour, was a strong fort of fifty guns in a strategically important position. It was from here that James II embarked after his flight from the Boyne in July 1690. The fort was subsequently captured by the Williamites after a short siege.

Phillips's report on the harbours, towns and forts of Ireland, submitted to the government in 1686, is a major source of information on the subject; it includes a number of 'Prospects' or topographical perspectives, such as this one, which provide invaluable information as to the actual appearance of Irish towns and harbours at the time of the Jacobite war. In his report he criticises Duncannon Fort because it was overlooked by the high ground to the left of the picture.

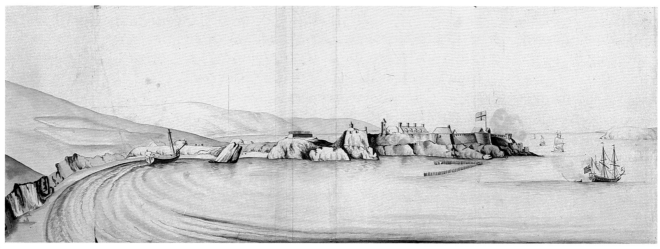

**185**

**186**

**186** *Intree van syn Koninglyke Mayesteit binnen Dublin den 16 July/Entree de sa Mayesté Brittannique dans la ville de Dublin le 16 Juillet*
(William entering Dublin 16 July 1690)

ENGRAVING PUBLISHED IN AMSTERDAM BY ADRIAAN SCHOONEBEEK
ULSTER MUSEUM, BELFAST
REPRODUCTION

Like many of the Irish scenes from Schoonebeek's *Théâtre d'Angleterre*, this engraving does not show an actual view or incident. It was either composed for the purpose by a Continental engraver or, more likely, adapted from an existing plate of a Continental scene.

## 187 *Mortuary-hilted sword, c.1640*

ENGLISH
ROYAL ARMOURIES, TOWER OF LONDON (IX.2859)

Length overall 100.6 cms, blade length 83.8 cms, weight 1.14 kg.
Iron hilt, wooden grip, steel blade.
Returned in 1986 from loan to the NPG, where it had been since 1969.
Exh:  *Parliament and the Glorious Revolution 1688-1988*, Banqueting House, London 1988.

Iron hilt consisting of a pommel, to which are pegged a knuckle-guard and two side knuckle-guards. The knuckle-guard widens to form a boat-shaped stool with a broad wrist-guard. The side knuckle-guards split and join the stool at their root. The knuckle-guard is joined to each side knuckle-guard by a pair of S-shaped bars. There is a modern wooden grip. The stool is pierced and chiselled with eight bearded heads around the blade and one at the front of the stool. The pommel is chiselled with scrolls and petals. The blade is broad, straight and double-edged, with a 5 cm long ricasso and four narrow fullers 23 cms long. The blade has an inlaid mark in copper on each side; one is a stylised running wolf, the other an orb surmounted by a cross.

The modern term 'mortuary sword' is applied to a particular type of broadsword of the mid-seventeenth century which is peculiar to Britain. As part of their decoration, many have chiselled heads of a typically seventeenth century appearance, with long hair and Van Dyck beards. It is from these that the swords have derived their name. Egerton Castle in *Schools and Masters of Fence* (London, 1885) said of them, 'Swords of this type are often called "mortuary" as a number of them were made in memory of Charles I and bear his likeness upon the hilt.' There is no contemporary evidence, however, to support this claim.

## 188 *Sword, c. 1680*

ENGLISH
ROYAL ARMOURIES, TOWER OF LONDON (IX.2788)

Length overall 84.8 cms, blade length 70.1 cms, weight 0.47 kg.
Silver hilt, steel blade.
Purchased from Gordon Knight Antiques in 1985.

The silver hilt consists of a pommel of slightly flattened section with a vestigial tang-button, a rear quillon with a beast's head terminal turned outwards and a loop-guard linking the half-way point of the rear quillon with the knuckle-guard. The latter has a small central knop and ends in a flourish by the pommel. The space inside the loop-guard is filled with a plate. The cast and chased decoration consists chiefly of figures and a linear motif of very fine transverse reeding, chased to resemble bullion wire, which decorates all the edges of the hilt and, on the pommel, alternates with latitudinal plain bands. The wooden grip is covered with canvas and spirally bound with wire. There is a Turk's-head ferrule at either end. A maker's mark, either BP or EP, above what may be a *fleur-de-lis* within a shield, is stamped on the pommel. The straight blade is of flattened lozenge section but the forte is transformed into a hexagonal section by a single deep fuller on either side, which runs for 20.3 cms from the hilt. The blade is pierced in the bed of the fuller with three slots alternating with holes.

This type of hilt first appeared in the late 1630s and 1640s and can be seen in many Dutch paintings of the period. It can also be seen in British portraiture of c.1670. A sword of this general type was presented to Lieutenant Walter Locke RN by the future William IV, as late as 1786.

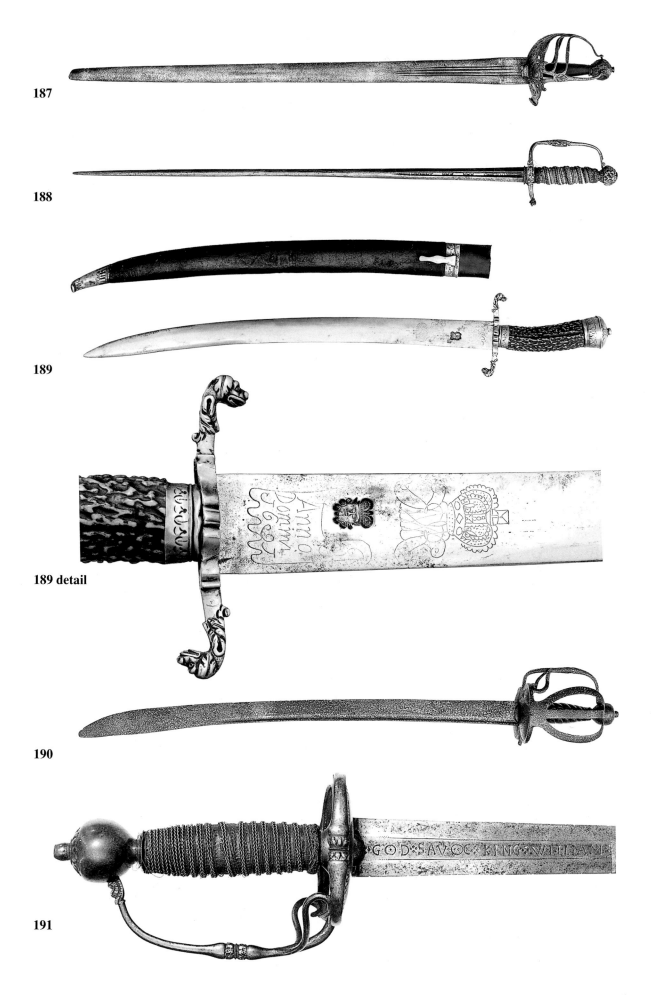

**187**

**188**

**189**

**189 detail**

**190**

**191**

GOD·SAV·OC·KING·N·HITAM·

## 189 *Hunting sword and scabbard, 1691*

ENGLISH
ROYAL ARMOURIES, TOWER OF LONDON (IX.1371)

Overall length of sword 60 cms, blade length 47 cms, weight 0.51 kg.
Length of scabbard 47.5 cms, weight 0.11 kg.
Hilt of silver and stag antler, steel blade. Scabbard of wood covered in black leather
with silver mounts.
Inscr: 'ANNO DOMINI 1691/GOD SAVE KING WILLIAM AND QUEEN MARY' on blade.
Acquired in 1974 from the Williams collection.

The hilt is silver with a cap pommel and tang-button engraved with foliate
motifs. There are short recurved quillons with terminals in the form of dogs'
heads. The grip is of stag antler. The short curved back-edged blade is deeply
stamped on each side with a king's head mark. Engraved on the outside of the
blade is a crowned monogram WM and below, in a panel, ANNO:DOMINI:
1691. On the inside of the blade, engraved in a panel, is GOD SAVE KING
WILLIAM AND QUEEN MARY, with engraved profile portraits of the king
and queen in an oval medallion below. The back edge of the blade is sharpened
for 17 cms from the point.

The short curved hunting sword or hanger was popular in Britain from the
sixteenth century, and by the beginning of the seventeenth century had evolved
into a particularly English style. This example is typical of the form which the
English hanger had acquired by the end of the seventeenth century. The
scabbard is of wood covered in black leather, with a silver chape and locket
decorated *en suite* with the pommel.

Source:     H.L. Blackmore, *Hunting Weapons* (1971).

## 190 *Military hanger, late seventeenth century*

BRITISH
ROYAL ARMOURIES, TOWER OF LONDON (IX.2566)

Length overall 85.7 cms, blade length 69.2 cms, weight 1.1 kg.
Steel.
Purchased from Arbour Antiques, Stratford-upon-Avon in 1982.

The hilt, of blackened and corroded steel, consists of a barrel-shaped pommel
slightly tapered towards the grip, a knuckle-guard plugged into the pommel and
the remains of a short rear quillon curved towards the blade, supporting an oval
side-ring filled with a plate on each side. The knuckle-guard is linked by a
scroll-guard on each side, just beyond its centre, to the forward edge of the side-
rings. In addition, an oval plate pierced to look like three separate ribbon-like
guards is mounted on the centre of the outside side-ring and plugged into the
outside of the pommel. The blade is flanked by very short langets. The grip is
brass with a twisted pattern. The single-edged curved blade expands slightly
towards the spear-point and has a false edge of about 15 cms in length, with
about 1.5 cms missing from the tip. A narrow fuller runs from the hilt along the
back of the sword for 47.5 cms. The inside flat of the blade is stamped with a
mark like a very elaborate *fleur-de-lis*, while the outside flat bears traces of a
similar mark.

The military hanger was a development of the hunting hanger,which was
found to be so suitable as a weapon that it soon became used for self defence
and then for military use. A similar hilt to this is illustrated in G. Neumann,
*Swords and Blades of the American Revolution* (Newton Abbot, 1973). This is
dated 1690 WR on the blade and inscribed SHOTLEY BRIDG, which was a
blade-making centre in the second half of the seventeenth century.

## 191 *Military sword*

THE HILT PROBABLY ENGLISH, THE BLADE POSSIBLY MADE IN GERMANY
BETWEEN 1688 AND 1694
ROYAL ARMOURIES, TOWER OF LONDON (IX.2142)

Length overall 93.5 cms, blade length 82 cms, weight 0.8 kg.
Steel hilt.
Inscr: 'GOD SAVE KING WILLIAM/AND QUEEN MARY' on blade.
Purchased from the collection of the late Sir James Mann in 1981.
Lit:    A.R. Dufty, *European Swords and Daggers in the Tower of London* (1974), pl. 50a.

Hilt of blued steel, consisting of an egg-shaped pommel with a barrel-shaped tang-button and a knuckle-guard and rear quillon with its end broken off, supporting on each side an oval side-ring made in one with its plate, each linked to the knuckle-guard by a small scroll-guard. Small curved langets. The decoration consists of rather crudely chiselled acanthus tips. These encircle the top of the pommel and appear as calyxes at the centres of the side-ring and the knuckle-guard, while a row of acanthus tips encircle the plate in each side-ring on the side towards the blade. The end of the knuckle-guard is incised to look like a dolphin's head. The wooden grip is spirally bound with copper herringbone of medium thickness and very fine copper twist, now badly damaged. Copper Turk's head ferrule towards the blade.

Hilts of this type are very common on cavalry swords of the late seventeenth and early eighteenth centuries. A sword of the same kind in the Royal Armouries (IX.1243) belonged to King George II and may have been used by him at Oudenarde in 1708. The blade of this latter sword is straight and two-edged, of a flattened oval section with a central fuller 16.5 cms. long, inscribed in capital letters outside the hand GOD SAVE KING WILLIAM, followed by an incised running wolf mark. The inscription continues on the inside with AND QUEEN MARY, followed by a second incised running wolf.

## 192 *Halberd, seventeenth century*

POSSIBLY ENGLISH
ROYAL ARMOURIES, TOWER OF LONDON (VII.1000)

Length of head 47 cms, length of langets 38 cms.
Steel head.

Blade of flattened diamond section, axe-head with convex crescentic cutting edge balanced at the rear by a down-curved fluke. The axe and fluke are pierced and decorated with incised lines. The square-section socket is pierced to take square-section side spikes. The langets have been restored and the haft is modern.

## 193 *Halberd, early seventeenth century*

DUTCH
ROYAL ARMOURIES, TOWER OF LONDON (VII. 1016)

Length of head 71.8 cms, length of langets 51 cms.
Steel.

Long narrow blade with a pronounced medial rib. At its base is a pierced hollow ball and octagonal socket fastened to a modern haft by two separate cheeks riveted to its lower end. The axe blade and fluke are each pierced and fretted with the figures of two Tritons, the points slightly reinforced.

This particular design of halberd was widely used by the Dutch Civic Guards of the early seventeenth century and can be seen in group portraits of guardsmen.

Source:    M. Carasso-Kok and J. Levy-van Halm, *Schutters in Holland* (Haarlem, 1988).

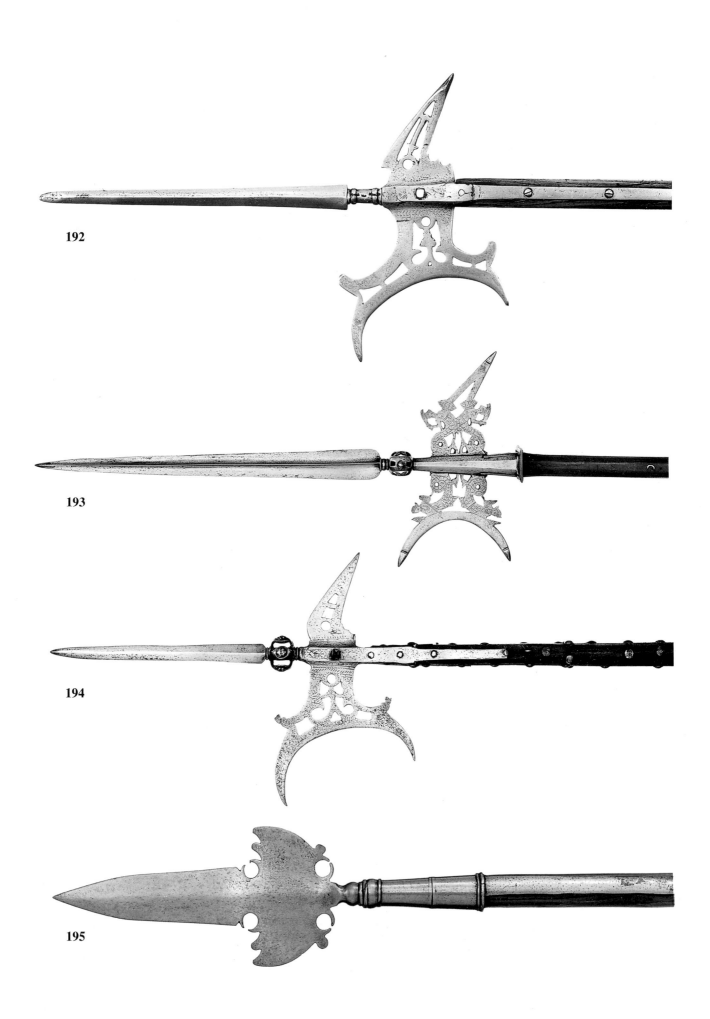

192

193

194

195

## 194 *Halberd, seventeenth century*

PROBABLY DUTCH
ROYAL ARMOURIES, TOWER OF LONDON (VII.1010)

Length of head 51.5 cms, length of langets 13 cms.
Steel.

Top spike of flattened diamond section, with a group of six half-rings chiselled with masks at its base. Axe blade with a crescentic cutting edge, large fluke at the rear; the axe and fluke are decorated with irregular piercings and incised lines. There is a transverse square-section bolt through the four-sided tapering socket, which has two short cheeks. The haft is heavily studded and has remnants of a fabric covering.

The halberd was generally carried by infantry sergeants from the sixteenth to the eighteenth centuries.

## 195 *Partizan, late seventeenth century*

BRITISH
ROYAL ARMOURIES, TOWER OF LONDON (VII. 250)

Length of head 28.5 cms, length of cheeks 28.5 cms.
Steel.

Short blade with sharply tapered point with an upturned and cusped fluke at the base on each side. The neck of the head where it joins the socket is formed by baluster mouldings. The socket itself has narrow mouldings at each end and in the middle. From the base of the socket two cheeks run down the haft.

The partizan was the weapon generally carried by infantry officers throughout the seventeenth century. The long cheeks were to strengthen the haft and prevent damage by sword cuts.

## 196 *Harquebusier's armour, c. 1650*

ENGLISH, LONDON
ROYAL ARMOURIES, TOWER OF LONDON (III. 1942, 1976, 2021, IV. 887)

Comprising a pott, breastplate and backplate made by members of the Armourers' Company of London and a buff coat.
Total weight 20 lb 5 oz.
Purchased 1985; from the armoury at Littlecote House.
Exh: *Parliament and the Glorious Revolution 1688-1988,* Banqueting House, London 1988.

This armour is one of about thirty from the Popham family armoury at Littlecote House, near Hungerford, Berkshire. The armoury may have been established in the house at the end of the Civil Wars and is thought to have belonged to the troops of Colonel Alexander Popham (1605-67). It was certainly displayed in Littlecote's Great Hall by 1840, which Joseph Nash illustrated in *Mansions of England in the Olden Time.* After an international public appeal in 1985, the armoury was purchased by the Royal Armouries, the National Museum of Arms and Armour.

The main group of armour at Littlecote was for harquebusiers, who were light cavalry armed with carbines and swords. Many of the pieces bear stamped and inscribed marks recording their makers and owners. The helmet, of the characteristic English form fitted with a triple-bar faceguard and known as a 'pott', is struck with the mark of the London maker, Edward Bunion, who was freed of his apprenticeship to William Crouch in 1633 and died in 1657. It is also struck with two indistinct marks, possibly a cross of St George, with which English armour was marked during the Commonwealth, 1650-60, and the mark of the Armourers' Company of London, an A surmounted by a helmet, which was used during the same period. The cuirass is unmarked. Unlike the vast majority of the Littlecote armours, the breast and backplate seem to belong together, but this can only be demonstrated by matching the internal construction marks.

Like many of the Littlecote buff coats, this example has an inscription referring to an owner and is inscribed inside the collar, 'Ph. Mann(e)ring.' It also retains its lining, which was formed of a layer of coarse linen inside the upper body down to the waist, and a layer of finer linen inside this and the sleeves. The coat was fastened down the front of the chest with a row of hooks and eyes attached to the lining; the laces were simply wound through to eyelet holes at either side for a decorative effect. The buff leather equipment for these armours was completed by a carbine sling and a baldrick (a belt or girdle, worn from one shoulder across the breast, to support a sword or bugle).

Sources:  T. Richardson, 'Armour in the Popham Armoury at Littlecote House,' *The 38th London Arms Fair,* Spring 1987; T. Richardson, 'The Buffcoats at Littlecote House,' *Arms Collecting,* vol. 26, no. 1, February 1988.

## 197a-b *Pair of flintlock holster pistols, c.1695*

ENGLISH; BY PIERRE MONLONG
ROYAL ARMOURIES, TOWER OF LONDON (XII. 3829 AND 3830)

Length overall 53.3 cms, barrel length 35.3 cms, calibre 1.3 cms, weight 1.22 kg.
Steel locks, barrels and furniture, walnut stocks, silver and gold decoration.
Inscr: 'MONLONG LONDINI' on both lock plates.
From the collection of the Duchess of Westminster.
Purchased in 1975 with the aid of the National Art-Collections Fund, the Pilgrim Trust, the Worshipful Company of Goldsmiths and a public appeal.
Exh:   *Exhibition of Steel and Ironwork,* Burlington Fine Arts Club, London 1900.
*Treasures from the Tower of London,* Sainsbury Centre for Visual Art, Norwich 1982; Cincinnati Art Museum, Cincinnati, Ohio 1982-83; Royal Ontario Museum, Toronto 1983.
*The Quiet Conquest: The Huguenots 1685 to 1985,* Museum of London 1985.
*William and Mary, Tercentenary of the Accession,* Kensington Palace, London 1988.
Lit:    J.S. Gardner, *Iron and Steel Work* (London, 1900),   pl. LXIII.
J.F. Hayward, *The art of the gunmaker* (London, 1963), pp. 66-7.
H.L. Blackmore, 'The Monlong Pistols,' *Huguenot Society Proceedings,* 1975, pp. 463-4.
H.L. Blackmore, 'The Monlong Pistols,' *Connoisseur,* September 1975, p. 72.
A.V.B. Norman and G.M. Wilson, *Treasures from the Tower of London* (1982), pp. 84-5.

The lockplates are chiselled with demi-figures, masks and delicate scrolls terminating in heads and are engraved MONLONG LONDINI. The cocks, one of which is cracked across the neck, have restored top jaws and screws and are engraved with demi-figures and foliate scrolls. The cock-screws are chiselled with a bust portrait, possibly of William III. The frizzles and pans are chiselled with scrolls and lions' masks. The frizzle-rings terminate in a foliate head and scroll finial. The full-length figures' walnut stocks are carved in low relief with scrolls terminating in heads and are profusely inlaid with silver wire and cut and engraved silver-sheet, with scrolls, birds, animals and figures including Diana flanked by hounds on the butt. In front of the trigger-guard is Apollo driving the Sun chariot and near the fore-end, Fortitude.

The steel  furniture is chiselled to match the lock plate and has an acanthus foliage pattern. The butt caps terminate in a grotesque mask within a cartouche of masks and scrolls. The side plates are pierced with scroll work terminating in a demi-figure and grotesque masks. The ramrods have been restored. The barrels are in three stages separated by mouldings and are chiselled with masks, foliate scrolls and figures, and damascened with gold scrolls. The muzzles are chiselled with a ring of acanthus foliage and the foresights are in the form of a mask surrounded by gold scrolls. Monlong's mark, an M under a heart within a circle, is stamped under the breech.

Monlong began his career as a gunmaker in Anger, probably around 1660. In 1664 he was appointed one of the gunmakers to the French royal household and moved to Paris. Despite this prestigious appointment, he went into partnership with the Parisian gunsmith Pierre Frappier, instead of setting up in business on his own. In 1684 he emigrated to London with his wife and three children and was granted citizenship in 1688. He established a business near Charing Cross, an area favoured by immigrant craftsmen on account of its location outside the City of London yet close to the Court at Whitehall. In this particular district, foreign workers could find a certain degree of protection from the City Companies, who jealously guarded their privileges and fought hard against competition from foreign craftsmen. Monlong's great talent was quickly recognised by the Court and in 1689 he was appointed 'Gentleman Armourer to His Majesty-in-Ordinary.' He died in 1699 and was buried in St Martin-in-the-Fields on 23 November.

**197 (a - b)**

**196**

The pistols are decorated on the lock with a portrait bust which appears to be based on a medallion of William III; it is therefore possible that they may have been made for the king himself. The general style of much of the ornament seems to derive from the pattern books of Claude and Jacques Simonin, published in Paris in 1685 and 1693. The style of the remainder, together with the form of the lock, appears to relate to early pattern books like those published by Jean Berain in 1659 and C. Jacquinet in 1660. It is probable that for pistols of this quality, a special set of designs was made, although it is impossible to tell whether these were produced by Monlong himself. Hayward (as above) suggests that they may have been furnished by Simonin before Monlong left Paris.

## 198 *Flintlock pistol, one of a pair, c. 1685*

ENGLISH
ROYAL ARMOURIES, TOWER OF LONDON (XII.742)

Length overall 53.5 cms, barrel length 35.4 cms, weight 1.47 kg.
Iron lock, barrel and trigger-guard, brass furniture, modern stock.

The lock-plate is decorated with a simple incised line around the edge, BROOKE in a scroll and a crown over JR. Swan-necked cock. The stock is fitted with a steel trigger-guard, brass ramrod pipes and butt-cap. The barrel is octagonal at the breech, changing to sixteen facets and then to round, the change to round being marked by a baluster moulding. Swamped muzzle. The barrel is stamped with a crown over IR, crown over rose, maker's mark RB and a square illegible mark. The barrel tang is stamped with a crown over a rose.

Flintlock pistols of this type were carried in pairs by cavalry, in holsters hanging on either side of the saddle.

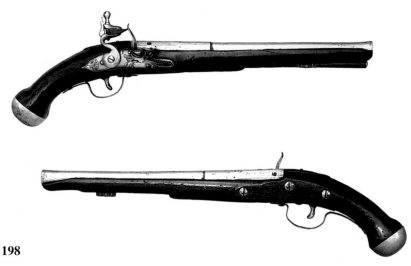

**198**

**199**

## 199a-b *Pair of Italian flintlock holster pistols*

BY DOMENICO BONOMINO (1635-1700)
N.A. WHITTLEY

Length 58 cms.
Lit:    H. Schedelmann, *Die Grossen Buchsenmacher* (Braunschweig, 1972), p.188.
       F. H. Cripps Day, *A Record of Armour Sales, 1881-1924* (London, 1925), p. 15, no. 206.

The pistols have walnut full stocks and finely chiselled steel locks and mounts. The Brescian gunmakers, of whom Bonomino was one of the most famous, produced much of this fine steelwork during the seventeenth and early eighteenth centuries. A pair of his pistols is in the Musée de l'Armée, Paris and a similarly chiselled pair, with barrels by Comminazo, is in the Historisches Museum, Dresden.

## 200a-b *Pair of flintlock holster pistols*

BY PAUL IGNAZIUS POSER OF PRAGUE (1646-1730)
N.A. WHITTLEY

Length 54 cms.
Lit:    J.F. Hayward, *The Art of the Gunmaker* (London, 1963), vol. II, p. 124.
       H. Schedelmann, *Die Grossen Buchsenmacher* (Braunschweig, 1972), p. 226.

The pistols have walnut full stocks, chiselled shell locks and silver mounts. The barrels are by Lazarino Comminazo, one of a noted family of Brescian gunmakers who sold their superbly light yet strong barrels all over Europe.

    Much of Poser's work is preserved in the former Imperial Collection in Vienna.

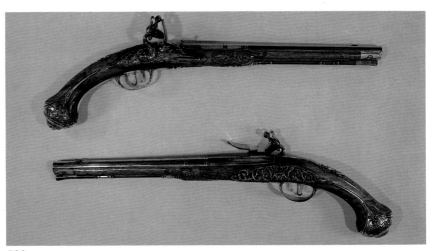

**200**

**201**

## 201 *Flintlock pistol, 1695*

N.A. WHITTLEY

Iron, length 48 cms.
Inscr: IO STVART on lockplate and dated 1695 on barrel.

This all-metal pistol with scroll butt, which is engraved and inset with silver plaques, is a good example of the firearms being made by several gunsmiths in towns and burghs up the east coast of Scotland in the late seventeenth century. Superficially the lock looks like a European flintlock of the period, but is a Scottish type of mechanism with a small 'dog' catch at the base of the cock to hold it in half-cock position. It is not known where Stuart worked, but at least nine other pistols by him survive, including one dated 1691.

## 202 *Matchlock musket, c.1690*

BRITISH
ROYAL ARMOURIES, TOWER OF LONDON (XII.24)

Length overall l85 cms, barrel length ll8 cms, calibre 2.1 cms.
Iron lock, barrel and furniture, wooden stock.

Slightly curved lockplate secured by three side-nails with an integral flash-pan with cover and flashguard. Curved serpentine or cock of D-shaped section with a clamp in the form of a stylised monster's head for holding a match. Iron butt-plate, trigger-guard, ramrod pipe, ramrod retaining band and side-plate. The barrel is octagonal at the breech and is stamped on the top flat with a crown over an illegible mark and an illegible circular mark. The ramrod is modern.

The matchlock musket was used by British forces from the sixteenth to the end of the seventeenth centuries. Ignition of the powder charge was achieved by means of a slow match, namely a piece of slow-burning cord. This was clamped into the cock and when the trigger was pulled, the cord was lowered into the flash-pan, igniting a small priming charge which in turn ignited the main charge in the barrel through a touch-hole in the side of it.

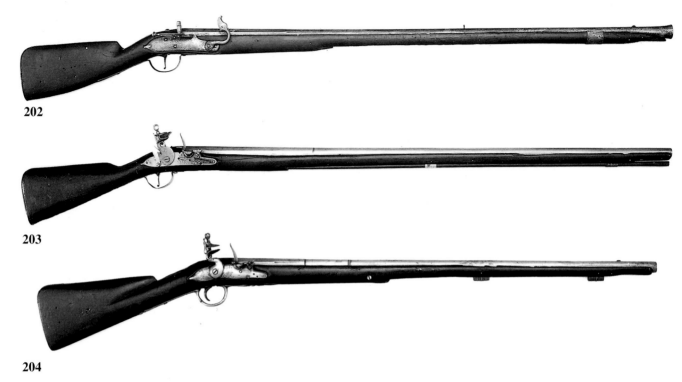

202

203

204

## 203 *Flintlock musket, c.1690*

BRITISH
ROYAL ARMOURIES, TOWER OF LONDON (XII.71)

Length overall l85.5 cms, barrel length ll8 cms, bore 2 cms.
Iron lock and barrel, brass and steel furniture, wooden stock.

Flat lock-plate with bevelled edge retained by three side-nails. Large flat ring-necked cock with restored dog-catch. The lower arm of the frizzle-spring is decorated with filed notches and has a leaf-shaped terminal. The lock-plate is engraved with WR under the crown. The stock has a brass butt-plate and ramrod pipes and an iron trigger-guard. The barrel is octagonal at the breech changing to round, the change marked by baluster moulding. The barrel is stamped crown over W?, with a rose and possibly EG.

The flintlock, in which ignition was achieved by a flint (held in the jaws of the cock) striking against the frizzle and sending a shower of sparks into the priming charge in the flash-pan, first appeared in an early form, called a snaphaunce, in the sixteenth century. However, it was not until the mid-seventeenth century that it became widely used on military firearms. It did not entirely supersede the matchlock until the end of the seventeenth century.

## 204 *Flintlock carbine, c. 1685*

ENGLISH
ROYAL ARMOURIES, TOWER OF LONDON (XII.153)

Length overall 115 cms, barrel length 79 cms, calibre 1.7 cms.
Iron lock, barrel, trigger-guard, brass furniture, wooden stock.

The lock-plate is decorated with a single incised line around its border, BROOKE in a scroll and a crown over J2R. Swan-necked cock and three side-nails. The stock has a butt-plate, escutcheon plate, two ramrod pipes, trigger-plate of brass and an iron trigger-guard. An iron screw through the stock held one end of the sling-bar, which is now missing. The other end was probably secured by the forward side-nail. The barrel is octagonal at the breech, changing to sixteen facets and then to round, the change to round being marked by a baluster moulding. The barrel is stamped with a crown over IR, a crown over a rose, two illegible marks and engraved with a crown over J2R. Brass foresight.

Carbines were carried by cavalry troopers and were suspended from a shoulder-belt by means of a spring-clip, which would clip through a ring running along a bar fixed to the left side of the gun.

**205**

## 205 *Bit and pair of stirrups, c.1660*

ENGLISH
ROYAL ARMOURIES, TOWER OF LONDON (VI 327, A, B AND C)

Height of bit 28 cms, height of stirrups 18 cms.
Cast brass, enamel and gilt.
Acquired in 1942; from the Morgan Williams and Lockett collection.

The bit is of the curb type. The S-shaped side branches are fitted with hooks and rings at their lower ends for attaching the reins and at the upper with hooks (one of which is missing) for the curb-chain. Mouthpiece of two slender linked bars pivoted to the branches at either side. Riveted to each branch is a large brass boss cast in relief with a floral design including poppies and Tudor roses partly enamelled in reddish-brown and partly gilt on a white enamelled ground. The stirrups are of cast brass with enamelled and gilt decoration similar to that of the bit and are possibly *en suite*. The arches are of semi-circular form with broad treads which have a serrated flange at the leading edge.

Enamel decoration of this type is generally known as 'Surrey' enamel. The attribution of this kind of enamel to Surrey was made by the late Charles Beard, in an article published in the *Connoisseur* in 1931. For some time, however, this attribution has been considered to be without any foundation. More recently the existence in some London churches of London-made pewter dishes with enamelled copper or brass central bosses made c. 1660, of similar technique to the 'Surrey' enamels, has led to a belief that 'Surrey' enamel was actually made in London.

Sources: *Burlington Magazine*, vol. 16, 1910; Charles R. Beard, 'Surrey Enamels of the Seventeenth Century,' *Connoiseur*, October 1931; Charles R. Beard, 'More about Surrey enamels,' *Connoiseur*, July 1932; J.G. Mann, 'Stuart enamels,' *Country Life*, vol.93, 1943.

**206**

## 206 *Cannon barrel, 3 pdr., 1685*

ENGLISH
ROYAL ARMOURIES, TOWER OF LONDON (XIX.172)

Length 203.2 cms, calibre 8.2 cms, weight 404 kg.
Bronze.
Inscr:   'IACOBUS IIs MAG BRIT FRA ET HIB REX ANNO REGNI SUI PRIMO. DN'
GEORGIUS LEGGE BARO DE DARTMOUTH REI TORMENTARIAE
BELLICAE PRAEFECTUS GENERALIS.'
Transferred from the Rotunda Museum, Woolwich in 1930, where it was no. II. 24.
Lit:     H.L. Blackmore, *The Armouries of the Tower of London, The Ordnance*, 1976, p. 67.

The second reinforce bears the monogram of James II within a wreath in relief.
The inscription above is on the first reinforce. Incised below the inscription is
NO 7 3pr. and on the base ring is the weight 7-3-23. The cascabel button is
unusually large and doughnut-shaped.

George Legge, first Baron Dartmouth (1648-97) - he of the inscription - was
the son of Colonel William Legge and was created Master General of the
Ordnance in 1682. A supporter of James II, he was sent to the Tower in 1691,
where he died within a few months. His father, Colonel William Legge, was the
last Master of the Armouries before the re-establishment of the post in 1935.

## 207 *Bronze or gunmetal cannon, c. 1700*

N. A. WHITTLEY

Length 87 cms, calibre 4.2 cms.
Prov: Powerscourt collection.

The six-stage barrel is cast, with dolphin handles and a vacant shield below a
coronet. Both the base of the barrel and the cascabel are decorated with acanthus
ornament. The piece would have been mounted originally on a small field
carriage. A gun of this size was probably used by private or irregular troops
rather than a regular army.

207

208

## 208  *Bronze or gunmetal cannon, seventeenth century*

N. A. WHITTLEY

Length 47 cms, calibre 2.3 cms.

The five-stage barrel is cast, with lion rampant device in a shield below a coronet.

## 209  *Tschege or lobster-tailed helmet, c. 1670*

CENTRAL EUROPEAN
N. A. WHITTLEY

Worn by cuirassiers (heavy cavalry), this form of helmet with its fluted skull was lighter and had a better weight-to-strength ratio than the earlier solid plate. The articulated lames or overlapping plates allow considerable movement whilst still affording protection to the neck. The pierced earpieces are also flexible. In action, the sliding bar nasal was lowered to protect the face against sabre slashes.  The helmet would originally have had a padded lining of wool or horse hair for comfort and to absorb shock.

Similar helmets can be seen in the Royal Armouries, Tower of London.

## 210  *A Prospect of Limerick Bearing DueWest*
*Exactly shewing ye Approaches Batteries & Breach etc*

FROM STORY'S *CONTINUATION* (1693)
REPRODUCTION

This plate was used by Story to illustrate the first (1690) siege of Limerick, which was conducted by William III himself.  Despite the poor state of the defences and lack of proper arms and supplies, the Irish garrison resisted so stoutly that William was forced to abandon the siege after Sarsfield had destroyed his siege train, en route to Limerick, in a daring night raid.

**209**

**211** *John Churchill, first Duke of Marlborough (1650-1722), general, with an allegory of Time revealing Truth*

By Pieter Tanje, after Sir Godfrey Kneller (1646-1723)
National Gallery of Ireland, Dublin

Line engraving 26.2 x 21.3 cms (plate 23.5 x 18.8).
Lit:    Adrian Le Harivel,ed., *National Gallery of Ireland Illustrated Summary Catalogue of Prints and Sculpture* (Dublin, l988), pp. 324-5, repr.

John Churchill was the second but eldest surviving son of Sir Winston Churchill, an ardent but impecunious Royalist who in the early l660s spent some time in Dublin as one of the commissioners appointed under the Act of Settlement to hear claims for forfeited Irish land.Handsome and immensely charming, he gained admission to the court of Charles II in l667 through the influence of his father and his sister Arabella, who was the mistress of James, Duke of York. He became first a page and then a gentleman of the bedchamber to James.  His position in the York household, as well as his evident ability, helped to advance his military career under Charles, and when James became king he was made a peer (as Baron Churchill) and promoted to lieutenant - general. Hewas second-in-command of the royal forces at Sedgemoor in l685, when Monmouth (whose life he had once saved) was defeated. His marriage to the penniless Sarah Jennings (whose sister Frances married first a brother of Anthony Hamilton and then Richard Talbot, later Earl of Tyrconnell) left him dependent for support on his career but was to advance that career enormously later, when Sarah's mistress and friend the Princess Anne became queen.

Despite his closeness to James, Churchill resisted all  pressures and temptations to change his religion, and he always claimed his devotion to Protestantism as the reason why in November l688, when effectively commander-in-chief of the royal army, he suddenly defected to William. This was a final blow to James and therefore a considerable service to William. Though despising such treachery, and always doubtful of Marlborough's loyalty to himself, William rewarded him with an earldom and made him a privy councillor; he gave the major commands in his armies to Schomberg and his own Dutch generals, however, while Marlborough had to be content with subordinate appointments.

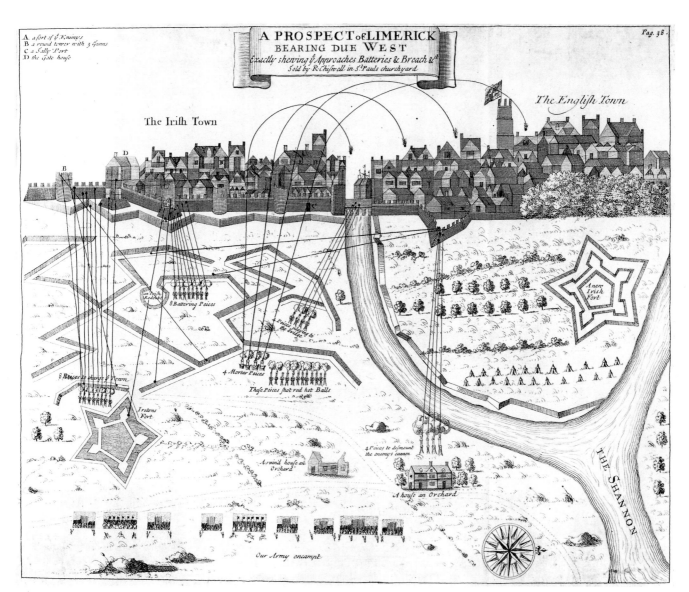

Following William's failure to take Limerick in 1690, Marlborough's proposal for a sea-borne attack on Cork and Kinsale was accepted and he was given the command. Landing at Cork late in September, he was joined by a mixed force under the Danish commander Würtemberg. Cork was taken after an assault lasting two days, its garrison surrendering as prisoners of war. The forts at Kinsale were then quickly taken. This brilliant brief campaign demonstrated both Marlborough's ability as a commander and also his grasp of the importance of sea power in combined operations. William commented that he knew of no man so fit to be a general who had seen so few campaigns. Marlborough's hopes of being made commander in Ireland were disappointed, however, Ginkel being preferred. After spending the winter in Ireland he departed to the Continent with William in 1691 and played no further part in the Irish war.

Intensely ambitious, and dissatisfied with his rewards so far, Marlborough then entered into secret correspondence with the exiled James (from whom he obtained promise of a pardon in the event of a Jacobite restoration) and put himself at the head of the growing opposition in England to William and his foreign favourites. William dismissed him from the privy council in June 1691, and he remained out of favour till 1698, thus missing all chance of military employment during the remaining six years the war lasted. In 1698, however, William appointed him governor to Princess Anne's son. Later, when renewed war with France became inevitable, William effectively made him his political heir by appointing him commander-in-chief of the forces in Holland and chief negotiator of the Grand Alliance.

The accession of Anne and the outbreak of war in 1702 at last gave Marlborough full rein to display his genius as a general and brought him all the rewards - including a dukedom, a palace and immense wealth - that even his

**211**

ambition could wish for. At Blenheim and many other battlefields he triumphantly accomplished against the might of France what William had attempted with much less success. He fell from power during the later years of Anne's reign, but was reappointed captain-general and master of the ordnance by George I. His last years, overshadowed by illness, were passed under the domestic tyranny of his formidable duchess.

The theme of Time revealing Truth was a common one in the sixteenth and seventeenth centuries. In this allegory Father Time,the bearded figure with the scythe to the right, draws back a veil from the image of Marlborough, beside whom stands the naked figure of Truth. The allegory appears to be indicating that the passing of time had revealed Marlborough's true genius as a military commander.

Sources: *DNB*; D.G. Chandler, *Marlborough as Military Commander* (London, 1973).

## 212 *Plan of the siege of the City of Cork, showing the progress of the siege of October 1690*

No cartographer or date given but possibly Thomas Phillips
British Library, London (Add. MSS., 61343)

Scale bar of 100 yards at 100 yards to 2.4 inches [1:1500].
No compass points but west at top. 63.4 x 100 cms. Imperfect, with only an irregularly - shaped fragment, measuring 31 x 15 cms at its largest points, remaining from the right side of plan.
Pen, pencil and coloured inks and washes on six sheets of paper stuck together without backing.
Extent: North Gate (north), south of Cat Fort (south), marshes (east), St. Finbar's Cathedral (west).
Unfinished, the positions of the besieging forces south of Cat Fort being sketched in pencil
Gradients, buildings and street plan in suburbs indicated in grey wash, street plan within walls, fortifications, trenches, batteries (with range of fire) and manoeuvres of besiegers (for which see D. Chandler, *Marlborough as Military Commander* 1973, pp. 38-41) indicated in red and black ink and yellow and pink washes. Miniature view of St Finbar's Cathedral.

This campaign map, and the following one of the siege of Kinsale, came from the Blenheim Archive. Their survival among Marlborough's papers (they are almost the only pre-1702 material) suggests that he intentionally retained them as souvenirs of the 1690 campaign, his first independent command and an early demonstration of his abilities as a general.

**212**

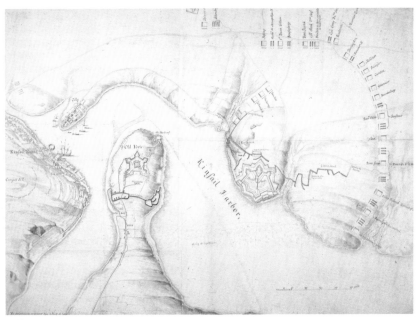

**213**

## 213 *Plan of the siege of Kinsale in October 1690*

NO CARTOGRAPHER OR DATE GIVEN BUT POSSIBLY THOMAS PHILLIPS
BRITISH LIBRARY, LONDON (ADD. MSS., 61343)

Scale bar of 500 yards at 500 yards to 5.5 inches [approx. 1:3273].
No compass points, but east at top. 60.6 x 82 cms.
Pen, coloured inks and washes on four sheets of paper stuck together without backing.

Shows town, harbour, Fort Charles, Old Fort and River Bandon. Bird's-eye
view in grey wash of Kinsale Town. Hills, fortifications, positions of English
and allied troops, trenches, batteries (with range of fire) and manoeuvres of
besiegers indicated in coloured inks and washes. Annotations relative to the
progress of the siege (for which see Chandler, no. 212, pp. 41-2).

214

### 214 *'Prospect' of Charles Fort, Kinsale, 1685*

BY THOMAS PHILLIPS (C.1635-93)
NATIONAL LIBRARY OF IRELAND, DUBLIN

Watercolour on paper 63 x 98.5 cms.

Ringcurran Fort, later renamed Charles Fort, was started in 1678 on the site of earlier works, to strengthen the defences of Kinsale harbour. In his survey of 1685 Phillips noted critically that it was overlooked by high ground to the north and east, 'so very ill situated under the command of hills, that it is a very hard matter to cover the inhabitants thereof, on any occasions that they shall have to stand by the guns, or the sea batteries ...' In October 1690 Marlborough and Würtemberg (joint commanders of the Anglo-Danish army sent to attack Kinsale and Cork) used precisely this weakness to capture the place.

Source:     P.M. Kerrigan, 'Charles Fort, Kinsale,' *The Irish Sword*, vol. XIII (1917-9).

### 215 *Williamite account book 1690*
*The Accompt of Cha Fox & Thoms Coningsby Esqrs Receivrs & Paymastrs Genll. of their Mat Revenue and Forces in Ireland —'*

BELFAST CITY COUNCIL

Charles Fox and Thomas Coningsby were appointed to office on 2 June 1690. This account book covers the period from that date till 11 March following (still 1690 according to the old calendar, by which the year changed on 25 March, not 1 January). In the preamble, 11 March is described as 'ye date of the Praecept Receivd from the Honble y Commissrs for putting in Execution ye Act intituled an Act for appointing Commissionrs to examin take & state the publick Accompts of the Kingdom'. This account book is evidently a fair copy prepared for the auditors.

Payments made are accounted for under the following heads: Officers Generall; Forces on the Irish Establishment; Dutch Forces; Hosspitalls; Regiments on the English Establishment; Ordnance & Trayns of Artillerie; Contingent Payments; English Reformd Officers; French Reformd Officers;

**216**

Other Reformd Officers as of his Mas Bounty; Half pay to Deserters from the Enemy (£117 16s. 9d.); Standing Allowances; Commissarys genl. of the Provisions; Comissary genl. of the Bread; Extraordinary Payments; Paid of 3000 Receivd from the Heer Van Averquere in London; Lords Justices of Ireland; Charge of management of the Treasury in Ireland. The total sum accounted for is £338,497 19s. 4 3/4d. The total cost of the Irish war was more than six million pounds, an enormous sum. The wars in which England became engaged as a result of accepting William III as king necessitated a financial revolution and the creation of a permanent National Debt.

## 216 *A Proclaimation For a Fast*
*Printed by Edward Jones at the King's Hospital in Oxman-Town, Dublin, for the King and Queen's Most Excellent Majesties. 1690*

### J.A. GAMBLE

The proclamation, dated 1 August 1690, proclaims Friday 15 August, and every Friday for the duration of the war, as a day of 'Publick Fasting, Prayer, and Humiliation'. The preamble begins: 'Whereas We have, under the Protection of Almighty God, taken upon Us, the Deliverance of Our good Protestant Subjects of Ireland, from the Oppressions of Popery and Arbitrary Power, under which they lately groaned ....'

**217**

# 8. Athlone, Aughrim and Limerick

When the campaigning season opened in 1691 the Irish army held the country west of the Shannon, with strong garrisons in Athlone, Limerick and Galway. Louis XIV sent no more troops but he provided war material, supplies and officers. An experienced French general, St Ruth, took charge of all the Jacobite forces.

The Williamite commander, the Dutch general Ginkel, assembled his forces at Mullingar at the end of May and advanced towards Athlone early in June. His first attack secured the English town on the Leinster side of the river, but the Jacobite defenders successfully held the only bridge despite heavy bombardment (12,000 cannon balls and 600 bombs were fired) until a ford below the town, pointed out by deserters, was crossed by a party of Williamite grenadiers, who put to flight the raw troops on guard at that point. Because St Ruth had not demolished the remaining fortifications the Williamites, once in, could not be dislodged and the town was lost. It was an important victory for Ginkel, its importance reflected in the title with which he was rewarded - Earl of Athlone.

St Ruth retreated towards Galway as far as Aughrim, where he took up a good defensive position and awaited Ginkel's arrival. Both armies numbered about 20,000. In the battle that followed, which took place on 12 July by the old calendar, the Irish infantry fought with great courage and success until a stray cannon ball killed St Ruth. The Jacobite cavalry on the left, probably through the treachery of officers who believed the war could not be won and who wanted to save their estates, then let Ruvigny's Williamite cavalry through and what might have been an Irish victory became the worst military disaster in Irish history. Unprotected by their cavalry, the Jacobite infantry were slaughtered as they fled; only the coming of darkness saved them from a complete massacre. Even so, 7,000 were killed, including 400 officers, and all the guns and baggage were captured. About 2,000 Williamites were killed. Though a much greater battle than the Boyne, and the decisive one of the whole war, Aughrim attracted less attention, no doubt because it came after the Boyne and no kings were present.

Galway surrendered to Ginkel a week later, after he had offered generous terms, and Sligo was taken in September. The last Jacobite resistance was concentrated in Limerick, which underwent a second siege. Its walls, strengthened since the previous year, and ample supplies of food enabled the garrison to hold out without much difficulty. Desperate to finish the war before the coming of winter, Ginkel offered attractive terms. For reasons not entirely clear Sarsfield, hitherto the leader of Irish resistance, took the lead in negotiating a capitulation that would enable him to transport most of his army to France. A large French fleet with ample supplies, that might have persuaded the Irish to continue their resistance, arrived too late. A parley was arranged on 23 September, and the articles of peace were signed on 3 October.

## 217 *Godert de Ginkel, first Earl of Athlone (1630-1703) (1695)*

BY SIR GODFREY KNELLER (1646-1723)
NATIONAL GALLERY OF IRELAND, DUBLIN

Oil on canvas 125 x 100 cms.
Lit:    Lord Killanin, S*ir Godfrey Kneller and his times* (London,1948),p.19,repr.pl. 23.
        *National Gallery of Ireland Illustrated Summary Catalogue of Paintings* (Dublin, 1981),
        p. 89, no.486.

Godert de Ginkel, eldest son of Godard Adriaan van Reede, Baron Ginkel of Amerongen, was born in Utrecht.  He had a distinguished career in the Dutch army before accompanying William to England in 1688, where his first action was the suppressing of a mutinous Scottish regiment which refused to proclaim for the new monarchs. He travelled to Ireland with William in 1690 and played an active role at the Boyne and at the first siege of Limerick. On William's departure (5 September 1690), he was made commander-in-chief of the Williamite army, a post he retained for the duration of the war. After the fall of Athlone (a crucial success) and his great victory at Aughrim in the summer of 1691, he was at the centre of the peace moves which culminated in the treaty of Limerick early in October.

Ginkel was in fact reluctant to lay siege to Limerick, home of the main Jacobite army after Aughrim: there were difficulties moving heavy artillery from Athlone and William himself had failed to capture the town the previous year. He favoured granting generous terms for a quick surrender, maintaining that his belief 'was always to finish the war by giving the Irish a free pardon, if it could be done soonest that way; for one summer's war costs the king more than all the forfeitures will amount to' (*Jacobite Ireland*, p.243). At the most he favoured a blockade, which the lords justices felt would be a sign of weakness: they accordingly pressed for a formal siege.

Shortly after the treaty had been concluded, Ginkel left for London. On arrival he was publicly thanked by the speaker of the Commons for his services. In March 1692 he was created Baron of Aughrim and Earl of Athlone and was subsequently granted the forfeited estates of Lords Limerick and Slane, 26,480 acres in all.  His grant was confirmed by an act of the Irish parliament (the only one to be treated in this way) but was later cancelled by the English parliament under the Act of Resumption.

In March 1692 he went with William to the Continent and took part in the battle of Steenkirk. He also fought at Landen in July of the following year (where he was almost drowned trying to restore order during the allied retreat) and in 1695 commanded the Dutch cavalry in the army of the Elector of Bavaria. On the renewal of the war in 1702 he waived his claim to lead the Dutch forces and agreed to serve under Marlborough, of whom he magnanimously said, 'The success of this campaign is solely due to this incomparable chief, since I confess that I, serving as second in command, opposed in all circumstances his opinion and proposals' (*DNB*). He died at Utrecht on 11 February 1703, after a short illness.

The portrait, which is very finely executed, shows a burning building in the background and a bridge. These may perhaps represent King John's Castle at Athlone and the bridge of Athlone, both scenes of fierce fighting in the assault on the town.

Sources:    *DNB*; J.G. Simms, *The Williamite Confiscation in Ireland 1690-1703* (London, 1956); J.G. Simms, *Jacobite Ireland 1685-91* (London, 1969).

## 218 *Plan illustrating the siege of Athlone in June 1691*

FROM STORY'S *CONTINUATION* (1693)
REPRODUCTION

The fortified town of Athlone on the river Shannon consisted of two parts, one (left) in Leinster, the other in Connaught, joined by a single bridge. It was fiercely defended by the Irish when Ginkel attacked it in June 1691; even when he took the Leinster town the bridge proved impassable. In the end a force of grenadiers forded the river downstream from the bridge and drove back the defenders.

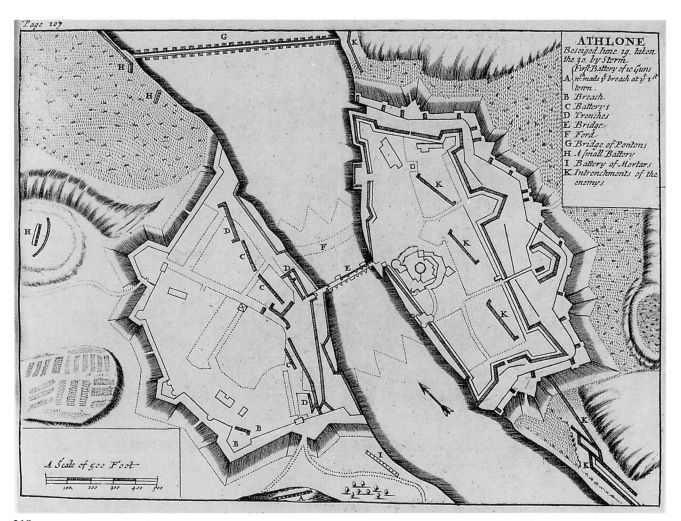

The taking of Athlone, the only major crossing of the Shannon north of Limerick, was regarded as an important Williamite victory. When raised to the peerage by William, Ginkel took the title Earl of Athlone.

## 219 *Gustavus Hamilton, Viscount Boyne (1639-1723)*

BY AN UNKNOWN ARTIST
PRIVATE COLLECTION
REPRODUCTION

Gustavus Hamilton, son of Sir Frederick Hamilton and grandson of the first Lord Paisley, served as a captain in the army towards the end of the reign of Charles II. On James's accession he was appointed to the privy council but resigned in protest against James's catholicising policies and unconstitutional conduct. In March 1689, as commander in charge of the garrison at Coleraine, he and his troops held off a numerically superior Irish force under Richard Hamilton for six weeks, before retreating to Derry, accompanied by large numbers of Protestants who were fleeing in terror from the advancing Irish army. (He is not to be confused with Gustavus Hamilton who was in command of the garrison at Enniskillen at this time). He thereafter suffered a breakdown in health, and on his recovery joined Schomberg's army at Loughbrickland with a regiment of Enniskillingers. He fought at the Boyne (where he was nearly killed and had his horse shot from under him) and at Limerick in August 1690.

He served under Ginkel during the remainder of the Irish campaign and distinguished himself at the storming of Athlone at the end of June 1691. He was subsequently appointed governor of the town. On the reduction of Ireland he was appointed to the privy council, was promoted to brigadier-general and was given a grant of 3,482 acres of forfeited land for his 'great and early services in the war in Ireland and for his wading in the Shannon and storming the town of Athlone at the head of the English grenadiers' (*The Williamite Confiscation*, p. 90). He was later promoted to major-general and commanded a regiment at the siege of Vigo. In 1714 he was created Baron Hamilton of Stackaller and Viscount Boyne three years later. He died in September 1723. The military scene in the background of the portrait may depict Athlone, with which he was so closely associated.

Sources: J. Willis, ed., *A History of Ireland in the Lives of Irishmen* (London and Edinburgh, n.d.), vol III; J.G. Simms, *The Williamite Confiscation in Ireland 1690-1703* (London, 1956); J.G. Simms, *Jacobite Ireland 1685-91* (London, 1969).

## 220 *Grenadier cap, Royal Regiment of Ireland, c. 1710*

NATIONAL ARMY MUSEUM, LONDON

Mitre cap, height 32.8 cms, width 22 cms.
Exh: *1688: Glorious Revolution?* National Army Museum 1988 (159).

Grenadiers were introduced into the British army in 1677. The diarist John Evelyn wrote of them in 1678: 'Now were brought into service a new sort of soldier called Grenadiers, who were dexterous to fling hand grenades, every one having a pouch full and had furr'd caps with coped crowns like Janizzaries which made them look fierce' (*Glorious Revolution* catalogue, p. 21). The grenades were hollow iron, wood, ceramic or glass balls, two or three inches in diameter and fitted with fuses. Grenadiers were the elite troops in the army, chosen from the tallest and fittest men. Their caps, originally of fur but later of cloth, replaced the broad-brimmed hat worn by most soldiers of the period because the latter hindered their grenade-hurling operations. Grenadiers were among the first troops to be supplied with bayonets.

This cap reputedly belonged to Captain Robert Parker, who served with the Royal Regiment of Ireland 1706-18, though it appears to be an other rank's cap. Parker's memoirs of his service under James II, William III and Anne (published in Dublin in 1746) are an important source of information about military life during the period. He served under William in Ireland.

Sources: *DNB*; A.S. Robertson, 'The Uniforms, Equipment and Weapons of the English Army of 1688,' in *1688: Glorious Revolution?* catalogue.

**219**

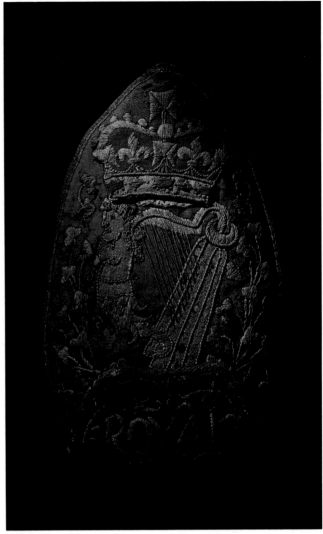

**220**

**221** *Birds-eye view of the battlefield of Aughrim*

FROM STORY'S *CONTINUATION* (1693)
REPRODUCTION

**222** *The French and Irish beaten near Aughrim by Ginkel*

ENGRAVING PUBLISHED IN AMSTERDAM BY ADRIAAN SCHOONEBEEK
ULSTER MUSEUM, BELFAST
REPRODUCTION

The Dutch and French titles of this engraving give the date of the battle as 22 July 1692, rather than 1691. The engagement between the Irish army commanded by the French general St Ruth and the English army commanded by the Dutchman Ginkel took place on 12 July 1691 by the old calendar, 22 July by the new. It was by far the bloodiest battle of the war in Ireland, about 7,000 of the 20,000 Jacobites being killed and about 2,000 Williamites killed or wounded out of an army of similar size.

This picture seems to be a general battle scene, rather than Aughrim in particular. It is just possible, however, that the figure on horseback in the background is meant to be Ginkel receiving Jacobite colours, of which more than forty were captured in the rout.

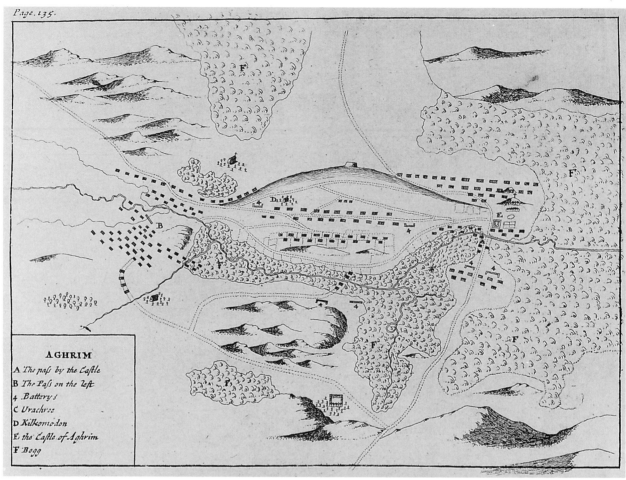

**AGHRIM**

A *The pass by the Castle*
B *The Pass on the left*
4 *Batterys*
C *Urachree*
D *Kilcomedon*
E *the Castle of Aghrim*
F *Bogg*

221

## 223 *Henri de Massue de Ruvigny, first Earl of Galway (1648-1720)*

BY AN UNKNOWN ARTIST
PRIVATE COLLECTION

Oil on canvas 123 x 97.5 cms (sight).

Henri de Ruvigny was the eldest son of Henri de Massue, marquis de Ruvigny, a distinguished French Huguenot general, formerly ambassaor at the English court and uncle of Rachel, wife of Lord William Russell. Ruvigny embarked on a military career at an early age and served with the French army in Portugal and Germany. In l678 he was sent to England (as Louis XIV's agent) to arrange a secret understanding between Louis and Charles II, his connection with the Russell family furnishing a plausible excuse for the visit.  In the same year he was chosen to succeed his father as deputy-general of the Huguenots at the French court. After the revocation of the Edict of Nantes in l685 he elected to leave France rather than stay and accept Louis's offer of preferential treatment. As a special concession, however, he and his father were allowed to take their personal property out of the country; in addition, he was permitted to enjoy the income from his French estates. In January l688 he, his father and brother Pierre settled in England.

After  his brother's death at the battle of the Boyne he decided to join the English army and fight for the Williamite cause, although by doing so he forfeited his French estates. He was appointed colonel of the Huguenot cavalry (Schomberg's former regiment) and in May l691 went to Ireland. At the battle of Aughrim on 12 July of that year he commanded the horse, which consisted of his own corps (composed entirely of French Protestants) and the Oxford regiment. His quick thinking at a crucial moment in the battle helped win the day for the Williamites. Würtemberg, the commander of the Danish troops, wrote afterwards to Christian V:'The action began to look very desperate on our side when, very luckily, three horse regiments, among them the Oxford Regiment,

222

Henri de Ruvigny
Earl of Galway.

**223**

commanded by Maj. Gen. Ruvigny, opened a passage for themselves fifty paces from the castle, formed up and drove the enemy back, and gave time for the rest of the cavalry from the right flank to come up, for these had to defile in twos, and this changed the aspect of the whole affair' (Danaher and Simms, p. 122). Ruvigny later served at the siege of Limerick and took part in the military negotiations for its capitulation.

In February 1692 he was appointed commander-in-chief of the forces in Ireland, and in the following November was created Viscount Galway and Baron Portarlington in recognition of his services at Aughrim. In 1693 he left Ireland and went to Flanders, where he commanded the English and Huguenot horse at the battle of Landen. In November of the same year he was appointed commander of the English forces in Piedmont and envoy to the Duke of Savoy in Turin. In 1696 he was granted the forfeited estates of Sir Patrick Trant, an area of over 58,000 English acres, mostly in Queen's County. In February 1697 William appointed him lord justice of Ireland; three months later he granted him an earldom. Since the two other lords justices appointed were caught up in other affairs, he had virtually sole charge of Ireland between February 1697 and April 1701.

Under his governance the first acts of the penal code against Catholics (and against the spirit of the treaty of Limerick) were passed in September 1697, although the Irish parliament had already embarked upon such a course two years before, at which time he was serving on the Continent (see no. 328). (History, however, has excoriated him as the perpetrator of the penal laws until recent times). During his years in Ireland, he established a Huguenot colony on his land at Portarlington and built and endowed two churches. In 1700 he was deprived of his Irish estates by the Act of Resumption; in compensation William gave him a pension of £1,000 a year and appointed him general of the Dutch forces. In 1704 he went to Portugal as commander of the English forces there. His latter years were spent in military service, apart from a second term as lord justice of Ireland, 1715-16. He died on 3 September 1720.

The portrait depicts him as a somewhat stern and determined individual. The battle scene in the background of the painting may perhaps be Aughrim, with which he was so closely associated.

Sources:     *DNB*; K. Danaher and J.G. Simms, eds., *The Danish Force in Ireland 1690-1691* (Dublin, 1962); P. Kelly, 'Lord Galway and the Penal Laws,' C.E.J. Caldicott, H. Gough, J.- P. Pittion, eds., *The Huguenots and Ireland* (Dun Laoghaire, 1987).

225

## 224a *Letter from General Ginkel to the Lords Justices,*
*from the 'Camp by Aughrim', 13 July 1691*

PUBLIC RECORD OFFICE OF NORTHERN IRELAND

MS. letter, in English, signed by Ginkel.

Dictated by the victorious general on the day after the battle of Aughrim, the letter begins: 'Mr Pulteney will tell Yr Ldships the Particulars of yesterday's action; I shall only say, that as it has pleased God to shew an Extraordinary Providence in giving us the Victory, so Yr Ldships will order a Publick Thankgiving in the other parts of this Kingdome, as I doe in that where the Army is.'

## 224b *Letter from General Ginkel to the Lords Justices,*
*written 'Aux Camp d'Aghrim', 15 July 1691*

PUBLIC RECORD OFFICE OF NORTHERN IRELAND

Holograph letter, in French.

After apologising to the lords justices (Lord Coningsby and Sir Charles Porter) for not having the time to write to them in his own hand as often as he would wish, Ginkel refers to the battle fought at Aughrim three days earlier, 12 July (OS) : 'C'est une très.. grande victoire que nous avons emporté par dessus les Ennemi, et le grand Dieu a beny les Armes du Roy' (It is a great victory that we have won over the enemy, and the great God has blessed the King's arms). In military terms Aughrim was a far greater battle than the Boyne (or any other during the Irish war). It was doubly disastrous for the Irish, to have lost when victory appeared to be within their grasp and to have lost in the end so calamitously (7,000 of them were killed, out of an army of 20,000). 'It isn't the loss of Aughrim' became a saying for any misfortune that was bearable (J.G. Simms, *Jacobite Ireland 1685-91*, p. 229).

## 225 *'Prospect' of Galway, 1685*

BY THOMAS PHILLIPS (C. 1635-93)
NATIONAL LIBRARY OF IRELAND, DUBLIN

Watercolour on paper 44.5 x 99.5 cms.

228

### 226 *Surrender of Galway to General Ginkel, 1691*

ENGRAVING PUBLISHED IN AMSTERDAM BY ADRIAAN SCHOONEBEEK
ULSTER MUSEUM, BELFAST
REPRODUCTION

Following his victory at Aughrim, Ginkel advanced to Galway. The leading
inhabitants, disheartened by Aughrim and anxious to save their property,
surrendered quickly when Ginkel offered generous terms. Under the Articles of
Galway, which served as a model for the terms offered at Limerick later in the
year, the garrison were allowed to march out to Limerick with their arms,
baggage and six pieces of artillery. Civilians who remained and submitted were
pardoned for their part in the war and were promised such freedom of religion
and property as in the reign of Charles II.

### 227 *Letter from General Ginkel to the Lords Justices,*
*written 'Aux Camp de Galloway' 21/31 July 1691*

PUBLIC RECORD OFFICE OF NORTHERN IRELAND

Holograph letter, in French.

After thanking the lords justices for congratulating him on his victory at
Aughrim - 'la glorieuse Bataille que nous avons donné et gagné contre les
Ennemis' - he goes on to say 'Voicy les effets .. la ville de Galloway vient de
capituler' (Here are the results .. the town of Galway has just surrendered).

Convinced by the defeat at Aughrim that the Jacobite cause was lost, and
anxious to save their estates and property while they could, the leading citizens
of Galway favoured peace. Ginkel was equally anxious to push on to Limerick
and finish the war. After a short siege he offered attractive terms. The Articles of
Galway, which foreshadowed those of Limerick, led to the speedy surrender of
the town. The garrison were allowed to march out with the honours of war and
make their way to Limerick.

### 228 *'Prospect of Sligo', 1685*

BY THOMAS PHILLIPS (C.1635-93)
NATIONAL LIBRARY OF IRELAND, DUBLIN

Watercolour on paper 44.5 x 100 cms.

**229**

### 229 *'Prospect' of Limerick, 1685*

BY THOMAS PHILLIPS (C.1635-93)
NATIONAL LIBRARY OF IRELAND, DUBLIN

Watercolour on paper 45 x 104 cms.

### 230 *Map illustrating the second siege of Limerick, 1691*

FROM STORY'S *CONTINUATION* (1693)
REPRODUCTION

The strong position of the city, with a fortified Irish Town guarding the bridge to
a fortified English Town on an island in the Shannon, made it difficult to take.
Until the closing stages of the siege the Williamite attack was entirely confined
to the Leinster side of the river, and the defenders could come and go freely on
the Connaught side. Even when carelessness (or treachery) let them cross to the
western bank, the besiegers were not much nearer success. Ginkel was glad to
offer generous terms in order to secure the surrender of Limerick before
winter came.

### 231 *'Limmerick' besieged, 1691*

FROM *HIBERNIA VINDICATA* (HAMBURG, 1691)
ANONYMOUS
REPRODUCTION

This illustration of the siege of Limerick is entirely fanciful.

### 232 *Letter from General Ginkel to the Lords Justices,*
*written 'Aux Camp devant Limmerick le 23 [septembre] a 7*
*heures du Soir'*

PUBLIC RECORD OFFICE OF NORTHERN IRELAND

Holograph letter, in French.

'Il y a deux heures que Mylord Lucan et Waecop ont demande a parley; et apres
quelques parolles que Messieurs de s'Gravenmore et Ruvigny ont passe avec eux
ils ont demande un Capitulation et une Cessation d'Armes' (Two hours ago Lord
Lucan [Sarsfield] and Wauchope [a Scottish Jacobite officer] asked for a parley;
and after some conversation between them and Messieurs Scravenmore and
Ruvigny [the Huguenot general] they asked for a capitulation and a cessation of
arms). Thus with immense relief Ginkel reported the successful end of the siege
of Limerick and the prospect of a happy end to the whole war. The next fortnight
was filled with negotiations over the articles of surrender. Ginkel was willing to

LIMMERICK.

**231**

offer generous terms in order to avoid another season's campaiging, but not so generous as the other side at first demanded. He agreed, however, that the articles should cover not only the citizens of Limerick and the soldiers of the Jacobite army but all those under that army's protection in the counties of Clare, Kerry, Cork and Mayo. Sarsfield had insisted on this, declaring that he 'would lay his bones in these old walls rather than not take care of those who stuck by them all along' (*Jacobite Ireland*, p. 252).

The lords justices were sent for and arrived on 1 October. The treaty was signed two days later in Ginkel's tent.

Sources:      J.G. Simms, *The Treaty of Limerick* (Dundalk, 1961);  J.G. Simms, *Jacobite Ireland 1685-91 (London, 1969)*.

## 233 *A portrait of a gentleman, possibly Patrick Sarsfield, Earl of Lucan (c. 1650-93)*

ATTRIBUTED TO JOHN RILEY (1646-91)

NATIONAL GALLERY OF IRELAND, DUBLIN

Oil on canvas 124 x 102 cms.

Prov:    Formerly at Malahide Castle.

Lit:      *National Gallery of Ireland Illustrated Summary Catalogue of Paintings* (Dublin, 1981), p. 139, no. 4163.

Sarsfield, the hero of the Irish army, was the son of Patrick Sarsfield and Anne O'More (daughter of Rory O'More) and was thus of Old English descent on his father's side, Gaelic Irish on his mother's. Educated at a French military academy, he served in Hamilton's regiment in France during Charles II's reign. Under James II, despite being a Catholic, he served in the English army and was seriously wounded at the battle of Sedgemoor in 1685; by 1688 he had reached the rank of colonel in the Life Guards. He followed James to France in 1688 and accompanied him to Ireland in the spring of 1689. In March of that year he was made a privy councillor and represented Co.Dublin in James's Irish parliament the following May. Appointed a brigadier-general, he subsequently served in Connacht and took Sligo in the autumn of 1689. He played only a minor role at the Boyne (he and his cavalry regiment were ill-positioned) but subsequently came to prominence during the first siege of Limerick in August 1690, when he acted as second-in-command to Boisseleau.

When the Jacobites fell back on Limerick, Tyrconnell felt the best move would be to surrender to William. Sarsfield, on the other hand, thought the army should fight on. Lauzun, fearing the town would fall, withdrew his French troops to Galway but left a French major-general, Boisseleau, in command of the garrison. Boisseleau, Sarsfield and Berwick thereupon urged resistance. William consequently was forced to lay siege to the town and sent to Dublin for heavy guns, ammunition and stores. With daring and enterprise, Sarsfield and a force of

**233**

cavalry crossed the Shannon one night and rode furiously through the Tipperary mountains to ambush the siege train as it lay encamped for the night at Ballyneety. (His ride thereafter became a popular subject for ballad and song). Many of the guns and supplies were destroyed. The delay and loss of ammunition had serious consequences for the Williamites: by the end of August they were forced to give up the siege because of lack of powder and shot and had to withdraw. Their retreat was a considerable boost to Jacobite morale. Furthermore, it justified the stand taken by Sarsfield and other die-hards and prolonged the war for over a year.

After Limerick, Tyrconnell went to France, leaving Berwick in charge but controlled by a council of war which included Sarsfield. The Irish army was now riddled with dissent: opposition to Tyrconnell was high and there were demands to send a deputation to James to request his removal as viceroy. Sarsfield was designated as the leader most acceptable to the army. However, by the time the delegation finally reached France, Tyrconnell had re-established himself in James's favour and was on his way back to Ireland. In an effort to placate the group, James agreed to its request to send a French general to Ireland, to hold an independent command. On his return in January 1691 Tyrconnell brought with him the earldom of Lucan for Sarsfield and attempted to heal the breach between himself and his arch-rival. Sarsfield, however, would have none of it, maintaining that Tyrconnell had displayed 'a thousand caresses and professions of friendship, but I know him too long not to be aware of how little faith I should place in his false words ... he is very jealous and despairs of my standing and the influence I have over the army...we await with impatience our French general and hope he will be independent of Lord Tyrconnell' (*Jacobite Ireland*, p. 196).

The long-awaited French general, St Ruth, finally arrived in May 1691 but his coming did not restore harmony: Tyrconnell still claimed authority over the army, which insisted St Ruth alone should command. Sarsfield's relations with St Ruth were also fraught; many Irish officers resented the fact that the French general had a higher ranking than their beloved Sarsfield. The effects of this division between Sarsfield and St Ruth were evident at the battle of Aughrim. Sarsfield, although second-in-command, was not given any orders or told of his general's plan. After St Ruth's death from a cannon shot (he was decapitated), Sarsfield was not placed in charge, and the Jacobite forces were routed in the chaos that followed.

Sarsfield took a leading part in the second defence of Limerick during August and September 1691, but subsequently led the peace negotiations when it became obvious that defeat was inevitable. His main aim was to obtain permission for the Irish army to go to France. He and the last of his 12,000 troops sailed from Cork on 22 December. Once in France, he was given
command of James's second troop of Life Guards and also given charge of the Irish troops intended for the invasion of England in May 1692 (a scheme thwarted by the defeat of the French fleet at Barfleur and La Hogue).Thereafter he fought in the service of France. He was mortally wounded at the battle of Landen on 29 July 1693 and died a few days later.

Sarsfield married Lady Honora De Burgh, daughter of the seventh Earl of Clanricarde. Two years after Sarsfield's death she married the Duke of Berwick. Sarsfield's Irish estate, seized by the commissioners of forfeitures after the Boyne, was successfully claimed by his niece Charlotte in 1696. After her marriage to Agmondisham Vesey and the Act of Resumption of 1700, the trustees reclaimed the estate. Vesey eventually got possession of it on payment of three times the rent at which the trustees had let it in 1702.

Sarsfield was of splendid physique, handsome and with pleasant manners, but he apparently lacked caution and (according to some sources) brains. Berwick described him as 'a man of an amazing stature, utterly devoid of sense, very good-natured and very brave' (*Jacobite Ireland*, p.158). This portrait shows a handsome young man with a confident manner and challenge and determination in his eyes. The fortification in the right background may represent Limerick. John Riley, to whom the picture is attributed, had a substantial practice in London between 1680 and 1691. Among his sitters were Charles II and James II. After the Revolution of 1688 he, together with Kneller, became chief painter to William and Mary.

Sources: *DNB*; J.G. Simms, *The Williamite Confiscation in Ireland 1690-1703* (London, 1956); J.G. Simms, *Jacobite Ireland 1685-91* (London, 1969).

## 234a-b *Pair of sugar casters, c. 1690*

BY ROBERT GOBLE, CORK
NATIONAL MUSEUM OF IRELAND, DUBLIN (7/8-1976)

Silver, height 19 cms.

Cylindrical body reeded around the base and rim, the base having in addition a raised rope-work band. Engraved with a coat of arms, probably those of the Sarsfield family impaled with those of Osborne. The lids are of a push-on type, decorated with reeding and a raised rope-work band around the rim, with baluster finial and cut-cord work above, pierced mainly with quatrefoils, trefoils and *fleurs-de-lis*. Each is stamped twice underneath with the maker's mark R G (Robert Goble) and with a castle, a town mark of Cork.

The casters were apparently owned by the Sarsfield family from their time of manufacture until their acquisition by the NMI in 1976.

## 235 *Colonel John Browne (1638-1711)*

BY SIR GODFREY KNELLER (1646-1723)
WESTPORT HOUSE, CO. MAYO
REPRODUCTION

Lit: The Marquess of Sligo, *Westport House and The Brownes* (Ashbourne, 1981), repr. p. 16.

John Browne, second son of Sir John Browne of the Neale, was born in 1638, educated as a barrister and practised at the Connaught bar. He acquired large estates in Mayo and Galway and built his family seat, Westport House, on the foundations of an O'Malley castle, Cahenamart (his wife was a great-great-granddaughter of Grace O'Malley, the renowned sea pirate and 'Queen of Connaught' in Elizabethan times). A Catholic and staunch Jacobite, he raised two regiments for James II, one of which was sent to France in 1690 and the other disbanded at the capitulation of Limerick. Besides his military service, he had contracts to make firearms, bayonets and ball for the Jacobite army at his ironworks at Knappagh, Foxford and Westport. (During the winter of 1689 he employed 150 men in Dublin, mostly Protestants, making musket barrels for firelocks).

**234a**                                                          **234b**

After the siege of Limerick in the autumn of 1691, he took part in drawing up the articles of capitulation of the Jacobite forces and was one of the signatories to the treaty signed on 3 October of that year. Under the terms of the treaty Catholics were to be granted the same religious privileges as they had enjoyed under Charles II; if they were prepared to take an oath of allegiance to William and Mary they would be pardoned and could keep their property and maintain their professions; those who chose to go to France were excluded from the benefit of terms and would be liable to lose their property. Browne, claiming that Sarsfield and Tyrconnell had commandeered goods which he had ear-marked to pay his Protestant creditors, got a clause inserted into the articles whereby a charge would be levied on every estate restored to a Catholic under the treaty.

Owing large sums to both Protestants and Catholics, Browne was almost ruined after the treaty. Imprisoned for debt and his lands confiscated, he was released at intervals and permitted to go to Dublin to help disentangle his extremely complicated financial affairs. In 1703 or 1704 he absconded on one of these trips and went into hiding. He was officially declared dead by the government in 1705 but in fact survived until 1711 or 1712, a respected figure in Co.Mayo. Westport and the other estates he had salvaged from the wreck of his fortunes were inherited by his son Peter who, in order to preserve them, brought up his only son as a Protestant.

Sources:       J. T. Gilbert, ed., *A Jacobite Narrative of the War in Ireland 1688-1691* (Dublin, 1892, reprinted Shannon, 1971); J.G. Simms, *The Williamite Confiscation in Ireland 1690-1703* (London, 1956); J.G. Simms, *Jacobite Ireland 1685-91* (London, 1969); The Marquess of Sligo, as above.

## 236 *A Diary of the siege & surrender of Lymerick:*
*with the articles at large, both civil & military... London, printed for R. Taylor... 1692*

THE QUEEN'S UNIVERSITY, BELFAST

quarto:   [4], 32 pp.
Lit:      Wing D1376.

A Dublin edition of this pamphlet, printed by Robert Thornton, also appeared in 1692. Thornton was the publisher of the official Williamite paper, the *Dublin Intelligence,* 1690-93 and King's Printer from 1692.

235

## 237a *Battle of Aughrim*

MEDAL BY J. SMELTZING (FL. 1685, D.1695)
NATIONAL MUSEUM OF IRELAND, DUBLIN

Silver, 54 mm.
Lit:           *Medallic Illustrations*, 29, no. 201.
Description:   obv.  conjoined busts of William and Mary, both laureate and draped, he over
                armour.
                legend: GUIL: ET MARIA D.G. M.BRIT:FR:ET HIB:REX ET
                REGINA. [William and Mary, by grace of God king and queen of Great
                Britain, France and Ireland].
         rev.  a cavalry attack from the right, with flags and clouds of smoke, in one of
                which an opposing horseman can be seen falling. To the left more cavalry
                flee, with fallen men, an abandoned flag and drum in the foreground.
                Further fighting can be seen in the background. The exergue line is formed
                in the manner of the capital of an ionic column, with masonry behind.
                legend: HIBERNIS. GALLISQ:DEVICTIS. [the Irish and the French
                defeated]; in exergue: PUGNA AD AGHRIM XXII IUL: MDCXCI. [the
                battle of Aughrim, 22 July 1691].

237(a) obv.

237(a) rev.

The great importance of the battle is reflected in its medallic treatment, ten
varieties being listed by *Medallic Illustrations*. It is emphasised that the Dutch
and English were fighting against the Irish, although there were Irish on both
sides.This was a suitable simplification for a foreign audience. On the medals
Aughrim is spelt in a variety of ways, none of which follow the modern
orthography.

237(b) obv.

237(b) rev.

237(c) obv.

237(c) rev.

## 237b *Battle of Aughrim*

MEDAL BY F.D. WINTER (FL. 1688-95) AND T. NEALE (1678-99)
NATIONAL MUSEUM OF IRELAND, DUBLIN

Silver, 51 mm.
Lit:             *Medallic Illustrations*, 31-32, no. 206.
Description:   obv.   laureate bust of William III, draped over armour.
                    legend: WILHELM.D.G.ANGSCO FRANC.ET.HIB.REX [William, by
                    grace of God king of England, Scotland, France and Ireland].
               rev.   a lion pounces on a dog which is lying on its back. With one forepaw the
                    lion holds down the dog by its throat, with the other it lashes out at a cock
                    which is running off to the right. The ground is realistically depicted.
                    legend: SIC. UNOFERIT . UNGUEDUOS. [Thus with one claw he strikes
                    both]; in exergue: IACOBO. ET LVDOVICO HIBERNIA . PVLSIS
                    ADAGHRIM 1692 [James and Louis beaten from Ireland at Aughrim,
                    1692].

One of the most interesting things about this medal is that it is an inept English
copy of another by Smeltzing. Both Ns in the main reverse legend are reversed
and the spacing of the letters is most uneven. The prototype manages to make the
design balanced and animated, fitting neatly into the circular space available.
The bust is handled much better - perhaps because Neale was master of the mint
and Winter worked for him, and was therefore used to this type of work. The
obverse legend, with its inclusion of Scotland in the list of titles, is a further
indication of British origin. The date should be 1691, not 1692.

The symbolism is simple enough - the dog is an Irish wolf hound, the cock
represents France and both are defeated by the English lion.

## 237c *Battle of Aughrim*

MEDAL BY J. SMELTZING (FL. 1685, D. 1695)
NATIONAL MUSEUM OF IRELAND, DUBLIN

Silver, 48 mm.
Lit:             *Medallic Illustrations* 32, no. 207.
Description:   obv.   laureate bust of William III.
                    legend: GUILM:III D.G.M. BRIT:FR:ET HIB:REX F.D.P.A. [William
                    III, by grace of God king of Great Britain, France and Ireland, defender of
                    the faith, pious and august].
               rev.   Hercules, wearing a loin cloth, club raised, stands over a pleading figure
                    lying on the ground with its head resting on a shield with a harp. Behind,
                    to the right, another clothed figure flees right, carrying a shield with three
                    *fleurs-de-lis*.
                    legend: IMPARES UNI [unequal to one]; in exergue: HIBERNIS
                    SUBIECTIS GALLIS FUGATIS MDCXCI [Ireland subjugated, France
                    put to flight, 1691].

This design in its brutal triumphalism emphasises the importance of the victory.
The fallen Irishman is being given the *coup de grace* by Hercules, representing
William's forces. The Frenchman scurries off, leaving his ally to his fate. Louis
used NEC PLURIBUS IMPAR as his motto, and the main legend here is a direct
riposte to that claim.

The design was copied in a larger version which was produced in England,
in the style of no. 284b. This in turn was copied by the Dutch.

**238(a) obv.**

**238(a) rev.**

**238(b) obv.**

**238(b) rev.**

## 238a *Galway taken*

MEDAL BY ? J. SMELTZING (FL. 1685, D. 1695)
PHOTOGRAPH OF AN ENGRAVING

55 mm.

Lit:       *Medallic Illustrations* 34, no. 211.
           N. Chevalier, *Histoire du Roy Guillaume III*, pp 228-29.

Description:  obv.  bust of William III, laureate and draped over armour.
              legend: WILHELM.III.D.G.M.BRI FRANC.ET HIB.REX.F.D. [William
              III, by grace of God king of Great Britain, France and Ireland, defender of
              the faith].

              rev.  shield with the arms of Galway, over crossed palms and between (to the
              left) a cap of liberty and (to the right) a book representing the bible; the
              main part of the field filled with the legend, across; below crossed
              branches of laurel.
              legend: GALLOWAY REBELLIVM ET GALLORUM PENULTIMVM
              REFUGIUM POST FLURIMAS STRAGES GUILIELMO*III*MAGNO
              RESTITUTORI RELIGIONIS AC LIBERTATIS CUM.ARMAMENTARIIS
              SIMUL AC.NAVIBUS REDDITUR [Galway, penultimate refuge for the
              French and the rebels, gave itself up after much bloodshed, to William III, the
              Great, restorer of religion and liberty, together with its arms and ships].

The same remarks apply to the authorship of this piece as to 238b. It may be that
the succession of victories did not allow enough time for separate celebratory
medals to appear and that the compendium medal by Smeltzing for the taking of
Athlone, Galway and Sligo superseded them. Certainly the reverse of this piece
is fairly dull.

## 238b *Athlone taken*

MEDAL BY ? J. SMELTZING (FL. 1685 D. 1695)
PHOTOGRAPH OF AN ENGRAVING

55 mm.

Lit:       *Medallic Illustrations* 28-29, no. 200.
           N. Chevalier, *Histoire du Roy Guillaume III*, pp 223-24.

Description:  obv.  bust of William III, laureate and draped over armour.
              legend: WILHELM.III.D.G.ANG.SCO. FRANC.ET.HIB.REX [William
              III by grace of God king of England, Scotland, France and Ireland].

              rev.  walled town with mountain behind, a battle raging in front; in the
              foreground a fortified battery of cannons, with tents. Men are streaming in
              and a river flows between the battery and the town.
              legend: DISSIPATIS GALLIS ET REBELLIS [The French and the rebels
              having been dispersed]; in exergue: ATHLONE LIBERTATUR MDCXCI
              [Athlone freed, 1691].

No specimen of this medal is recorded by *Medallic Illustrations* and its
description relates to a medal signed by Winter and Neale. Chevalier shows both
this piece and no. 238a as being signed 'D.S.'. The same signature is shown on
his plate of the battle of Aughrim medal known to be by Smeltzing, so it is
possible that the initials stand for 'Delinit Smeltzing,' indicating that he
designed,but did not necessarily engrave such pieces, and that some of the
designs, like no. 237b, were produced, rather ineptly, by Winter and Neale.

The siege of Athlone was the first major confrontation between Ginkel and
St Ruth, who badly underestimated the attacking forces. After a massive
bombardment and fruitless assaults on the only bridge across the Shannon, the
Williamite army forded the river and, finding the town lightly defended, took it
with little loss. Ginkel was rewarded with the title Earl of Athlone.

239 obv.

239 rev.

240 obv.

## 239 *Athlone, Galway and Sligo captured, 1691*

MEDAL BY J. SMELTZING (FL. 1685, D. 1695)
PHOTOGRAPH

Silver, 51 mm.

Lit:        *Medallic Illustrations*, 35, no. 212.
Description:   obv.   conjoined busts of William and Mary, he laureate and in armour, she
                    draped.
                    legend: GUILELM:REX  MARIA REGINA F.D.P.A. [William king,
                    Mary queen, defenders of the faith, pious and august].
              rev.   three scenes within laurel circlets, all topped by mural crowns: at top
                    ATHLON XXX IUN:N.IUL, with a battle raging; bottom left:
                    GALLOWAY D. XXVI IUL. V AUG., a walled town with an army in
                    front; bottom right: SLEGO D.XV SEPT. XXV., a similar view. There is
                    a central cartouche with harp, and all is imposed on a lance which carries a
                    Phrygian cap. Behind run a crossed sword and sceptre, with branches of
                    laurel to the left and orange to the right.
                    legend: ARMIS. NOMI: NISQ: TERRORE [by arms and not less by the
                    terror of his name]; in exergue MDCXCI. [1691].

The die of this reverse is used with two obverses, one of which is not signed and
shows William by himself. The obverse die shown here was used for a
coronation medal.

The reverse design is very triumphalist. Normally the Phrygian cap
(representing liberty) is shown on the staff of maintenance, whereas here it is
very firmly on a lance. Often two sceptres are crossed; here a sword replaces a
sceptre. The towns, shown in very fine detail, are Continental in appearance,
being mere symbols, the victories they represent being more important than the
territory taken. The dates are given in both old and new style.

## 240 *Capture of Limerick*

MEDAL BY J. LUDER (FL. 1680-1710)
NATIONAL MUSEUM OF IRELAND, DUBLIN

Silver, 38 mm.

Lit:        *Medallic Illustrations*, 37-38, no. 217.
Description:   obv.   bust of William III, in armour, with a mantle over his left shoulder.
                    legend: GVILIELMVS.III.D.G.MAG.BRIT. FRAN.ET.HIB.REX
                    [William III, by grace of God king of Great Britain, France and Ireland].
              rev.   a crowned shield with the arms of Great Britain and Ireland is on the trunk
                    of an orange tree, with a little foliage at the top. At the foot of the tree to
                    the left, a kneeling female clasps the trunk.  Behind her are the attributes
                    of religion - a cross and a crozier - lying on the ground; there appears to be
                    a broken shackle on her ankle. To the right a similar female grasps the tree
                    with one hand and holds her slipping dress up with the other.  In the
                    background are ships and a city under bombardment.
                    legend:  BONA.CAUSA TRIUMPHANT [the good cause triumphs]; (in
                    the field on either side of the tree): LIMME RICA ANGL: HIBERN: [?
                    Limerick, English and Irish; or (following Chevalier) Limerick in Ireland
                    submits to the English]; in exergue: VICTA REBELLIONE [the rebellion
                    vanquished].

The two females on the reverse pose some difficulties of interpretation. *Medallic
Illustrations* suggests that they represent Religion and Liberty; however, there
does not appear to be any particular reason for the latter identification. It may be
that Liberty? is either a rescued Hibernia or intended to symbolise the civilian
population of Limerick (the Orange party put considerable emphasis on
William's clemency at the time).

240 rev.

**241** obv.

**241** rev.

**242** obv.

**242** rev.

## 241 *The pacification of Ireland, 1691*

MEDAL BY D.TRAPENTIER (FL.LATER PART OF THE SEVENTEENTH CENTURY)
ULSTER MUSEUM, BELFAST

Silver, 55 mm.
Lit:          *Medallic Illustrations,* 39-40, no. 220.
Description:  obv.  conjoined busts of William (in armour and draped wearing a laurel wreath)
                    and Mary (draped).
                    legend: GULI.ET MARIA D.G.M.BRIT.FR:ET HIB REX ET REGINA
                    [William and Mary, king and queen of Great Britain, France and Ireland].
              rev.  a lion, head raised and fangs bared, mauls a Hydra; behind, a lioness
                    looks towards him, while a spaniel fawns at her feet; behind this again is a
                    port with some ships at sea.
                    legend, above PARCERE SVBIECTIS, ET DEBELLARE SVPERBOS.
                    [to spare the humble and subdue the proud]; in exergue HIB: PACATA
                    CICCCXCI [Ireland pacified, 1691].
              edge. ET. REGNARE PARES ET INTER AMARE. [equal in governing and the
                    admirable love they have for each other].

The many-headed Hydra, which was killed by Hercules, symbolises evil and
rebellion. Given the obverse and edge inscription, the male and female lions may
be taken to refer to William and Mary, the spaniel being an insulting reference to
the defeated Jacobites. This is a Dutch medal, but emphasises that William's
claims depended largely upon his wife, especially as any personal cult could
only reinforce his unpopularity. The Hydra and spaniel appear on other medals
to make similar points.

## 242 *Ireland brought under the rule of William III*

MEDAL BY G. HAUTSCH (FL. 1683-1712)
ULSTER MUSEUM, BELFAST

Silver, 41 mm.
Lit:          *Medallic Illustrations,* 38-39, no. 219.
Description:  obv.  draped bust of William III, wearing laurel wreath.
                    legend: WILH.III.D.G.ANG.SCO.  FR.ET.HIB.REX,DEF.FID. [William
                    III, king of England, Scotland, France and Ireland, defender of the faith].
              rev.  William as a Roman, being crowned from behind by Victory with a
                    wreath, gives an olive branch to a kneeling Hibernia, distinguished by a
                    shield bearing a crowned harp.
                    legend, above HIBERNIA RESTITVTA. [Ireland restored; in exergue
                    MDCXC [1690].
              edge. ARMIS IVNGIT AMOR NVNC TERTIA REGNA DVOBVS [Affection,
                    brought about by arms, now joins a third kingdom to the other two].

This small medal is quite common. It is possible that William is receiving the
olive branch from Hibernia, although her role is usually passive. The symbolism
is linked to the rendering of feudal fealty, which was a type of definite contract
involving responsibilities on both sides. It is interesting that the clearest message
of the piece, the edge inscription, is put on the most obscure location.

## 243 *Ireland reunited with Great Britain, 1692*

MEDAL BY J. LUDER (FL. 1680-1710)
HUNTERIAN MUSEUM, GLASGOW

Silver, 46 mm.
Lit:          *Medallic Illustrations* 50, no. 214.
Description:  obv.  bust of William III, laureate and draped over armour.
                    legend:  GVILIELMVS MAGNVS [William the Great].
              rev.  William, in Roman dress and laureate, leads a dejected-looking female
                    representing Hibernia, with a shield bearing a harp, towards a crowned
                    cornucopia. To the right is an empty armchair and two females. In the
                    middle of the exergue is a crowned shield with the royal arms.
                    legend: REX AUGET REGINA TENET [the King increases, the queen
                    possesses]; in the exergue: GUIL.III.NAS LIB. PAC REST BRITAIN
                    REGI.IMPERII [William III of Nassau, restorer of liberty and peace to
                    Britain, ruler of the Empire] {?}; 1692 either side of the shield.

**243** obv.

**243** rev.

**244** obv.

**244** rev.

The description of William as 'The Great' is an imitation of, and a comment on, Louis XIV's use of the same style.

The reverse appears to show William leading Hibernia to a chair beside Anglia and Scotia, where there will be prosperity, represented by the cornucopia. The exergue legend refers to the fact that William had gone off to Holland, leaving his co-ruler, Mary to look after the British Empire, which was once again united.

### 244 *William's victory in Ireland: 'The Deventer Testimonial'*

MEDAL BY J. LUDER (FL. 1680-1710)

ULSTER MUSEUM, BELFAST; NATIONAL MUSEUM OF IRELAND, DUBLIN

Silver, 47 mm.

Lit:          *Medallic Illustrations*, 48, no. 237.

Description:   obv.  bust of William III draped and in armour.
                     legend: GVILIELMVS MAGNUS [William the Great].
               rev.  William, in Roman armour and costume, holding a standard with a
                     christogram banner, has his hand kissed by a kneeling female, representing
                     Ireland. Behind her is a shield with a harp upon it, to her left a cornucopia
                     spills over and at her feet lies a crown. Behind William stand two females:
                     one wearing a mural crown and leaning on a shield with a spread eagle,
                     represents the city of Deventer; the other is a Genius (? Fame) who holds a
                     laurel wreath in her left hand and with her right places a medallion with
                     'SAL PUBL' [public safety or prosperity] on a column. Three ships can be
                     seen in the far background and also some tiny men carrying a flag up a
                     precipitous slope to the left.
                     legend: HIBERNIA SURGE [Ireland, Arise!]; in exergue:
                     DAVEN.F.F.CVR.LM CI I CLXXXXI. [this represents: Struck at
                     Deventer by the generosity of the Master of the Mint, 1691].
               edge. SPONSOR.  SECVRITAS. PVBLICAE. [Guarantor of public
                     safety].

This medal was struck at the expense of Peter Sluysken, master of the mint at Deventer, and presented to officials of the town. On the obverse the portrait of William is more than usually close to that of Louis XIV, for whom the title of 'Magnus' was commonplace. On the reverse there are a number of references to Roman coinage: the emperor with christogram standard was a common design from the time of Constantine I onwards, to whom there may be direct reference. Designs showing emperors raising female personifications of countries rescued from recent danger are also not unusual. It may be, in view of the legend, that William is in fact raising Hibernia from her prostrate position, the interpretation offered by *Medallic Illustrations*. The alternative, that she is expressing fealty and offering her riches, signified by the cornucopia and crown, may also be accepted. The exact significance of the female with the wreath is hard to decipher, especially as she appears to have a small windmill on her winged helmet. Again, the medallion with 'Sal Publ' is lifted directly from a Roman coin reverse.

### 245 *Hibernia vindicata, oder des britannischen*
*Glücks-Wechsels anderer Theil... Königreich Irrland... auch/was sonst rares und merckwürdiges darinnen zu sehen; und die so wohl vor Alters/als isst geführte Krieges - Geschichte... Hamburg, gedruckt und verlegt durch Thomas von Wiering... 1691*

THE QUEEN'S UNIVERSITY, BELFAST

quarto: [8], 188, [3], 8 pp., 21 plates (of which 1 folding), folding map.

The first sixty-four pages of this book are devoted to a general description of Ireland, but the remainder contains an illustrated account of the war between William and James. A number of the etchings are by P. van den Berge. The volume is extremely rare: this may be the only one in the British Isles.

**246** *Kirby, Richard*

*Catastrophe Galliae, & Hiberniae restitutio, an impartial judgement, denoting the reduction of Ireland, this revolution, 90. (ending March the 10th. 1691)... prophetically deduced from the characters of heaven... London, printed for Tho. Hawkins... 1690*

THE QUEEN'S UNIVERSITY, BELFAST

quarto: 48 pp.
Lit:     Wing K619.

Astrological prediction was still a respectable profession in late seventeenth century England. This pamphlet of 1690, foretelling William's victory from the stars, was correct as to the outcome but more than six months too soon as to the date. The author, despite the usual claims on the title page, was far from impartial. Much of the pamphlet consists of confused astrological disagreement with a Jacobite practitioner, John Gadbury, who had predicted in 1686 that there would be 'an eternal settlement in England of Romanists.' Gadbury was suspected of being implicated in the 1690 plot against William.

# 9. The War at Sea

Though the course of naval events was much less spectacular than that of the war on land with its battles and sieges, the struggle for control of the seas around Ireland and France was vital to the outcome of the war. To intervene in Ireland to any effect, both William and Louis needed to be able to land troops and keep them supplied. The French sent no fewer than eight naval expeditions to Ireland, only one of which was seriously challenged. The battle of Bantry Bay, fought on 1 May 1689, was the greatest naval battle ever fought in Irish waters, despite the fact that no ships were actually sunk or taken on either side. Although the French thus appeared to come and go with impunity, even landing and recovering a substantial force of troops in 1690, they did not even try to disrupt Williamite operations at other vital times. William was able without any interference to relieve Derry by sea and to transport whole armies to Ireland in 1689 and keep them supplied, and these interventions were decisive. Nearer home, the French made little use of their victory off Beachy Head in 1690, and the Anglo-Dutch triumph at La Hogue two years later ended James's hopes of invading England. The fact is that William put more resources into naval operations in Irish waters than Louis was prepared to do and thus ensured his success on land.

Irish waters were fairly thoroughly charted by the end of the seventeenth century, especially by the Dutch: Irish charts are included in Blaeu's *Zeespieghel* (ten or more editions of which were published between 1623 and 1658) and in Van Keulen's *Zee Atlas* (first published in 1683). Early in 1690 a French expedition made detailed surveys of Galway Bay and the Shannon estuary which were included in the first French marine atlas, *Le Neptune François* in 1693. *Great Britain's Coasting Pilot*, published in the same year, contained the surveys of Irish waters carried out by Collins in the 1680s.

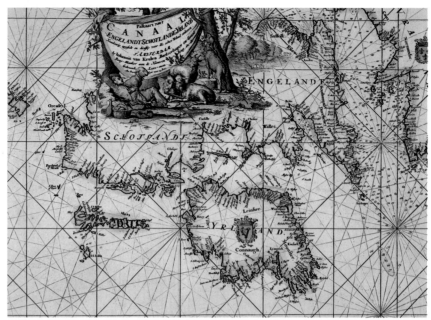

**247**

## 247 *Paskaart van't Canaal Engelandt Schotlandt en Yrland*
*(Chart of Ireland and the north, west and south coasts of Great Britain), 3rd state, c.1754*

JOHANNES VAN KEULEN (1654-1715), FROM *DE NIEUWE GROOTE LICHTENDE ZEE-FAKKEL*
PROFESSOR R.S.J. CLARKE

Line engraving, hand-coloured 50 x 88 cms. Oriented with east at top.

Lit:    C.Koeman, *Atlantes Neerlandici* (Amsterdam, 1970), vol. IV.
R.S.J. Clarke, 'Early printed charts of Irish waters,' *Proceedings of the Belfast Natural History and Philosophical Society*, 2nd ser., vol.10, (Belfast, 1983), p.22.

The *Zee-Fakkel* (Sea Torch), the atlas from which this and the following chart (no.248) come, was first published by van Keulen in 1681, the year after his *Zee Atlas*. Both of these works were very popular and continued to be issued in expanding and revised editions until well into the eighteenth century. The *Zee-Fakkel* contained five charts showing the Irish coastline: (1) a general chart, listed above; (2) a chart of the Irish sea, oriented with west at the top; (3) a chart of the northern part of Ireland with the west coast and islands of Scotland; (4) a chart of the west coast of Ireland; (5) a chart of the south coast (no. 248).

The publisher of the *Zee-Fakkel*, Johannes van Keulen, was the founder of a firm of chart and instrument makers and nautical publishers in Amsterdam that existed for over two hundred years until 1885. From 1693 onwards it incorporated the other well-known Amsterdam nautical publishing firm of Hendrik Doncker.

Sources:    R.V. Tooley, *Tooley's dictionary of mapmakers* (New York and Amsterdam, 1979); Clarke, 'Early printed charts ... ,' as above.

## 248 *Nieuwe Pascaert, vande suyt syde van Yrlandt*
*(Chart of the south and south-west coasts of Ireland from north Kerry to Waterford harbour), 1st state*

JOHANNES VAN KEULEN (1654-1715), FROM *DE NIEUWE GROOTE LICHTENDE ZEE-FAKKEL*
PROFESSOR R.S.J. CLARKE

Line engraving, hand-coloured 50 x 88 cms.

Lit:    Koeman, as above.
Clarke, 'Early printed charts ... ,' as above, p.22, repr. facing p.24.

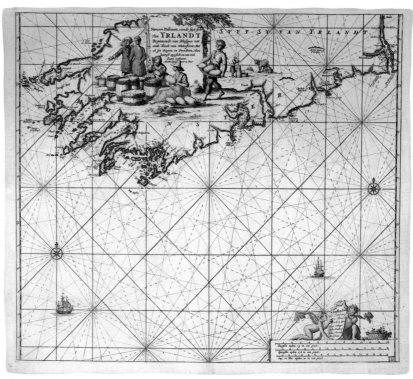

**248**

The title of this chart is charmingly embellished with figures illustrating the production of butter - the main export of Munster through the port of Cork - from milking and churning to packing in tubs.

## **249** *Title page of 'Le Neptune François,' 1693 edition*

JAN VAN VIANEN, ENGRAVER (FL. 1693-1729)
ULSTER MUSEUM, BELFAST

Line engraving on paper, hand-coloured 50.6 x 37 cms.
Purchased 1989.
Lit:     Clarke, 'Early printed charts ...,' as above, p.22.
         R.S.J. Clarke, 'The Irish charts in *Le Neptune François:* their sources and influence,' *The Map Collector,* no. 30 (March 1985), p.10.

*Le Neptune François ou Atlas Nouveau des Cartes Marines* was the first French marine atlas, having been published originally in Paris in 1693. It was not the work of a single cartographer, but was produced under the principal editorship of Charles Pene, with the assistance of a number of other cartographers and surveyors. The atlas contained three charts of the Irish coast, all of which are displayed in this exhibition (nos. 250, 251 and 252). Two of these are based on earlier Dutch charts; that covering Galway Bay and the Shannon estuary can, however, be traced back to two surveys of these waters carried out by the French Ministry of Marine in 1690 (see note on no. 251).

In the same year as the authentic edition of *Le Neptune François*, a pirated edition in Dutch, French and English text versions was issued by Pierre Mortier of Amsterdam jointly with the Parisian bookseller Hubert Jaillot. The chief feature that distinguishes the authentic from the pirated edition is its watermark, which consists of a double-headed swan and the name 'By- colombier,' a reference to the French papermakers Colombier. Other differences, however, occur in the Irish charts, the most notable betrayals of the pirated edition being the absence of the engravers' signatures in the lower left corners of the Galway-Shannon chart (no. 251) and the *Carte Generale..* (no.252), and the misleading insertion in all three titles of the phrase 'Levée et Gravée par ordre du Roy. A Paris 1693.'

A new edition of *Le Neptune François* was published in 1753 by the Dépôt des Cartes et Plans de la Marine. It was virtually unchanged from the original edition except for the introduction of multiple scales of longitude and the addition of an historical preface by the editor Jacques Nicolas Bellin. In 1757

LE NEPTUNE FRANÇOIS

**249**

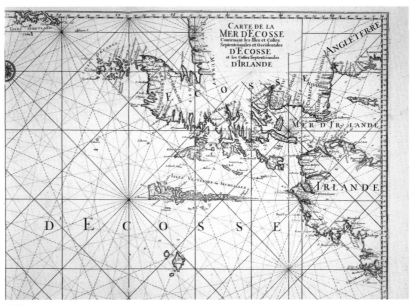

**250**

Bellin produced five new and more accurate charts covering the British Isles. These were of south England, north England, south Scotland, north Scotland and Ireland. All but the north Scotland chart include parts of Ireland. In 1773 there appeared a third edition of the atlas, which for the first time advertised a price: 30 sols. After the Revolution of 1789 a further edition was published in which only the Galway-Shannon chart of the Irish charts appears; other changes in this edition were the raising of the price to 50 sols, and the omission of the *fleur-de-lis* or its replacement by the cap of liberty. A copy of the Galway-Shannon chart has been found with the *fleur-de-lis* scored out, presumably at the time of the Revolution.

Sources:         Clarke, as above.

**250** *Carte De La Mer D'Ecosse Contenant les Isles et Costes Septentrionales et Occidentales D'Ecosse et les Costes Septentrionales D'irlande*
*(Chart of the northern and western coasts and islands of Scotland and the coastline of the northern half of Ireland)*

CHART FROM *LE NEPTUNE FRANÇOIS*, 1693 EDITION
PROFESSOR R.S.J. CLARKE

Line engraving on paper, hand-coloured outlines, 59 x 85 cms. Oriented with east at top.
Lit:     Clarke, 'Early printed charts ...,' as above, p.22.
         Clarke, 'The Irish charts ...,' as above, p. 10.

**251** *Carte Particuliere Des Costes Occidentales D'irlande, Qui comprend la Baye de Galloway Et la Riviere de Lymerick, Comme elles paroissent a basse mer dans les grandes Marees*
*(Chart of the west coast of Ireland from Galway Bay to the Shannon estuary) with inset CARTE DU PORT DE KINSAL EN IRLANDE (Chart of Kinsale harbour)*

CHART FROM *LE NEPTUNE FRANÇOIS*, 1693 EDITION
PROFESSOR R.S.J. CLARKE

Line and stipple engraving, hand-coloured margins and compass points, 59 x 85 cms. Oriented with east at top.
Lit:     Clarke, 'Early printed charts ...,' as above, p.22.
         Clarke, 'The Irish charts ...,' as above, p. 10, repr. p.10.

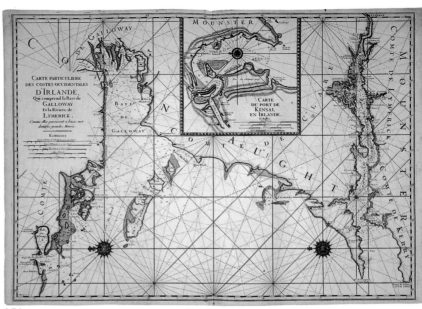

**251**

The origin of this chart can be traced back to two surveys, of Galway Bay and the Shannon estuary, carried out by the French Ministry of Marine in 1690. The manuscript charts resulting from these surveys are now in the Bibliothéque Nationale in Paris. The link between the printed chart and the surveys is most evident on comparison of the areas for which soundings are given in the printed and manuscript charts (there being virtually no soundings given on the printed chart for the coast of Co. Clare between the Aran Islands and Loop head - not surveyed in 1690).

The reason for such detailed surveys of inlets on the west coast of Ireland being carried out at this time by the French must be sought in the context of the continuing war between William of Orange and the deposed James II of England. In the winter of 1689-90 James, having suffered some reverses in Ireland, accepted an offer of French troops in exchange for Irish, and in March 1690 the French general Lauzun landed in Kinsale with 6,000 troops. The purpose of the surveys, which were probably made around the time of this event or not long afterwards, may have been to explore the possibilities of other landings on the west coast, which remained under James's control even after his defeat at the Boyne. The insertion on the printed chart of the inset of Kinsale harbour (albeit with only limited sounding marks) may indicate that some kind of survey of this area was also made, possibly at the time of Lauzun's landing.

The Galway Bay and Shannon estuary surveys influenced post-1690 editions of van Keulen's *Zee-Fakkel* (see nos. 247 and 248) and *The English Pilot;* the *Zee-Fakkel* from 1704, and *The English Pilot* from about 1701 when it was taken over by the firm of Mount and Page, both introduce soundings and other features of the survey charts into their relevant charts.

Source:     Clarke, 'The Irish charts ...,' as above.

## 252 *Carte Generale des Costes D'Irlande, et des Costes Occidentales D'Angleterre avec une Partie de celles D'Ecosse*
*(Chart of the whole Irish coastline, with the west coast of England and south-west coast of Scotland) with inset chart of the estuary of the River Dee to Chester and Holt*

CHART FROM *LE NEPTUNE FRANÇOIS*, 1773 EDITION
PROFESSOR R.S.J. CLARKE

Line engraving, hand-coloured 59 x 85 cms.
Lit:     Clarke, 'Early printed charts ...,' as above, p.22.
        Clarke, 'The Irish charts ...,' as above, p.10, repr. p.10.

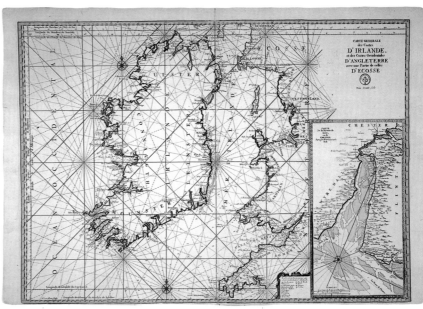

**252**

# 253 *Chart of Dublin Bay, 1687-8*

CAPTAIN GREENVILE COLLINS (FL. 1669-93)
ULSTER MUSEUM, BELFAST

Line and stipple engraving on paper, hand-coloured 45.7 x 57.8 cms.
Inscr:  'To His Grace IAMES Duke of ORMOND &c. This is humbly Dedicated & Presented, by
Capt. G. Collins.'
Purchased 1979
Exh:  Ulster Museum 1982-3.
Lit:  C. Verner, 'Captain Collins' Coasting Pilot,' *Map Collectors' Circle*, no. 58 (1969).
Clarke, 'Early printed charts ...,' as above, p.22.

This chart and the three following (nos. 254, 255 and 256) form part of a survey
of the coasts of Great Britain and Ireland carried out by Captain Collins between
1681 and 1688. The charts in the survey were printed and issued as they were
completed, the Irish charts being produced towards the end of the survey. They
were first published collectively in 1693 (the same year as *Le Neptune François*)
under the title *Great Britain's Coasting Pilot*, which consisted of forty-eight
charts on forty-five sheets. This work was far in advance of any previous attempt
to chart the British coastline, and has the distinction of being the first complete
pilot book of Britain in the English language. It was re-issued nine times from
1723 to 1792, unchanged but for the fact that the chart of Cork Harbour, which
for some reason had been omitted from the 1693 edition, was now included.

The surveyor, Greenvile Collins, was a captain in the Royal Navy who in
the 1670s had gained experience of surveying in the South Seas and the
Mediterranean. In 1681 he was appointed Hydrographer to the King, and was
ordered to survey and chart the coasts and inshore waters of the kingdom. There
is little further firm information about him; however, he may well be the 'Capt.
Collins' mentioned in the key to the inset engraving 'A Prospect of CARRECK-
FERGUS' on the chart of Carreckfergus Lough (no. 254), as being commander
of the yacht *Mary* from which King William III landed at Carrickfergus.

Sources:  *DNB*; R.V. Tooley, *Maps and map-makers* (New York, 1970); R.V. Tooley,
*Tooley's dictionary of mapmakers* (New York and Amsterdam, 1979); Clarke,
'Early printed charts ...,' as above.

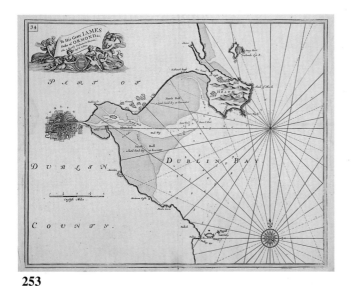

253

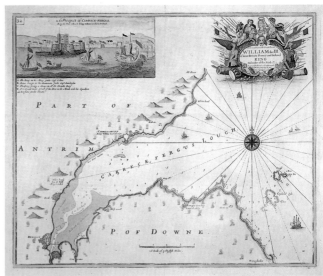

254

## 254 *Chart of 'Carreckfergus' Lough (Belfast Lough) 1687-8*

CAPTAIN GREENVILE COLLINS (FL. 1669-93)
ULSTER MUSEUM, BELFAST

Line and stipple engraving on paper, hand-coloured 44.8 x 54.8 cms.
Inscr:    'To the most Potent and Heroick Prince WILLIAM the III of Great Britain France and
Ireland KING Defender of the Faith &c.  This is most humbly Dedicated and Presented by
Your Majes. most Dutifull and Loyall Subject and Servant Capt. G. Collins.'
The following notes on locations are included: 'CARRECK-FERGUS King Will: Landed 1690';
'White House here K. Will. Army Landed'; 'Bangor Scomberg Landed 1689.'  The locations of
bonfires on the shore are marked.  There is an inset engraving entitled 'A Prospect of CARRECK-
FERGUS,' representing the arrival there of King William III's fleet.
Purchased 1977.
Exh:    Ulster Museum 1982-3.
Lit:    Verner, as above.
Clarke, 'Early printed charts ....,' as above,  p.22,   repr. facing p.28.

## 255 *The Harbour of Cork, 1687-8*

CAPTAIN GREENVILE COLLINS (FL. 1669-93)
ULSTER MUSEUM, BELFAST

Line and stipple engraving on paper, hand-coloured 44.8 x 53.5 cms.
Purchased 1979.
Exh:    Ulster Museum 1982-3.
Lit:    Verner, as above.
Clarke, 'Early printed charts ...,' as above, p.22.

This chart was omitted from the first edition of *Great Britain's Coasting Pilot*,
but does appear in the 1690 edition of John Seller's *The English Pilot*. It was
included in the 1723 and 1744 editions of Collins's *Pilot*, but later a new chart
was produced and introduced into both atlases from 1759 onwards.

Source:    Clarke, as above.

## 256 *Chart of 'Kingsale' Harbour, 1687-8*

CAPTAIN GREENVILE COLLINS (FL. 1669-93)
ULSTER MUSEUM, BELFAST

Line and stipple engraving on paper, hand-coloured 46.5 x 58.5 cms.
Inscr:    'THIS CHART OF KINGSALE HARBOUR is Humbly Dedicated  and Presented To the
Right Honble. Sr. Robert Southwell Knight Vice Admirall of Munster and Principall
Secretary of State for the Kingdom of Ireland. by Capt. Greenvile Collins.'
Purchased 1979

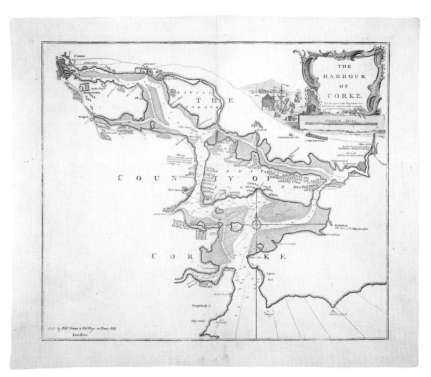

**255**

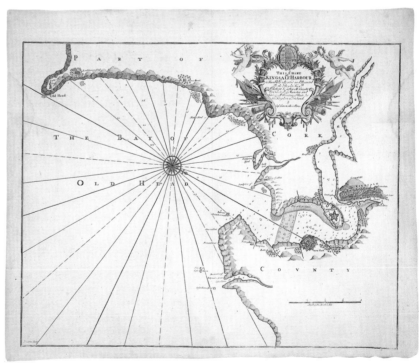

**256**

Exh:    Ulster Museum 1982-3.
Lit:    Verner, as above.
        Clarke, 'Early printed charts ...,' as above, p.22.

## 257 *Rigged model of a Dutch ship of 70-76 guns, c. 1665*

### NATIONAL MARITIME MUSEUM, LONDON

Length 152, breadth 63, height 122.2 cms.
Scale:   1:44 (4 ft to 1 in, Dutch).
Dimensions of ship (taken from model, English measure):
Length on gundeck 151 ft, beam 42 ft.

**257**

1100 tons burden (approx).
Donated by Dr R.C. Anderson in l946.
Exh:    Science Museum, London.
        *Parliament and the Glorious Revolution*, London 1988.

This is a half-size copy of a seventeenth century model, formerly in the
Hohenzollern Museum, Berlin, which was destroyed during World War II.The
original model is believed to have been given to Prince William of Orange by
the Dutch Admiralties in l666. It represented a type of ship built by the
Amsterdam Admiralty and bore the arms of the city and Prince William.

This copy was made in 1923-4 by Captain W. Brandt of the German navy
and was rigged in l925 by Miss B.P. Derrick and Dr R.C. Anderson, from
photographs of the original and contemporary evidence. The model is pierced for
seventy-six guns but probably did not carry more than seventy. The guns are
somewhat too large.

## 258  *The Schip, c. 1689*

DUTCH
CITY OF ABERDEEN DISTRICT COUNCIL, CITY ARTS DEPARTMENT

Length ll6, breadth 58, height 131 cms.
On loan from the Aberdeen Shipmaster Society.
Prov:   Commissioned by Alexander Mackie of the Aberdeen  Shipmaster Society c. l689, and hung
        as a votive model in the Seamen's loft of St. Nicholas's church until l836. Thereafter moved
        to the Shipmaster Society offices, Regent Quay, where it remained until the 1970s.
Exh:    Aberdeen Maritime Museum.
Lit:    Alexander Clark, *A Short History of the Shipmaster Society Or The Seamen's Box of
        Aberdeen* (Aberdeen, l911), repr.

Made in Holland - hence the Dutch title given to it by the Aberdeen Shipmaster
Society - the 'Schip' is a model of a fifth-rate warship of the period. Warships
were rated by the number of guns they could carry, ranging from more than
ninety in a first-rate to fewer than thirty in a sixth rate; a fifth-rate had thirty to
forty. The rate of a ship also determined the pay of its officers.

The model was fully restored in l983-84, preserving eighty per cent of the
original material, and rigged in accordance with its original design. Its history
and associations have made it an important part of Aberdeen's
maritime heritage.

**258**

## 259 *HMS Dartmouth? 1675?*

BY WILLEM VAN DE VELDE THE YOUNGER (1633-1707)
NATIONAL MARITIME MUSEUM, LONDON

Pencil and wash 28.6 x 53.9 cms.

Lit:  Michael Robinson,*Van de Velde Drawings. Catalogue of Drawings in the National
     Maritime Museum made by the Elder and the Younger Willem van de Velde* (Cambridge,
     1958), pp. 89, 164, repr. p. 362, pl. 112.

The ship is probably the *Dartmouth*, a thirty-two gun fifth rate frigate built in
Portsmouth in 1655. The *Dartmouth* was one of a fleet of thirty, commanded by
Major General Percy Kirke, which sailed on 31 May 1689 to relieve Derry. The
sight of the fleet in Lough Foyle during the second week of June caused great
rejoicing in the besieged town, hopes which were soon dashed, however, when
Kirke proceeded to do nothing (probably because he had no pre-arranged plan
and was going to decide on a course of action once he had arrived). He had two
options: to sail straight up the Foyle and smash through the boom (a course he
considered too dangerous because of shore batteries) or to go back down Lough
Foyle, sail around Malin Head and up Lough Swilly to Inch Island, which was a
convenient base for both Derry and Enniskillen. The fact that he had no idea of
the urgency of Derry's plight made his decision all the more difficult. Eventually
he decided to wait in Lough Foyle for reinforcements, using as a reason for his
inactivity the excuse that the town's inhabitants had not notified him of their
condition. A few volunteers went out from the fleet as spies but failed to bring
back worthwhile intelligence.

On 3 July Schomberg wrote sharply to Kirke, pointing out that his excuse
for not taking decisive action was 'no otherways grounded than upon supposition
that it is uncertain whether the Boom and chain that are said to be laid crosse the
River can be broken or the Boates that are reported to be sunck past over'
(Macrory, p. 308). Schomberg ordered Kirke to attempt an attack on the boom;
accordingly, three small provision ships with forty musketeers on each, the
*Phoenix,* the *Jerusalem* and the *Mountjoy*, were set in readiness. (The *Jerusalem*
was held back until a successful passage had been forced). Escorted by the
*Dartmouth* under the command of Captain John Leake , the *Mountjoy* and
*Phoenix* set sail on 28 July.  At Culmore the *Dartmouth* engaged the enemy
batteries and neutralised the fort, while the *Phoenix* and *Mountjoy* sailed past
towards the boom, which the latter broke after the crew of a longboat had
attacked it with axes. The *Mountjoy,* however, ran aground after the collision, to

**259**

the exultation of the Jacobites, who prepared to seize the ship. On firing a salvo at the approaching cavalry (only a pike's length away), the vessel lurched back into deep water and refloated. Led by the *Phoenix*, the *Mountjoy* passed through the broken boom and the two small ships sailed up to Derry, to relieve the starving population.

The Dutch marine painter Willem van de Velde the Younger settled in England c. 1672, and was shortly joined by his father, Willem van de Velde the Elder. Both men, the foremost naval war artists of their day, were appointed painters to Charles II, at a salary of £100 each per year and served as official war artists to the British Navy. Van de Velde the Younger had an enormous influence on British marine painting and was highly prolific; during the course of his career he drew or painted almost every kind of English and Dutch vessel afloat.

Sources:     Rev. P. Dwyer, A.M., ed., *The Siege of Londonderry in 1689* (London 1893; reprinted Wakefield, 1971); P. Macrory, *The Siege of Derry* (London, 1980).

## **260** *HMS Dartmouth: excavated relics*

NATIONAL MUSEUMS OF SCOTLAND, EDINBURGH

The *Dartmouth*, a fifth-rate frigate (i.e., a warship carrying thirty to forty guns), was built by John Tippets at Portsmouth and completed in 1655. She had a keel length of 80 feet (24.4 m) and a burden of 266 tons.

In the summer of 1689, under the command of Captain Leake, *Dartmouth* played a leading part in the relief of Derry. The redoubtable Leake, under the description 'Ye Capt. of ye Dartmouth', was one of the three individuals portrayed on the great tapestry of the Siege forty years later (see no. 159a). In 1690, under the command of Captain Edward Pottinger, *Dartmouth* was sent with two smaller ships to patrol the west coast of Scotland in order to discourage Jacobite activity there and to enforce the authority of the new government. On 9 October, as they sheltered from a storm in the Sound of Mull, *Dartmouth* parted from her anchors and was driven on to a rocky island. She was a total loss: of the 130 or so on board, only six survived. Local tradition attributed the loss of the ship to Jacobite witchcraft; whatever about that, extended patrolling duties had certainly put a heavy strain on the ship and its equipment.

The remains of the ship were rediscovered by amateur divers in 1973 and were excavated over the next two years under the guidance of the Scottish Institute of Marine Studies, in collaboration with the National Museum of Antiquities of Scotland. The excavation was published in a series of articles in the *International Journal of Nautical Archaeology*, starting in 1974. For the ship and its construction, see C.J.M. Martin, 'The *Dartmouth*, a British frigate wrecked off Mull, 1690. 5. The Ship', *IJNA*, vol. 7, no. 1 (1978), pp 29-58.

260 (iii, iv, v, vi, vii, viii)

260 (i)

**(i)** *Ship's bell* (NMS Dartmouth no. 1)

Cast bronze, ht 43 cms, diam. at mouth 37 cms.
Inset.:    DH 1678.
Lit.:    J.R. Adams, *IJNA*, vol. 3 (1974), pp. 269-74.
The DH - for Dartmouth - and the pheon (arrowhead) cast on the bell led
to the identification of the wreck as the *Dartmouth*. The date is that of a
major overhaul of the ship in 1678.

**(ii)** *Rigging block* (NMS no. 2)

Wood, 20.5 x 16 cms.

**(iii)** *Protractor* (NMS no. 5)

Brass, 12 x 7.5 cms.

**(iv)** *Compass case* (NMS no. 6)

Brass, diam. 3.5 cms.

**(v)** *Dividers* (NMS no. 7)

Brass, 10 x 4 cms (closed).

**(vi)** *Dividers* (NMS no. 8)

Brass, 10 x 3 cms (closed).

**(vii)** *Folding rule* (NMS no. 9)

Wood and brass, full length 61 cms (2 feet).

**(viii)** *Folding rule* (NMS no. 10)

Wood, full length 61 cms (2 feet).

**(ix)** *Plum bob* (NMS no. 11)

Lead, ht 8 cms, diam. 6.5 cms.

**260 (x, xi)**

**260 (xvi, xii)**

**(x)    4 Cannonballs** *(NMS no. 12-15)*

Cast iron, diams 7 ins, 4 ins, 3¹/2 ins, 2 ins (20.3, 10.2, 8.9, 5.1 cms).
The largest guns in use on the *Dartmouth* appear to have been demi-culverins, taking shot
of 4.2  or 4 ins diameter. The 3.5 inch shot was for a six-pounder, the 2 inch
shot for a falconet. The 7 inch ball was probably ballast.
P. McBride, *IJNA*, vol. 5 (1976), pp. 189-200.

**(xi)    2 Hand grenades** *(NMS no. 16-17)*

Cast iron, diam. 9 and 7.5 cms.
The larger is intact with its charge; the smaller has its beechwood plug still in place.

**(xii)    Mortar** *(NMS no. 18)*

Cast bronze, ht 8 cms.
It is decorated on both sides with a poorly defined head.

**(xiii)   Ointment pot** *(NMS no. 19)*

Tinglazed ware, ht 4.5 cms.
Three ointment jars like this were recovered from the stern region of the wreck, along
with other utensils and pieces of equipment which may have belonged to the surgeon. The
jar is probably of English make.
R.G. Holman, *IJNA*, vol. 4 (1975), pp. 253-65.

**(xiv)   Flagon** *(NMS no. 20)*

Stoneware, ht 12 cms.
The remains of three small flagons were found on the wreck site.  They are probably
imported Rhenish ware from the kilns at Frechen, near Cologne.
Holman, as above.

**(xv)    Drinking mug** *(NMS no. 21)*

Stoneware, ht 9 cms.
The blue and purple patterned salt glaze on this piece is typical of the products of kilns at
Westerwald in Germany. It is possible that it was part of a set made to commemorate the
coronation of William and Mary in 1689.
Holman, as above.

**(xvi)   'Wine taster'** *(NMS no. 22)*

Pewter, diam. 7.5 cms.
Although silver and pewter vessels such as this are often known as wine-tasters, this one
may have served the ship's surgeon as a bleeding bowl.

**(xvii)  2 Wine bottles** *(NMS no. 23-24)*

Glass, hts 15 cms.

**260 (xiv, xv, xvii, xviii)**

**260 (xix)**

### *(xviii)* Spoon *(NMS no. 25)*

Pewter, length 18.3 cms.

This is a typical late seventeenth century spoon with trefoil end to the stem.

### *(xix)* Brooch *(NMS no. 26)*

Brass, diam. 12 cms.

The brooch is made of a strip of flat metal formed into a circle and riveted together where the pin straddles it. The front is decorated with an interlaced design, the back with three simple cross designs. Such ring brooches were typical of the Highlands of Scotland in the seventeenth century and are thought to have been used, normally by women, to fasten plaids.

### *(xx)* Gun stock *(NMS no. 27)*

Wood, length 36 cms.

Curved, fluted gun stocks like this were made in Scotland in the late seventeenth century. Most of the gunsmiths working in the main burghs probably fashioned stocks conforming to contemporary English and Continental models; this piece, however, was probably the work of a gunsmith based in the Highlands or Islands.

## 261 *The battle of Bantry Bay, 1 May 1689: French and English ships in action during the War of the English Succession*

By Adriaen van Diest (1655-1704)
National Maritime Museum, London

Oil on canvas 94 x 137 cms.

After James landed at Kinsale on 12 March 1689 (OS), the French ships which had conveyed him there returned to Brest, to transport his Irish infantry and cavalry units which had been formed in exile. This second Jacobite convoy set sail on 26 April, under the command of Chateaurenault, and consisted of twenty-four ships of the line, two frigates and six fire-ships. It neared Kinsale on 29 April but, sighting English men-of-war, changed course for Bantry, about forty miles to the west.

Though England and France were not formally at war at this time, there was a *de facto* state of hostilities between them. The English fleet spotted by the French was under the command of Admiral Herbert and was somewhat inferior

253

**261**

in size, consisting of eighteen ships of the line, one frigate and three fire-ships. Herbert, on the trail of the French, judged Kinsale to be their destination. His scouts subsequently ran across them near there and on 30 April located them in Bantry Bay, where they had already succeeded in landing men and stores.

On the morning of 1 May Herbert also put into Bantry Bay and hostilities commenced between the two fleets. The battle raged throughout the afternoon until 5 o'clock, when the two fleets separated, the English withdrawing towards the Scillies, the French going back into Bantry Bay. Cloudisley Shovell, John Leake and George Rooke took part in the action, Leake in particular distinguishing himself by setting fire to the *Diamant* (of fifty-four guns) with a 'cushee-piece', a gun invented by his father. Little real damage was done to the ships of either fleet. The English lost ninety-three men and suffered about two hundred and fifty wounded; the French had forty killed and ninety-three wounded. The results of the engagement were indecisive.

Nevertheless, both sides claimed to have won. The English, however, had failed to prevent the French from landing men and supplies. In France the result was treated as an outright victory. James, when told of the English 'defeat', forgot himself and is said to have exclaimed tartly, 'it is the first time, then' (Simms, p. 69). In England the result was also treated as a victory: Herbert was created Earl of Torrington, two of his captains (Shovell being one) were knighted and each sailor was promised ten shillings. These rewards were partly political, as a gesture of thanks to Herbert for his part in William's expedition to England (he had carried the invitation to William across to Holland), and as an attempt to appease the navy, which had been neglected (it needed to be reorganised and had insufficient ships to stop the French from reinforcing the Jacobites in Ireland).

The picture, which is full of drama and action, shows the English and French fleets in battle. Adriaen van Diest, a Dutch landscape and portrait painter, came to England c. 1673 and was patronised by the Earl of Bath. Among his sitters were General Wade and Lord Carpenter.

Sources: *DNB*; J.G. Simms, *Jacobite Ireland 1685-91* (London, 1969).

**262**

## 262 *Sir George Rooke (1650-1709) (c. 1701-2)*

BY MICHAEL DAHL (1656-1743)
NATIONAL MARITIME MUSEUM, LONDON

Oil on canvas 127 x 101.5 cms.

Lit:   E.H.H. Archibald, *A Preliminary Descriptive Catalogue of Portraits in Oils,* National
       Maritime Museum 1961, p. 118.
       *The Concise Catalogue of Oil Paintings in the National Maritime Museum,* 1988,
       p.142, repr.

George Rooke, son of Sir William Rooke of St Lawrence, Canterbury, entered
the navy as a volunteer during the Dutch wars and subsequently served in the
Mediterranean. In May 1689 he took part in the battle of Bantry Bay and shortly
afterwards accompanied Kirke to the relief of Derry, as commander of the
squadron which carried troops and supplies to the besieged town. In May of the
following year he was promoted to rear-admiral and took part in the battle of
Beachy Head on 30 June following. He played a decisive role in the battle of La
Hogue in May 1692 and received considerable praise for his destruction of part
of the French fleet. The following month King William rewarded him with
a knighthood.

In April 1694 he was appointed one of the lords commissioners of the
admiralty. In 1702, when war broke out once again between England and
France, he commanded an Anglo-Dutch fleet which was sent to take Cadiz but
failed. Fortunately for his reputation he learnt of the arrival of a Franco-Spanish
treasure fleet at Vigo and succeeded in destroying or capturing all the ships.
Although much of the treasure had already been taken ashore, the British were
able to retrieve £1,000,000 (considerably more was probably sunk). He returned
to England in November 1702 in a blaze of glory, the ignominious failure of
Cadiz forgotten. On taking his seat in the House of Commons as MP for
Portsmouth he received the thanks of the House for the success at Vigo and was
nominated to the privy council. In July 1704, in conjunction with Sir Cloudisley
Shovell, he attacked and captured Gibraltar, a key prize which henceforth gave
Britain an important foothold in the Mediterranean. The following month he
engaged the French fleet as it attempted to seize Gibraltar and, after a fierce
battle, forced it to withdraw to Toulon.

263

He received much commendation for these successes and was hailed by the Tories as Marlborough's peer. The Whigs, however, in power at the time and resentful of the comparison with the great duke, exerted political pressure and had him removed from command. He thereupon retired from public life and spent his last years as a Kentish gentleman. He died on 24 January 1709.

Michael Dahl, a Swedish painter, worked in London and Italy before finally settling in London in 1689. He was patronised by the Duke of Somerset, Prince George of Denmark and Princess Anne and, after the latter's accession to the throne in 1702 painted a number of presentation royal portraits. This picture was probably executed between November 1702 and October 1703 and shows Rooke resplendent in a red velvet coat with gold braiding, leaning against a cannon with the fleet in the background. A portrait of him, from Dahl's studio, is in the NPG; another, by Dahl, is in the collection of Lord Brabourne at Mersham Le Hatch.

Sources:      *DNB*; D. Piper, *Catalogue of the Seventeenth Century Portraits in the National Portrait Gallery* (Cambridge, 1963); P. Macrory, *The Siege of Derry* (London, 1980).

## 263  *Sir John Leake (1656-1720)*

BY SIR GODFREY KNELLER (1646-1723)
NATIONAL MARITIME MUSEUM, LONDON

Oil on canvas 127 x 101.5 cms.
Inscr:    'Sr John Leake, Vice Admll of the Blew, by Sir Godfrey Kneller' b.r.
Lit:      E.H.H. Archibald, *A Preliminary Descriptive Catalogue of Portraits in Oils,* National Maritime Museum 1961, pp. 80-81.
          *The Concise Catalogue of Oil Paintings in the National Maritime Museum,* 1988, p. 237, repr.

John Leake, son of Richard Leake, master-gunner of England and storekeeper of the king's ordnance at Woolwich, served with his father on board the *Royal Prince* in 1673 and after a period in the merchant marine was appointed a gunner. In 1688 he was promoted to commander of the *Firedrake.* The following year he took part in the battle of Bantry Bay and using the 'cushee piece,' a kind of howitzer invented by his father, set fire to the French ship *Diamant.* So impressed was Admiral Herbert with his performance that two days later (on 3

May 1689) he placed him in command of the frigate *Dartmouth*, which was to play an important role in the relief of Derry a few months later.

It was largely due to the resourcefulness of Leake and the captains of the *Phoenix* and *Mountjoy* that the boom was finally broken. Leake in particular showed a cool head when the *Dartmouth* came under heavy fire at Culmore fort. A contemporary account reported that he 'behaved himself very bravely and prudently in this action, neither firing great nor small shot though he was plied very hard with both, till he came on the wind of the castle and there beginning to batter, that the victuallers [the *Phoenix* and *Mountjoy*] might pass under shelter of his guns, he lay between the castle and them within musket shot and came to an anchor' (Macrory, p. 310). Kirke himself confirmed that Leake's conduct and courage had been extraordinary.

He subsequently served on the *Oxford* and in May 1690 was appointed to the *Eagle* and took part in the reduction of Cork. He later served at Barfleur (May 1692), where the *Eagle* sustained considerable damage and heavy casualties; 220 men out of a crew of 460 were killed or wounded. In July 1702 he was sent to Newfoundland as governor and commander-in-chief, a post he held for six months. He received a knighthood in 1704. In the same year he took part in the capture of Gibraltar and stayed in the Mediterranean in command of a squadron which defeated a number of Franco-Spanish attempts to re-capture the Rock. During a second tour of the Mediterranean in 1706 he relieved Barcelona and returned to England to a hero's welcome; both Queen Anne and Prince George rewarded him with generous gifts. In 1710 he was appointed chairman of the board of admiralty, a post he held until the queen's death in 1714. He was forced into retirement (the result of political machinations) on the accession of George I.

The portrait shows him standing in front of a rock (presumably Gibraltar), with the fleet in the background. His demeanour and appearance are decidedly dashing and bespeak the daring that made him a successful commander.

Sources:     *DNB*; P. Macrory, *The Siege of Derry* (London, 1980).

## 264  *Sir Cloudisley Shovell (1650-1707)*

By Michael Dahl (1659-1743)
National Maritime Museum, London
Reproduction

Cloudisley Shovell entered the navy at the age of fourteen under the patronage of his countryman and probable relative, Sir Christopher Myngs. On Myngs's death Sir John Narborough, also a countryman and possibly a relative, became his patron. (Patronage was an essential feature of the navy in those days, with promotion depending more upon influential friends than upon personal ability). In 1677 he was appointed captain and between then and 1686 served in the Mediterranean, hunting Barbary pirates. In 1689 he received a knighthood for his services in the battle of Bantry Bay. The following year he was given command of a squadron in the Irish sea and was promoted to rear-admiral. After escorting King William to Carrickfergus in June 1690 he assisted General Kirke in the reduction of Duncannon fort, an importantly-sited garrison of fifty guns commanding Waterford harbour. He played an important part in the battle of Barfleur (La Hogue) of May 1692, breaking through the French line, a manoeuvre which ultimately led to the total defeat of the French fleet.

During the 1690s his role in the navy was one of increasing importance. In 1693 he was vice-admiral under Lord Berkeley in an expedition to Camaret Bay and in 1695 was again second-in-command to Berkeley in the attack on St Malo and Dunkirk. The following year he was promoted to admiral. In 1704 he was sent to the Mediterranean with reinforcements for Sir George Rooke and took part in the capture of Gibraltar. In 1705 he was appointed admiral and commander-in-chief of operations off Portugal and Spain. Two years later he helped annihilate the French Mediterranean fleet in an engagement off Toulon. On the return voyage to England most of his fleet was wrecked off the Scilly Isles. He himself was washed ashore, barely alive, and was found by a woman who, coveting his emerald ring, buried him alive in the sand. (She confessed to the deed thirty years later and the ring was returned to his family. His body was thereupon exhumed and subsequently interred in Westminster Abbey at the government's expense).

**264**

A full-length portrait by Dahl is in the NPG. This three-quarter length picture was probably painted not earlier than 1696, with a possible dating of 1702-8, during which time Dahl painted a number of admirals. The portrait is a fine example of his work. Shovell's face, with its stern no-nonsense expression, is full of character and his costume, with its delicately-executed gold braid, is painted with considerable skill. The flags on the ship in the background have probably been repainted; that on the main is white and the ensign is red, which is an incorrect conjunction.

Sources:     *DNB*; E. Waterhouse, *Painting in Britain 1530-1790* (London, 1953); D. Piper, *Catalogue of the Seventeenth Century Portraits in the National Portrait Gallery* (Cambridge, 1963).

## 265 *The battle of La Hogue, 23 May 1692*

BY ADRIAEN VAN DIEST (1655-1704)
NATIONAL MARITIME MUSEUM, LONDON

Oil on canvas 90 x 112 cms.
Inscr:   'A. Diest f.'

The battle of La Hogue was the culmination of the battle of Barfleur of 19 May 1692, when a French fleet of forty-four ships commanded by Admiral Tourville was defeated by an Anglo-Dutch fleet of eighty-eight ships, under the command of Admiral William Russell. In the action Sir Cloudisley Shovell, as rear-admiral, played a leading part. After the battle three French ships, including the *Soleil Royal* (the pride of the French navy), took refuge at Cherbourg, where they were destroyed by English fire-ships.

Another thirteen French ships took shelter in the bay of La Hogue. They too were destroyed by the English a few days later, in an action led by Vice-Admiral Sir George Rooke. (Shovell, to whom the task would have fallen as junior admiral of the fleet, was indisposed). James II, Tourville and a number of French officers watched this latter action from nearby cliff tops. James did nothing to endear himself to the French when, in an outburst of patriotic fervour, he exclaimed 'Ah mes bons Anglais!' (van der Zee, p. 362).

265

The painting shows the French ships engulfed in flames in the shallows of La Hogue. The dark plumes of smoke and the glowing fires on the vessels lend an atmosphere of drama and tension to the picture.

Sources:     *DNB*; *Chambers's Encyclopaedia*; H. and B. van der Zee, *William and Mary* (London, 1973).

### 266 *Canailje't Canael uyt*
*(Sweeping the scum from the Channel)*

<small>BY AN UNKNOWN ARTIST
ATLAS VAN STOLK, ROTTERDAM</small>

Print with contemporary colouring 51 x 30.5 cms; Dutch text.

The print celebrates the overwhelming victory of the Anglo-Dutch fleet over the French at Barfleur and La Hogue, 29 May - 1 June 1692, which ended French plans to invade England. A terrified French officer is shown begging a Dutch rating to accept his sword in surrender; another is about to be slaughtered. In the background French ships are shown burning and sinking. The democratic tone of the print is remarkable.

### 267 *Battle of La Hogue, 1692*

<small>MEDAL BY J. BOSKAM (FL. C.1680-1710)
HUNTERIAN MUSEUM, GLASGOW</small>

267 (obv.)

267 (rev.)

Silver, 55 mm.
Lit:            *Medallic Illustrations*, 53-54, no. 248.
Description:    obv. bust of William III, draped over armour.
      legend: GVILIELMVS . III. D.G. MAG. BRITT.FR.ET.HIB.REX.F.G.
      [William III, by grace of God king of Great Britain, France and Ireland and
      Defender of the Faith - it is assumed that the final 'G' is a mistake for 'D'].
    rev. a unicorn and a lion, crouching over a trident, chase a cock. In the
      background is a naval battle scene, with clouds of smoke.
      legend: IMPERIVM . PELAGI . NOBIS [to us belongs command of the
      maritime world]; in exergue: INCENSA.GALL.CLASSE
      ANG.ET.BAT.VICTORES MDCXCII [the French fleet burnt, the English
      and Dutch victorious].

**266**

**268** (obv.)

**268** (rev.)

## 268 *Battle of La Hogue, 1692*

MEDAL BY J. SMELZING (FL. 1685, D.1695)
HUNTERIAN MUSEUM, GLASGOW

Silver, 56 mm.

Lit:                *Medallic Illustrations*, 53, no. 247.

Description:    obv.  conjoined busts of William and Mary, he in armour and laureate, both
                              draped.
                              legend: GUL:ET MARIA D.G.  M.BRIT:FR:ET HIB:REX ET REGINA.
                              [William and Mary, by grace of God king and queen of Great Britain,
                              France and Ireland].

                     rev.  three large warships fighting, with clouds of smoke billowing from the
                              guns, others in the background. In the foreground two ships are sinking,
                              with heads and a rowing boat visible in the sea.
                              legend: ASSERTA MARIS IMPERII GLORIA [the glory of the ruler of
                              the sea asserted]; in exergue: GALLORUM CLASSE DELETA D.XIX,
                              XXIX MAJI MDCXCII [the French fleet destroyed, 19/29 May 1692].

During the reign of Louis XIV France attempted to claim dominion of the seas,
which was particularly galling to the successful maritime tradition of the Dutch.
The battle of La Hogue was a turning point: it lasted six days, during which
French naval power was devastated by a combination of the English and Dutch
fleets. *Medallic Illustrations* lists twenty-six different medals associated with the
action, which gives some idea of the importance placed upon the victory.

The date is given in both old and new style.

# 10. Peace in Ireland and Europe

With the defeat of the Jacobites, many Protestants who had fled from Ireland returned to share the spoils of victory. All the acts of the Jacobite parliament were repudiated, and the corporations were restored to their former state with Protestants (including, until 1704, some Presbyterians) in control. The substantial rewards given by William to those who had conquered the country will be mentioned later; some of the gifts he made to those who had done him personal service still survive, unlike the over-numerous trees to which he reputedly tied his horse in 1690.

With Ireland under control he was at last able to give his full attention to the war in the Low Countries. Not that things went well at first, for William was not a great general. The allied armies under his command in 1692 lost the great fortress of Namur and suffered heavily at the battle of Steenkirk; in the following year Landen (where Sarsfield too met his end) was another costly defeat. The death or retirement of Louis's best generals altered matters, however, and in 1695 William achieved the triumph of his military career by recapturing Namur. By then the French were becoming as weary as the English and Dutch.

The death of Queen Mary at the close of 1694 struck William very hard. It also reawakened the hopes of James and his supporters. The discovery early in 1696 of a plot to assassinate William and invade England from France caused a wave of support for him and dashed James's hopes for the last time. By 1697 Louis was glad to make peace. In the treaty of Rijswijk in September of that year he even recognised William as king by the grace of God and promised not to assist James any longer. When the nine years' war thus came to an end, William had become the leading statesman of Europe and the equal of Louis XIV.

**270**

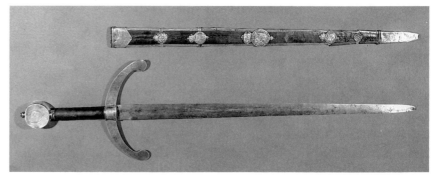

**271**

## 269 *Royal charter of William III*
### *to the Corporation of Drogheda, 1697*

CORPORATION OF DROGHEDA

Parchment; in English; portrait of monarch.

Dated 22 March 1697, the charter replaced that of James II (1687), which had been revoked after William's victory at the Boyne.

## 270 *Mace of the town of Drogheda, 1699-1700*

BY THOMAS BOLTON, DUBLIN
DROGHEDA CORPORATION

Silver, length 161.5 cms.

The mace consists of seven detachable parts mounted on a wooden core. It is decorated in repoussé and chasing on the shaft, with floral and foliate motifs. Around the head are a crowned rose, thistle, *fleur-de-lis* and harp, each of them between the letters WR and within laurel wreaths linked by foliate female busts. Above, on the cap, is the royal arms of William III.

The present mace and sword (no. 271), together with a halberd, were presented to the Corporation of Drogheda by William III; earlier regalia had apparently been melted down by the Jacobite corporation to assist James II's cause. According to D'Alton's *History of Drogheda* (1844), William also gave the corporation two Jacobite kettle-drums found on the field of the Boyne, 'painted in lively colours with the royal arms of the doomed monarch, and his titles. They were beat for him at the battle, and, by the deep stains in the parchment, the drummer appears to have only resigned them with his life ...' They were exhibited in the old Tholsel, but when D'Alton was writing had 'very recently disappeared'.

## 271 *Sword and scabbard of the town of Drogheda*

DROGHEDA CORPORATION

Sword, length 109 cms; scabbard, length 83.5 cms.

The sword has a silver-gilt hilt and pommel. The hilt is C-shaped, flat and broadened and rounded at the terminals and engraved with foliate sprays and spirals, with stars at the centre. The pommel is in the form of a closed cylinder, and is engraved with a crescent and star.

The scabbard is leather, with silver-gilt mounts along the edges, at the top and at the tip and has five silver-gilt plaques, two of which represent the royal arms, two a rose crowned, and one a rose.

272

Photo Pieterse-Davison International, Dublin

## 272 *Great chain and medal of the Lord Mayor of Dublin*

DUBLIN CORPORATION

Gold, circumference 200 cms.
Given to the City of Dublin by William III in 1698.

The chain, the maker of which is unknown, is formed of a linked pattern of
twelve roses, representing the Tudor rose; twelve trefoil knots and two harps,
symbolising Ireland; and twenty-six S-hooks with animal-head terminals. The
chain is divided into halves by two portcullises diametrically placed.

The medal, by James Roettier, pendant from one of the portcullises, has on
the obverse (which is very worn) a bust of William III armoured and draped to
right, with the inscription GVLIELMVS TERTIVS D.G. MAG. BRIT. FRANC.
ET HIB. REX (William III by grace of God king of Great Britain, France and
Ireland). Originally on the reverse, but now totally rubbed, is the inscription
'GVIELMVS III ANTIQVAM ET FIDELEM HIBERNIAE METROPOLIN
HOC INDVLGENTIAE SVAE MVNERE ORNAVIT. BARTH VAN
HOMRIGH ARM. VRB. PRAETORE MDCXCVIII (William III decorated the
ancient and loyal Metropolis of Ireland with this memorial of his favour,
Bartholomew Van Homrigh, Esq., being Lord Mayor 1698).

## 273 *Copper gilt version of the gold medal on Lord Mayor of Dublin's chain*

MEDAL BY JAMES ROETTIER (1663-98)
ULSTER MUSEUM, BELFAST

Copper gilt, 84 mm.
Lit:        *Medallic Illustrations,* 197, no. 509.
Description:  obv.  Bust of William III, draped over armour, with hair flowing round to his
            breast.
            legend: GVIELMVS.TERTIVS.D.G. MAG.BRIT.FRANC.ET.HIB.REX.
            [William the Third by grace of God king of Great Britain, France and
            Ireland].
        rev.  legend: GVLIELMVS III ANTIQVAM ET FIDELEM HIBERNIAE
            METROPOLIN HOC INDVLGENTIAS SVAE MVNERE ORNAVIT.
            BARTH VAN HOMRIGH ARM. VRB. PRAETORE. MDCXCVIII.
            [William III decorated the ancient and loyal Metropolis of Ireland with
            this memorial of his favour, Bartholomew Van Homrigh, Esq., being Lord
            Mayor 1698].

263

This is a huge medal to have been produced by the die-struck process. Since a number of examples are known, there must have been some intention to have it act as a propaganda piece, as well as hanging from the mayoral chain as an example and an explanation of William's munificence. The cost of preparing the dies must have been substantial, and a one-off medal of similar type could have been made by several other methods.

A previous mayor of Dublin, a Jacobite, had fled with the city regalia. Van Homrigh was a Dutchman who had settled in Dublin in Charles II's reign. He was one of the Protestant aldermen of the city named in James II's charter of 1687. William appointed him Commissary General of Provisions, always a profitable post: he left a considerable fortune when he died in 1703. Swift's friend Vanessa was his daughter.

The following decanter, bowl and two pairs of gauntlets, all belonging to King William and associated with the Boyne campaign, were presented by the king to Sir John Dillon of Lismullen, Co. Meath on the morning of 3 July l690 (0S), two days after the battle of the Boyne. According to family tradition, King William slept at Lismullen on the night of 2 July and presented the family with these articles and a bed coverlet (not exhibited here). William often gave personal belongings as tokens of appreciation for services rendered; his gift to the Dillons was in keeping with his established practice. All five articles were donated to the NMI by Miss Millicent Dillon, a descendant of Sir John Dillon. For a detailed account see Catriona MacLeod, 'Some Hitherto Unrecorded Momentoes of William III, (l650-1702), Prince of Orange and King of England from Lismullen, Navan, Co. Meath,' *Studies* (Summer l976), from which the following entries are drawn.

## 274 *Decanter, c. 1689-90*

ENGLISH, WHEEL-ENGRAVED
COLLECTION THE NATIONAL MUSEUM OF IRELAND, DUBLIN

Height 26.5 cms.
Lit:     MacLeod as above, repr. p. 129.

The decanter is of heavy rather white flint-glass metal, containing some large and small bubbles. The body is globular; the tapered neck has a wide flat string-ring and clipped C-handle with thumb-rest in high relief and curled-up end. The bottom has a high kick-up with sharp pontil mark. The piece is wheel-engraved with a number of patterns above a heavily gadrooned base.

On the neck, among foliate stems with single roses and a large tulip, stands a bird with spread wings having long feathers and a leafed spray in its beak. Below, the main design consists of a square shield bearing the arms of William III as King of England.  To the right of the handle are grouped war trophies: a field gun, round shot, powder kegs, a drum, battle-mace, torches for ignition and arrows. To the left of the handle is a further group of trophies, consisting of two saddle-pouches, two partially unfurled banners, two pennants bearing a saltire cross, battle-mace, pistol, blunderbuss and sword. Below the handle, a scale representing justice is tied by a bow-knot.

The main patterns appear to have been taken from copperplate prints or from glass articles engraved with similar subjects by skilled craftsmen. War trophies of the type on the decanter, which represented victories by the house of Nassau, are not unusual and occur frequently in contemporary prints and in other media.  Likewise an eagle holding in its beak an olive branch, representing Peace in Victory, occurs on a number of William III medals.

The overall design on the decanter is balanced and the drawing of the birds and foliage is free. Many details, such as the pearled arches and the *fleurs-de-lis* on the royal crown, the Irish harp on the shield of arms and the curves of the cannon wheels and of the powder kegs in the trophies, are weak in execution and the lettering is inexpert. While the sturdy flint glass metal and the contemporary shaft-and-globe form with gadrooned base suggest that the piece was London made, the quality of the engraving does not match that of the glass and appears to have been executed by an inexperienced craftsman or by one working in an

274

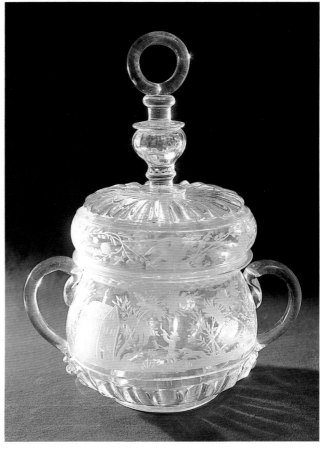

275

unfamiliar technique. The decanter represents a strong functional vessel which, while bearing the appropriate royal emblems, could, if broken, be easily replaced. Both the decanter and posset bowl are important first-hand evidence of the type of glassware provided for the royal table during a military campaign.

## 275 *Posset bowl and cover, c. 1689-90*

PROBABLY GERMAN, WHEEL-ENGRAVED
COLLECTION THE NATIONAL MUSEUM OF IRELAND, DUBLIN

Height 21 cms.
Lit:    MacLeod as above, repr. pp. 131, 132.

The bowl is of heavy white flint-glass metal, containing some splashes and both large and small bubbles and with the engraved bands on bowl and cover having a larger lead content than the gadrooned portions and the ring-knob. The bowl is flattened globular with an everted rim, gadrooned base and an applied foot ring. Underneath, there is a high kick-up with a sharp pontil mark and at the sides are C-handles with pinched and curled-up ends.

The bowl is engraved below the rim with a stylized leaf border and with, on one side, trees having both heavy palm-like and light pinnade leaves. Beside the trees is a high-gabled house with smoke plumes from the chimneys and diamond-paned windows. A countryman, in wide-brimmed hat, long belted coat, a rake in his right hand and a hunting horn held to his mouth with his left hand, approaches the house, followed by a hunting dog. Behind there is a stag being chased by a second dog. In the foreground are clumps of sedge-like plants.

The second side of the bowl is engraved with a basket of apples, pears, a large melon-like fruit and trailing clusters of vine with, on top, a bird pecking an olive branch. Below on either side are tulips and billing doves. The cover is flattened dome-shape with gadrooned top and with an elaborate grip consisting of a thick ring on a moulded hollow pear-shaped knop having a prominent pontil mark on the underside. At the base of the lid is a heavy applied ring, slanted

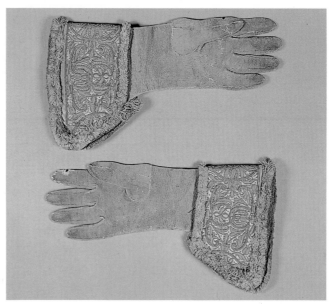

**276**

inwards in order to fit easily into the rim of the bowl. The engraved band depicts undulated foliate stems with drooping bell-flowers and many-petalled daisy-like flowers having cross-hatched centres and with fruited sprays and long-tailed birds.

The curved shape of the bowl does not conform with that of the contemporary English posset bowl, which was cylindrical in outline, and, while it had a stout ring-grip this did not surmount a high and elaborate stem but was usually attached to the lid by a low and simple arrangement. Neither is it Netherlandish in origin. While some of the motifs, such as the cross-hatched flowers and fruited sprays might wishfully be interpreted as sun-flowers and oranges - emblems associated with the Netherlands - these were part of the general contemporary repertoire and occur on late seventeenth century German glassware. The main pattern on one side of the bowl, that depicting the high-gabled house, the man, the hunting dogs and clumps of sedges, is also to be found on south German glass. It would seem therefore that the bowl is probably of German origin. Although the bowl itself is of stout structure and well designed, the engraving on it is weak and shallow and appears to have been executed by a less skilled craftsman who borrowed portions from the pattern of a master German engraver.

Posset, a preparation made by curdling boiled milk with some acidulous liquor such as white wine or old ale, was usually taken at bedtime and was considered beneficial for colds and coughs.

## 276 *Gauntlets, c. 1689-90*

PROBABLY NETHERLANDS
NATIONAL MUSEUM OF IRELAND, DUBLIN

Length 35 cms, greatest width 10.2 cms.
Lit:      MacLeod as above, repr. p. 136.

Made of buckskin, with the smooth surface on the inside. The glove and cuff are in one piece. The original fine overcast seaming has been largely replaced by coarse overcast stitches on the outside. The thumb has a centre front seam. The cuff is of lime-green satin, mounted on canvas, interlined with paper and lined with lime-green silk. The embroidered pattern consists of stylized tulips and petalled flowers within compartments, executed with lime-green silk thread in couched cord, satin stitch and French knots. The cuff is trimmed with fringes of lime-green silk.

While the gauntlets are of medium size, they are relatively narrow and due to the soft leather and a fair amount of wear, they have partially retained the shape of the hand. The undersides of the fingers are soiled and rubbed and the upper sides, especially of the first two fingers of the right gauntlet, retain deep creases

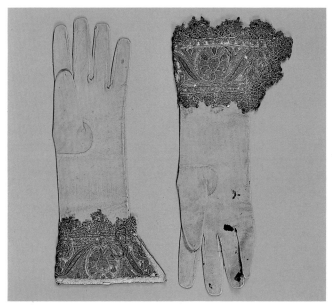

**277**

which appear to have been caused by pressure, possibly that of a rein. On the same gauntlet the small finger is so curved inwards as to suggest that the finger itself was bent. There are splashes of dark ink on the upper part of the thumb, first finger and cuff of the right gauntlet. This suggests that documents may have been signed with a gloved hand.

## 277 *Gauntlets, c. 1689-90*

PROBABLY NETHERLANDS
NATIONAL MUSEUM OF IRELAND, DUBLIN

Length 35.4 cms, greatest width 9.8 cms.
Lit:     MacLeod as above, repr. p. 136.

Made of doeskin, with the smooth surface on the inside, which is stained yellow from cuff edge down as far as the thumb. The glove and cuff are in one piece, with seams on the inside except for the thumb, which is attached by overcast stitches. The cuff is mounted on canvas and lined with cream silk. The embroidered pattern consists of stylized foliage and petalled flowers, having a heart in the centre, and is executed with gold and silver thread in raised work, couched cord, pearl-purl and spangles. The cuff is bordered with gilt-metal pillow-lace having a picot edge, trimmed with spangles, many of which are missing.

    The cream silk lining of both cuffs is mostly worn away. The gold lace border of the right cuff is lacking. The left-hand glove shows more wear than the right and there are large splashes of ink on the upper parts of the third and fourth fingers and on the third finger and palm of the left hand. The gold and silver threads consist of flat strips wound around a silk thread core.

## 278 *Ostrich egg cup, 1694-5*

BY THOMAS BOLTON, DUBLIN
NATIONAL MUSEUM OF IRELAND, DUBLIN (27-1955)

Height 24.5 cms.
Exh:     *The Company of Goldsmiths of Dublin 1637-1987*, NMI l987 (II), repr. p. 9; UM April-
         June l989.

Ostrich egg-shell bowl with silver-mounted rim and base and four vertical silver straps; silver stem, foot and lid, decorated with engraving and gadrooning. The lid is engraved with a forearm vested, holding a garland; this crest has not been identified.  Stamped under the foot with the maker's mark TB (Thomas Bolton) twice and with the harp crowned; also stamped on the lid with the maker's mark, the harp crowned and the date letter K for l694-5.

    Thomas Bolton was Lord Mayor of Dublin l716-17.

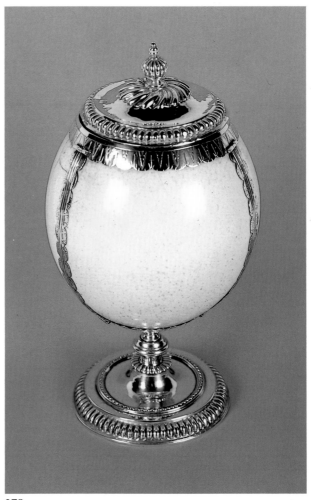

**278**

## 279 *Coconut cup*

LATE SEVENTEENTH OR EARLY EIGHTEENTH CENTURY; NO HALLMARKS
ULSTER MUSEUM, BELFAST

Coconut shell, silver mounted, height 10.8 cms. Engraved (later) with the crest of Hamilton incorporating a ducal coronet.
Bequeathed by Miss Ella Hamilton, per M.Sinclair and W.L.H.Roden 1947.

The coconut is mounted on a mounded silver pedestal foot and has a scalloped rim and three wavy ribs joining it to the foot. Coconut cups first gained popularity in the fifteenth century, when the extreme rarity and exotic nature of the shell, combined with their ideal shape for use as a cup and the fine patina which could be obtained from polishing, made them highly prized.

## 280 *Toilet casket, 1696*

BY JOHN HUMPHREYS, DUBLIN
ULSTER MUSEUM, BELFAST

Silver, height 10.5 cms, excluding feet, length 28.1 cms, width 20.3 cms, hallmarks on base and inside cover.
Inscr:'JAY SE RVY ET OB TENV' (J'ai servi et obtenu).
Purchased London 1958.

The rectangular casket has a gadrooned base and a hinged three-band stepped lid, with gadrooning at each level. The four bewigged masked feet may have been added later. The lid is engraved with contemporary armorials beneath a scrolling foliate mantling.The arms are those of Thompson impaling Wilmot and it is probable that they commemorate a marriage. The box would have formed part of a larger toilet set.

280

281

The toilet service did not become fashionable in England until after the Restoration, when the most important sets were either imported from France or richly decorated in the French manner. The toilet sets produced for the Stuart court were flamboyantly ornate, often depicting figures or whole mythological scenes.

The toilet set was generally a marriage gift and became the most important means of establishing the standing of the lady of the house. Gentlemen's toilet plate was primarily functional, consisting of shaving implements and candlesticks. By contrast, the lady's toilet set became increasingly diverse to cater for the complex cosmetic preparations which became fashionable in the early eighteenth century. The component parts of the toilet set varied but in general they consisted of a mirror, various rectangular, octagonal or oval caskets, candlesticks, a basin, a ewer and assorted brushes and bottles.

By the mid seventeenth century it had become fashionable for the nobility to receive particularly favoured friends and associates in the staged intimacy of their bedrooms and dressing rooms. These rooms fulfilled a formal purpose and so the ostentatious arrangement of an elaborate toilet set made a very direct reference to the wealth and standing of the owner. In addition to this formal function , the toilet set served so intimate a role in the daily life of its user that its fine form and elegantly wrought detail was intended to be examined and enjoyed during frequent use.

### 281 *Two handled cup and lid, 1696-8*

BY JOSEPH WALKER, DUBLIN
NATIONAL MUSEUM OF IRELAND, DUBLIN (5-1948)

Silver, height (overall) 27 cms.
Exh:  *The Company of Goldsmiths of Dublin 1637-1987*, NMI 1987 (12), repr. p. 10; UM
April-June 1989.

The U shaped body widens upwards and has a slightly everted rim, a spreading foot and horizontal strengthening band. It is decorated with repoussé and chasing with acanthus and palm leaves around the body and with acanthus leaves on the lid. The finial is in the form of an acanthus bud. The cup is stamped under the body and inside the lid with the maker's mark IW (Joseph Walker), the harp crowned and the date letter L for 1696-8.

### 282 *Funeral procession of Queen Mary II, 1695*

BY ROMEYN DE HOOGHE (1645-1708)
ULSTER MUSEUM, BELFAST

Sequence of six prints;combined size 39 x 118 cms (sheet size).

These six prints, forming a continuous display which (left to right) starts with the head of the funeral procession entering Westminster Abbey and ends with its tail

269

**282 (detail)**

leaving Whitehall, were published in Amsterdam in 1695 by Peter Persoy in a volume, with Dutch text by Samuel Gruterus, entitled *Lyk - Reden op de ontijdige Dood ... van ...Maria de II* (Untimely death of Mary II). Below each section, except the last, is a key to the people depicted, including a number of individuals; above, lively scenes of gun salutes and military parades.

The occasion, which was an extremely elaborate piece of ceremonial, was organised by the Duke of Norfolk and designed by Sir Christopher Wren (who appears in the procession). Wooden walkways, covered with black cloth and bordered on both sides by black hangings, were erected all the way from the Banqueting House at Whitehall (where the queen's body lay in state) to the Abbey.

William gave mourning cloaks to all the members of Parliament, which was in session at the time and which continued its existence, despite the death of a sovereign, because William and Mary were joint rulers and William's reign went on. Some time after these elaborate obsequies, Mary's request for a simple funeral was found among her papers, too late. It might have been ignored in any case, for the grief at her death was universal and genuine and probably demanded public expression. By contrast, William died in 1702 unlamented and was buried without ceremony.

# 283 *Death of Mary*

MEDAL BY R. ARONDEAUX (FL. 1678-1702)
HUNTERIAN MUSEUM, GLASGOW

Silver, 49 mm.

Lit:       *Medallic Illustrations* 108-9, no. 338.

Description:  obv.  bust of Mary, draped with a mantle over her dress, a pearl tiara in her hair. legend: MARIA D. G. MAG. BRIT. FRANC. ET HIB. REGINA [Mary by grace of God queen of Great Britain, France and Ireland].

              rev.  Mary, hands clasped, lying in a bed under an elaborate canopy. William half sits at the end of the bed, a bishop and two nobles kneeling in front of him. Two other men are visible behind, one weeping. A crowned royal arms imposed on crossed sceptres is under the canopy. legend, in exergue: POPULIS LIBERTATIS EREPTA OBIIT VII IAN MDCXCV [she died 7 January 1695, snatched from a freed people].

The bust was used by Arondeaux on a celebratory medal issued in 1693. On the reverse the Queen is shown lying in state. Her status as sovereign in her own right is emphasised by the obverse legend. The reverse indicates the genuine sorrow which her death induced.

# 284a *Plot to assassinate William III, 1696*

MEDAL BY I. BOSKAM (FL. LATE SEVENTEENTH AND EARLY EIGHTEENTH CENTURIES)
HUNTERIAN MUSEUM, GLASGOW

Silver, 58 mm.

Lit:       *Medallic Illustrations,* 150-51, no. 413.

Description:  obv.  bust of William, draped and laureate, holding a shield which covers his chest.

**284 a** (obv.)

**284 a** (rev.)

**284 b** (obv.)

**284 b** (rev.)

legend: WILHELMVS.III.D.G.MAG.BRIT. FRANC.ET.HIB.REX
[William III, by grace of God king of Great Britain, France and Ireland -
the 'X' disappears behind the shield]; on the shield, around the top:
NON.LAEDITVR.QVEM.TEGO [he is not injured, whom I cover]; in the
middle of the shield the Hebrew letters for 'Jehovah'.

rev. six bare-breasted females dancing in a circle, holding snakes and burning
torches or daggers. All are blindfolded. Cords come down from a cloud to
form nooses around their necks. They are against a background of trees
and foliage.
legend, above: DEXTRA.LATENS.COERCET. [a hidden right hand
restrains them]; in exergue: MDCXCVI [1696].

Sir George Barclay led a conspiracy to assassinate William which was
eventually discovered and a day of public thanksgiving declared. The obverse
suggests that William was under the direct protection of God. On the reverse, the
dissolute females, who may be Maenads in frenzy, represent the conspirators
being restrained by a heavenly force which they cannot see. Barclay and his
fellow conspirators were close to making their attempt several times but
circumstances always intervened to prevent them.

## 284b *Plot to assassinate William III, 1696*

MEDAL BY ANON
HUNTERIAN MUSEUM, GLASGOW

Silver, 43 mm.
Lit:            *Medallic Illustrations*, 151-52, no.44.
Description:    obv. conjoined busts of Louis XIV in front of James II.
                     legend: HERODES ATQVE PILATVS. [Herod and Pilate]; in exergue:
                     ACTOR.IV.26 [Acts, chapter 4, verse 26].

                rev. inside a nettled enclosure James II, wearing armour and a cloak, holding
                     up a sword, holds up a bag marked 'CM PISTO' (100,000 Pistols] with
                     Louis XIV, who is similarly dressed. To their left Father Petre holds up a
                     pyx. In the left foreground young Prince James rides backwards on a
                     lobster. Behind them are trees and a number of armed men running
                     around, with the figure '40' shown several times. Beyond this again is the
                     sea with a large fleet.
                     legend: IRRITA CONSPIRATION. [the ineffectual conspiracy]; on
                     ground line: GENESIS.XLIX.5.6 [Genesis chapter 49, verses 5 and 6]; in
                     exergue: ADVERS GVILIELMVM.III ANGLIAE REGEM
                     3.MART.1696. [against William III, king of England, 3 March 1696].

The obverse reference is to the killing of Christ by an alliance of Pilate and
Herod. The quotation from Acts is, 'The kings of the earth stood up, and the
rulers gathered together against the Lord, and against his Christ.' The reverse is
packed, both in design and symbolism. Father Petre is giving his blessing to the
plot, which was heavily backed with French cash. The '40' refers to the
supposed number of the conspirators, and the ships are the French fleet lying
offshore ready to invade. The lobster is used as a symbol for the Jesuits. St
Francis Loyola is said to have dropped his bible on the shore and it was brought
back to him by a lobster. The quotations from Genesis are: 'Simeon and Levi
are brethren: instruments of cruelty are in their habitations' (verse 5) and 'O my
soul, come not thou into their secret; unto their assembly, mine honour, be thou
not united: for in their anger they slew a man, and in their self-will they digged
down a wall' (verse 6).

## 285 *An Impartial account of the*
*horrid and detestable conspiracy to assassinate His Sacred*
*Majesty King William raise a rebellion in England Scotland and*
*Ireland, and to encourage an invasion from France. London,*
*printed for John Salusbury... 1696*

THE QUEEN'S UNIVERSITY, BELFAST

quarto: 38, [2] pp.
Lit:      Wing 170.

**286** (obv.)

**286** (rev.)

## 286 *Namur captured by the French, 1692*

MEDAL BY ? J. SOUBIRAN (FL. 1680-92)
PHOTOGRAPH

Silver, 72 mm.

Description:  obv.  laureate bust of Louis XIV, draped over armour.
legend: LVDOVICVS MAGN. GALL. REX PIVS AVG. [Louis the
Great, king of France and holy emperor].

rev.  a group of horsemen, the foremost ? Louis himself; a group of soldiers on
foot, making their way from the right, doff their hats. In the background is
the town of Namur with an army drawn up beside it.
legend: AMAT VICTORIA TESTES [Victory loves on-lookers]; in
exergue: NAMVRCVM EXPVGNAT:SPECTANTE AVRIACO ET
BAVARO CVM CENT:ARMATOR:MILLIB. XXXIVN:MDCXCII.
[Namur captured in view of the Prince of Orange, the Elector of Bavaria
and 100,000 soldiers, 30 June 1692].

This is a splendid example of the larger module used in Louis's medallic
histories. Namur was strategically important but fell after a relatively short siege,
in spite of the attempted intervention of William and his German allies with a
large army. As part of the surrender agreement the garrison was allowed to
march out with military honours. It may be that play was made of this, after the
bad publicity the French had received for their treatment of other
captured towns.

## 287 *Namur retaken by the allies, 1695*

MEDAL BY P.H. MULLER (1653-1718)
ULSTER MUSEUM, BELFAST (WHITE METAL)

White metal, 47 mm.

Lit:  *Medallic Illustrations*, 134-35, no. 388.

Description:  obv.  female personification of Namur, wearing a mural crown, a scarf flowing
behind, holding a shield with the town arms and a palm in her right hand, a
staff in her left, is seated facing between two river gods, with spilling
cisterns.
legend: *PROVINCIA RESTITUTA* [the province restored]; in exergue:
MDCXCV [1695].

rev.  a tablet (? representing the base of a commemorative obelisk), with the
goddess of ? War (Bellona) in helmet with shield and spear, pointing out
the lettering. Fame, winged and with her trumpet, is seated to the right on
the pedestal. A view of the town is on the plinth, with the ground
underneath realistically rendered. Behind are some classical arches.
legend: NAMVRCVM INDEFESSA VIRTVTE FOEDERATORVM ET
REDDI ET VINCI POTVISSE VILLAREGIVS DVX GALL.
LIBERATIONEM FRVSTRA TENTANS CVM INGENTI C.
{contraction mark over the 'C'} HOMINVM EXERCITV TESTIS ESSE
VOLVIT [Villeroy, the French general, wished to be a witness, with his
immense army of 100,000 men, that Namur could be reduced and
conquered by the untiring bravery of the Allies].

edge.  ERIPITVR GALLIS VRBS AC CASTELLA NAMVRCI. HOC
REX ANGLE POTES! TV QVOQVE BOIE POTES F.K. [The city and
castle of Namur snatched from the French. This, King of England and
Bavarian, you have been able to do!].

This appears to be one of those occasions on which medallic propaganda
transcends the medium and becomes a work of art in itself. The obverse is a
stunning composition, the flying scarf balancing the extended leg of the river
god which passes through the exergue line and over the 'D' of the date. In spite
of the small scale and the difficulty of the pose chosen, Namur's face suggests
contentment at being retaken by the allies. The manner in which her bare toes
seem to protrude from the comparatively low relief of the medal confirms
Muller's mastery and skill. A relatively large number of different medals were
struck to mark this important victory, but this stands out by its novel treatment
of the problem.

The reverse, by comparison, is unexciting, but the detail of the view of the
town on the base is astonishing in its exactitude.

The edge inscription is chronogrammatic, that is, certain letters (underlined
here) are picked out and, when added up, make the date in Roman numerals. The

288 (a)

288 (b)

initials at the end stand for Friedrich Kleinert, master of the mint at Nuremberg and pioneer in Germany of the use of machinery for inscribing the edges of medals.

The long inscription on the reverse deliberately echoes the boasts of the French when they took the town (see no. 286).

## 288a-b *De Vrede van Rijswijk*
### *(The Peace of Rijswijk)*

BY J. VAN VIANEN (?1660-1726)
ATLAS VAN STOLK, ROTTERDAM

Two engravings with contemporary colouring 40 x 25 cms; Dutch and French text.

The Peace of Rijswijk brought to an end the nine years' war between Louis XIV and the allies. Apart from the territorial arrangements, which were the chief concern of his Dutch subjects, the most important concession to William was on the question of James II. In the end Louis swallowed his pride and recognised William as king by the grace of God. He also undertook not to aid attempts to subvert William, but would not agree to oblige James to leave France. He rejected outright a demand that French Protestants should be allowed to settle in William's principality of Orange, which was to be restored.

The English and Dutch signed the treaty on 20 September 1697. The emperor at first refused to accept the terms but eventually did so on 30 October.

The two prints illustrate these two sets of negotiations. In the upper picture, the circular arrangement of the participants shows how prolonged disputes over precedence were solved.

## 289 *William III returning from the Peace of Rijswijk, Margate, 1697 (c.1701)*

BY SIR GODFREY KNELLER (1646-1723)
NATIONAL GALLERY OF IRELAND, DUBLIN

Oil on canvas 139 x 122 cms.
Lit:    *National Gallery of Ireland Illustrated Summary Catalogue of Paintings* (Dublin, 1981),
        p.89, no. 311.

The picture commemorates William's return from the negotiations which led to the Peace of Rijkswijk. The treaty was signed on 20 September 1697, William landed at Margate on l4 November and returned to London in triumph two days later. The painting shows the king in armour, wearing the collar of the Garter and riding along the shore over trophies of war. Greeting him to the right is Ceres, goddess of agriculture,with her cornucopia of Plenty (the horn-shaped container in her left hand). Behind her Flora, goddess of flowers, and a boy attendant strew flowers in William's path. To the left are Neptune, god of the

**289**

sea, and his son Triton. In the sky a female figure, probably Peace, and a putto
with a quiver of arrows, presumably Cupid, hold William's helmet. Mercury, the
messenger of the gods, wearing a winged hat, is beside Cupid. Peace (?) and one
of the attendant putti carry palm branches, symbol of victory, while another
putto bears a scroll with William's motto  JE MAINTIENDRAY
(I will maintain).

The painting may have another meaning besides the allusion to William's
activity as a peace maker at Rijswijk. Cupid's presence with William's helmet
suggests a reference in the *Aeneid* to Venus and Cupid showing Aeneas his arms.
William therefore appears to be identified with Aeneas or perhaps as his
descendant. A legend, current from the twelfth century and still very much alive
in Kneller's time, maintained that the kings of Britain were direct descendants of
Brutus, a grandson of Aeneas. The painting seems to be saying that William, a
sovereign of ancient Trojan lineage, has by his virtuous deeds fulfilled ancient
prophecies and brought about a splendid new golden age in a reborn world,
where peace and justice will reign and trade will prosper under victorious
Britain, heir of imperial Augustan Rome.

The picture is a smaller version, with minor differences, of the large work at
Hampton Court, which was painted for the Presence Chamber where it still
hangs. The Hampton Court painting, probably commissioned by William in 1700
and executed by Kneller the following year, bears an inscription from Virgil's
fourth Eclogue on its scroll:  PACATAVMQVE REGIT PATRIS VIRTVT
(IBVS ORBEM)  (And he reigns over the pacified world with the virtues of his
ancestors). The ships in the background of the two pictures are also different.

There are a number of oil sketches and drawings associated with the
Hampton Court picture and an engraving after it by Bernard Baron. Kneller used
several elements of the painting in his *modello* of the Triumph of the Duke of
Marlborough in the NPG, painted c. 1706.

Sources:       O. Millar, *The Tudor, Stuart and Early Georgian  Pictures in the Collection of Her
               Majesty the Queen* (London. 1963); J.D. Stewart, 'William III  and Sir Godfrey
               Kneller,' *Journal of the Warburg and Courtauld Institutes*, 33, 1970; J.D. Stewart,
               *Sir Godfrey Kneller* (NPG, 1971).

# 11. Spoils of War

In Ireland as everywhere else in Europe in the seventeenth century, social status and the right to exercise political power depended upon owning land. Before the Cromwellian period most of the land of Ireland was still in the hands of Catholic nobility and gentry. As a result of Cromwell's victory and the wholesale confiscations that followed, most of these families, whether of native Irish or Old English origin, lost their estates. The confiscated lands were distributed to Englishmen who had financed the conquest or to Cromwellian soldiers in lieu of arrears of pay. When Charles II was restored to the throne the Acts of Settlement (1662) and Explanation (1665) confirmed these new men in most of what they had gained, while many Catholic gentlemen who had fought for the King against them failed to recover their estates.

During the next twenty-five years, however, a number of these people - Richard Talbot is a good example - managed to purchase back some of their lost land; by 1689, it is estimated, Catholics owned between a fifth and a quarter of the profitable acreage of the country. The old Gaelic families- the Os and the Macs as James II and others called them - recovered least and consequently longed most for the Restoration Settlement to be overthrown. Their chance came when James needed their help to recover the throne he had lost in England. In the Jacobite parliament of 1689 they got their way, despite James's reluctance to diminish English influence in Ireland. Had James won the war, all the families which had owned estates in 1641 would have been restored.

His defeat in 1690, on the other hand, presented the Williamites with the prospect of confiscating most of the land still in Catholic hands. William himself wanted land with which to reward his friends and supporters; his English parliament, always against high taxes, wanted to use the forfeitures to pay for the cost of the war. The strength of Irish resistance after the Boyne, however, made William willing to limit the confiscations in order to end the war in Ireland quickly - much too willing, in the view of his Westminster critics and his more extreme Irish Protestant subjects. The terms he gave in the treaty of Limerick, and their liberal interpretation afterwards, ensured that most of the Catholic gentry who surrendered at that time and chose to remain in Ireland kept their estates. William further enraged his critics by giving large grants of forfeited land to Dutch favourites, and the whole of James II's 'private estate' to his mistress. The furious Commons forced him in 1700 to accept an act cancelling all his grants. The forfeited land was then put into the hands of trustees appointed by parliament, who dealt with claims and sold what remained - just over three-quarters of a million acres by modern reckoning.

In the end, as a result of the Williamite victory the proportion of Irish land owned by Catholics fell from about twenty- two per cent in 1688 to about fourteen per cent in 1703. This was a much less drastic outcome than Catholics had feared and Protestants had hoped in 1691. It was the effect of the penal laws rather than the Williamite confiscations themselves that reduced the number of Catholic landowners to a handful during the eighteenth century. By the 1770s, it was estimated, the proportion of the country owned by Catholics was no more than five per cent.

290

## 290 *Charles II (1630-85) (c.1665)*

BY AN UNKNOWN ARTIST
NATIONAL PORTRAIT GALLERY, LONDON

Oil on canvas 69.8 x 56.5 cms.

Lit:    David Piper, *Catalogue of the Seventeenth Century Portraits in the National Portrait Gallery 1625-1714* (Cambridge, 1963), pp. 66-7.

Charles was the elder of the two sons of Charles I, who was executed in 1649. He and his brother James, Duke of York, spent the 1650s in impoverished exile on the Continent, until the death of Cromwell and disputes in the army that had kept him in power brought the chance of a restoration of the monarchy. In Ireland a group of army officers and Protestant gentry seized Dublin Castle in December 1659 and summoned an assembly early in 1660 which denounced the execution of Charles I and petitioned Charles II for the calling of an Irish parliament and the confirmation of the enormous transfers of land that had taken place under Cromwell. They did not want anything like a complete return to the situation before 1641, when Catholic landlords - many of them Gaelic - had owned three-fifths of the profitable land of the country (and all the unprofitable).

Despite the fact that many of them had so recently profited by the defeat of the royal cause, Charles depended for his peaceful restoration in Ireland on coming to terms with these people. Holding most of the land and wealth of the country and controlling the large army, they would not easily be dislodged. Charles therefore broadly accepted the situation as he found it, while promising to restore or reward those who had been unjustly dispossessed and those who had suffered for supporting the royalist cause. The Duke of Ormonde recovered his enormous estates (and was made viceroy), but many Catholic claimants, especially those of Gaelic stock, got little or nothing. Influence at court counted greatly, and brought some notably unjust decisions. The lands that had been granted to the Cromwellian regicides - 120,000 acres in various counties - was given to the Duke of York as his 'private estate', instead of being returned to its former owners; and the huge O'Dempsey estate in Leix and Offaly went to Charles's courtier Arlington.

The religious settlement established a narrow Anglican church, whose adherents were reckoned in 1672 to be only one-third of the Protestant population, another one-third being Presbyterians and the remainder members of smaller non-conforming sects. So far as Catholics were concerned, there would

**291**

have been little freedom of worship if the Irish parliament, dominated by intolerant Protestants who feared concessions to them, had had its way. Fortunately, Charles was not obliged to call parliament again after 1665 and was therefore able - most of the time - to follow a policy of practical toleration. The fact that in the Treaty of Limerick in 1691 the Catholic negotiators accepted freedom to exercise their religion as in the reign of Charles II shows that on the whole they had found his favour a real protection.

A close version of the portrait, threequarter-length in armour but with a lace collar, is at Northwick Park, and a variant, showing the king in a buff coat and breastplate, is in the SNPG. There are also miniature versions in the Rijksmuseum and at Goodwood. It is not known who made the original study for this type of portrait.

Sources:     Piper, as above;  T.W. Moody, F.X. Martin, F.J. Byrne, eds., *A New History of Ireland III  1534-1691* (Oxford, 1976); D. Dickson, *New Foundations: Ireland 1660-1800* (Dublin, 1987).

## **291**  *Sir William Petty (1623-87)*

By Isaac Fuller (1606-72)
National Portrait Gallery, London
Reproduction

Sir William Petty, political economist, statistician and pioneer cartographer, evinced a talent for mathematics and mechanics from an early age and in his youth spent a period at sea. His maritime career lasted only a short time, however, as he was handicapped by short-sightedness and too precocious for his fellow shipmates, who were only too happy to abandon him on the coast of France when he suffered a broken leg. He thereupon spent some time at the Jesuit College in Caen and later studied at Utrecht, Amsterdam and Leyden, where he matriculated as a student of medicine in 1644.  On his eventual return to England he went to Oxford, where he resumed his medical studies. He was subsequently given a fellowship at Brasenose and was appointed professor of anatomy in 1651.  In 1652 he was made physician general to the Cromwellian army in Ireland.

In the same year the Commonwealth government embarked upon a far reaching scheme, the resettlement of Ireland, whereby land owned by Catholics was to be forfeited and given to the Commonwealth's creditors as payment. Creditors fell into three categories: Cromwellian soldiers whose pay was in arrears, London 'adventurers' who had financed the army and a number of miscellaneous claimants. (Proprietors deprived of their lands were to be transplanted to Connacht and Clare). In order to carry out the scheme the land had first to be surveyed, as the acreage to be confiscated (and indeed the size of the country as a whole) was unknown. After a dispute with the surveyor general, Benjamin Worsley, whose abilities he called into question, Petty was entrusted with the task of surveying the forfeited estates in 1654. His survey, completed in 1659 and known as the 'Down Survey' because it was set down in map format, was the first scientific large-scale survey of Ireland and a model of its kind. From the early days of the project, Petty envisaged publishing the survey as an atlas and in 1660 was granted royal approval to sell the work, which he got engraved in Amsterdam at his own expense. Publication of the atlas, called *Hiberniae Delineatio*, was postponed until 1685, however, possibly because he hoped to collect more information for it.

In 1659 he returned to London and acquiesced in the Restoration. By this time he had become a wealthy man, as his survey earnings had enabled him to buy large tracts of land in Ireland. Under the Restoration settlement, Catholics who had been loyal to the crown were to be given back some of their forfeited estates and Cromwellian supplanters compensated with equivalent land elsewhere. In 1662 he was given a knighthood and in 1666 returned to Ireland to manage his estates.

On the accession of James II in 1685 the maintenance of the settlement became one of Petty's chief preoccupations, and a frequent topic of discussion between himself and his kinsmen Sir Robert Southwell (see no.171). While regarding the settlement as far from equitable, he felt it should be maintained and sought assurance from both James and Tyrconnell on the subject. (The settlement eventually did come under attack by Tyrconnell, who proposed that parliament modify the acts by returning estates to old owners and compensating new owners with cash payments). The condition of Ireland remained close to Petty's heart; his last work, the *Treatise of Ireland*, which he presented to James II in September 1687, dealt with Protestant apprehension about the settlement's reversal, which was reflected in a considerable fall in Irish land values and increasing emigration to England.

A founder member of the Royal Society, Petty published numerous articles on applied mechanics, practical inventions and political economy. He abounded in novel ideas and was noted for his wit and humour; when challenged to a duel, he suggested the place and weapon suitable for his extreme short sightedness, namely a dark cellar and a hatchet. (By stipulating such conditions he turned the duel into ridicule and it never took place). John Aubrey in 1680 described him as 'a proper handsome man, measured six foot high, good head of browne hair, moderately turning up ... his eies are a kind of goose-grey, but very short-sighted, and as to aspect, beautifull, and promise sweetnes of nature, and they do not deceive, for he is a marvellous good-natured person ...' (Piper, p.276). He died in London on 16 December 1687.

Isaac Fuller studied in France before establishing practices in Oxford and then London. In addition to portraiture he painted a number of religious subjects. This portrait, which shows Petty holding a skull and pointing to a copy of Adrian Spigelius's *De Humani Corpus Fabrica* (1627), was probably painted at Oxford after he became a Doctor in Physic in 1649 or perhaps in 1651, when he became professor of anatomy.

Sources:     *DNB*; D. Ogg, *England in the Reign of Charles II* (Oxford, 1934); D. Piper, *Catalogue of the Seventeenth Century Portraits in the National Portrait Gallery 1625-1714* (Cambridge, 1963); J.G. Simms, *Jacobite Ireland 1685-91* (London, 1969); Dr. J.H. Andrews, introduction to Sir William Petty, *Hiberniae Delineatio* (Shannon, 1969); T.W. Moody, F.X. Martin, F.J. Byrne, eds., *A New History of Ireland III 1534-1691* (Oxford, 1976).

## 292 Petty, Sir William (1623-87)

*Hiberniae Delineatio quoàd hactenus licuit, Perfectissima Studio Guilielmi Petty... [London, the author, 1685]*

THE QUEEN'S UNIVERSITY, BELFAST

folio: port., contents leaf, 36 maps (some folding).
Scale (county maps): 2 Irish miles to 1 inch (1:161, 240).
Lit: Wing P1928 (second state of title leaf).

This atlas, based on Petty's 'Down' survey which was completed in 1657, contains general, provincial and county maps. Engraving work for the atlas commenced probably in Amsterdam about 1661 and may have been completed as early as 1675. Petty acted as his own publisher.

## 293 The Acts of Settlement (1662) and Explanation (1665)
*(14 & 15 Chas II, c.2 and 17 & 18 Chas II, c.2)*

TRINITY COLLEGE, DUBLIN
REPRODUCTIONS OF TITLE PAGES

(a) The Act of Settlement was designed to give effect to Charles II's declaration of 30 November 1660, the so called 'Gracious Declaration' which forms the preamble to the Act. On the basis of misleading statistics supplied by the former Cromwellian Broghill - whom he created Earl of Orrery - Charles promised both to confirm the new English settlers who had got the land confiscated from Irish Catholics under Cromwell and also to make provision for 'innocent Papists' and those who had supported the monarchy. The court of claims set up to administer the settlement soon found that these two promises were incompatible. After issuing 566 decrees of innocence to Catholics it suspended its work, leaving many claims unheard.

(b)The Act of Explanation modified the Act of Settlement. Most of the new English settlers were obliged to give up one third of the land they had held in 1659, in order to provide for 'innocent Papists' and royalists. This left the Protestants resentful and the Catholics far from satisfied.

The Restoration land settlement, overthrown in 1689 but restored and extended by William's victory, was the basis of landownership in Ireland for the next two and a half centuries.

## 294 C., J.

*The state of the Papist and Protestant proprieties in the kingdom of Ireland, in the year 1641... and how disposed in 1653... and how disposed in 1662... and how... stand this present year 1689... To which is added, a list of the present nobility of Ireland Protestant and Papist. London, printed for Richard Baldwin... 1689*

THE QUEEN'S UNIVERSITY, BELFAST

quarto: [4], 34, [2] pp.
Lit: Wing C74.

## 295 Lady Neil O'Neill (d. 1732)

BY GARRET MORPHEY (FL. 1680-1716)
THE LORD O'NEILL

Oil on canvas 127.6 x 100.8 cms.
Prov: Formerly at Malahide Castle, Co. Dublin.
Exh: *Irish Portraits 1660-1860*, NGI August-October 1969, NPG October 1969-January 1970, UM January-March 1970 (10), repr. p. 31.
Lit: Anne Crookshank and The Knight of Glin, *The Painters of Ireland* (London, 1978), p. 24, repr. p. 24.

**295**

Frances Molyneux, daughter of Sir Caryll, third Viscount Molyneux of
Maryborough, an English Catholic peer, married Sir Neil O'Neill (see nos. 67
and 173) in January 1677 and had four daughters: Rose, Anne, Margaret and
Elizabeth. After her husband's death on 18 July 1690, from wounds received at
the Boyne, she was left unprovided for and the family estate at Killelagh, Co.
Antrim was confiscated. On petitioning the government for redress, on the
grounds that her jointure was secured on the estate, she was granted a lease of
the property for forty-one years; the remaining term of this lease was sold in
1701. Lady O'Neill died in 1732.

The portrait was probably painted shortly after O'Neill's death, as it
contains a funerary urn carved with a skull and crossbones, a *memento mori* of
the transience of life. The sitter's thin elongated fingers and the delicate
execution of the draperies are typical of Morphey's style.

Sources:      M. Archdall, *The Peerage of Ireland* (Dublin, 1789); Rev. J. O'Laverty, *Diocese of
              Down and Connor* (Dublin, 1880), vol. II.

## 296  *Claud, fourth Earl of Abercorn (d.1691)*

BY AN UNKNOWN ARTIST
DUKE OF ABERCORN

Oil on canvas 73 x 61 cms (sight).

Claud, Lord Strabane and fourth Earl of Abercorn, second son of George, Lord
Strabane, travelled with James II from France to Ireland in February 1689. On his

**296**

arrival in Dublin, he was sworn as a privy councillor and sat in the parliament summoned for 7 May following (whose aims were the repeal of anti-Catholic laws and an end to the dependence of the Irish parliament upon the English). During the early days of the siege of Derry, James sent him to the town to negotiate a surrender. George Walker in his account of events records that on 20 April (OS) 'Lord Strabane came up to our Walls, makeing us many Proposals, and offering his Kings Pardon, Protection and Favour, if we would surrender the Town; but these fine words had no place with the Garrison. At that very time of his Capitulating with us, we observ'd the Enemy using that opportunity to draw their Canon to a convenient stand, we therefore desired his Lordship to withdraw, otherwise we would make bold to fire at his Lordship; his Lordship continued in his Complements, till we plainly told him, we would never deliver the Town to any but K. William and Q. Mary or their order. My Lord having ended all his Insinuations, found himself at last obliged to retire.'

In July 1689 he served with Lord Mountcashel's forces in the battle of Newtownbutler and was wounded in action. He later fought at the Boyne and at Aughrim. After Aughrim he was one of three envoys despatched to France to report the disaster to Louis XIV and to ask for further help. According to a Jacobite chronicler, the vessel in which he travelled 'met a Dutch man-of-war near Brest, by whom the ship was taken, and the earl killed in a fight, after escaping death in the bloody field of Aughrim, where he gallantly comported himself with his regiment on the right' (Gilbert, p. 150). His epitaph, from the same source states, 'He was a person of great bravery, zealous for his country, and most loyal to his prince.' He was outlawed posthumously and his estates and title of Strabane forfeited; however, the earldom of Abercorn remained in the family and devolved upon his brother Charles, fifth earl. Charles later obtained a reversal of Claud's outlawry and succeeded to the restored title of Strabane. On his death in 1701 he was succeeded by his kinsman, James, sixth earl (see no. 297).

Sources:     J. D'Alton, *King James's Irish Army List (1689)* (Dublin, 1855); *Burke's Peerage*; J. T. Gilbert, ed., *A Jacobite Narrative of the War in Ireland 1688-1691* (Dublin, 1892, reprinted Shannon, 1971); Rev. P. Dwyer, A.M., ed., *The Siege of Londonderry in 1689* (London, 1893; reprinted Wakefield, 1971).

**297**

## **297** *James, sixth Earl of Abercorn (1656-1734)*

BY AN UNKNOWN ARTIST
DUKE OF ABERCORN

Oil on canvas 98 x 70.5 cms (sight).

James, sixth Earl of Abercorn, was the son of James Hamilton and nephew of Anthony, Richard and John Hamilton, who fought on the Jacobite side. He served as groom of the bedchamber to Charles II and during James II's reign was captain of a regiment of horse. During the Revolution of 1688 he supported the Williamite cause. He played an important part in the siege of Derry, arriving there from England in the *Deliverance* on 20 March (OS) with 'Ammunition and Arms, 480 Barrels of Powder and Arms for 2000 Men, and a Commission from the King and Queen for Col Lundy to be Governour of the City, together with Instructions to swear all Officers Military and Civil, and assurance of speedy Supplies from England.'

Hamilton's orders were specific: not to hand anything over until Lundy had taken oaths of allegiance to William and Mary, in the presence of the mayor or chief magistrate. As the mayor had departed to fight for the Jacobites and his deputy's loyalty was questionable, Lundy took the oaths on board the *Deliverance*, in the presence of Hamilton and a few others. Rumour soon spread, however, that he had not sworn allegiance at all. Despite pressure the following day to take the oaths publicly, he declined - a refusal which caused many to regard his motives and loyalty with considerable distrust.

Hamilton was shortly afterwards promoted to colonel and served on Lundy's council of war (which consisted of fifteen officers besides Lundy). It was he (Hamilton) who suggested on 11 April that the council unite in their efforts to defend Derry to the utmost, by 'a mutual engagement [to] be made between all the Officers and other ranks and signed by every man ... None shall desert or forsake the service, or depart the kingdom without leave of a Council of War. If any do, he or they shall be looked upon as a coward and disaffected to the service.'

S‹ Rich⸱ Cox L‹ Chanc‹ one of y‹ L‹ Iuſt‹͡ 1704

**298**

Hamilton succeeded to the earldom of Abercorn in 1701, on the death of his kinsman Charles, fifth earl, and was created Viscount Strabane in the same year. He served as a privy councillor during the reigns of Queen Anne, George I and George II and died on 28 November 1734.

The two Abercorn portraits neatly illustrate how members of the same family could be at political and religious odds in Ireland in the late seventeenth century: while James Hamilton was inside Derry's walls during the siege, both his uncle Richard and his kinsman Claud were outside, fighting on behalf of James II.

Sources: J. D'Alton, *King James's Irish Army List (1689)* (Dublin, 1855); *Burke's Peerage*; *DNB*; Rev. P. Dwyer, A.M., ed., *The Siege of Londonderry in 1689* (London, 1893; reprinted Wakefield, 1971).

## 298 *Sir Richard Cox (1650-1733)*

BY AN UNKNOWN ARTIST
ROYAL HOSPITAL, KILMAINHAM
REPRODUCTION

Richard Cox was born at Bandon, Co. Cork and, orphaned at the age of three, was raised by his grandfather and uncle. He studied for a career in law and was appointed recorder of Kinsale. An ardent Protestant, he deemed it wise to move to England on the accession of James II, as he had made a public attack upon Catholics in the Cork quarter sessions. While in England, he spent part of his time writing *Hibernia Anglicana*, a history of Ireland from the English conquest to his own time. (The first part of this appeared in 1689 and the second part the following year). Inspired by the Glorious Revolution, he published *A Sheet of Aphorisms, proving by a fair deduction the necessity of making the Prince of Orange king, and of sending speedy relief to Ireland* and gave a copy to each member of the house on the first day of the Convention, which opened in January 1689.

In 1690 he was appointed secretary to Sir Robert Southwell and accompanied him to Ireland. He was present at the battle of the Boyne (where his accurate information was of considerable help to William) and was involved with Southwell in drafting the Finglas Declaration of 7 July (OS), which promised pardon to the poorer classes among the Jacobite supporters if they surrendered by 1 August. (This was an unsuccessful attempt to divide rank and file Jacobite supporters from the higher echelons). On the surrender of Waterford he was made recorder of the town and on 15 September 1690 was appointed second justice of the common pleas. The following year he was made military governor of Cork, a position which he held until the reduction of Limerick in September.

In April 1692 he was admitted to the privy council, as a reward for his services to Ginkel during his governorship of Cork, and in the November following was given a knighthood. In February 1693 he was appointed one of nine judges to hear claims under the terms of the treaty of Limerick. This court of claims came in for considerable criticism from the inquiry commissioners of 1699, who accused its members of being too benevolent. Cox, in a stirring riposte, repudiated their charge emphatically: 'What is but common justice they may call favouring the Irish and a lessening of the forfeitures, and we cannot help that. We got nothing but trouble and censure by that court of claims, and if the justice we administered there will distinguish us and preserve us from the destroying angel when he comes to punish the oppressions and perjuries, notorious and public, committed against the claimants it is all the reward we desire or expect' (Simms, p. 52). As a result of his views, which annoyed many of the more extreme Protestants, he was removed from the privy council in June 1695. (He was readmitted in 1701).

His expertise in Irish affairs was widely recognised by the end of the century. On Queen Anne's accession in 1702 he was summoned to London to advise and consult about matters in Ireland. In 1703 he was appointed lord chancellor of Ireland, remaining in office until 1707. He was chief justice of the Queen's Bench between 1711 and 1714; thereafter he retired from public life.

The portrait shows him wearing the robes of lord chancellor. To the left can be seen the embroidered purse of the Great Seal of Ireland and the mace resting on a draped table. The painting was presented by him to Kilmainham Hospital.

Sources:    *DNB*; J.G. Simms, *The Williamite Confiscation in Ireland 1690-1703* (London, 1956).

## 299 *Arnold Joost Van Keppel, first Earl of Albemarle (1669-1718)*

BY AN UNKNOWN ARTIST, AFTER SIR GODFREY KNELLER (1646-1723)
NATIONAL TRUST

Oil on canvas 126.5 x 96.5 cms (sight).

Keppel, the son of a distinguished Dutch family, entered William's household as a page and accompanied the prince to England in 1688. He rose rapidly in William's favour, becoming his amanuensis, then gentleman of the bedchamber and finally constant and close companion, much to the chagrin of the jealous Portland. Of the king's two favourites he was much the more popular, on account of his friendly and open nature. Lord Sunderland aptly summed up the difference between the two rivals when he said of Keppel 'This young man brings and carries a message well, but Portland is so dull an animal, that he can neither fetch nor carry' (van der Zee, p. 415). William granted him large estates in Ireland, 108,633 acres which included the estates of Lord Clare and a number of other forfeiting proprietors.

By 1697 his influence on the king was enormous. In January of that year he was created Baron of Ashford, Viscount of St Edmondsbury and Earl of Albemarle - an elevation which annoyed the English at court, who were infuriated to see yet another Dutchman join their aristocracy. One of the numerous lampoons of the day commented accordingly:

**299**

> Proceed my muse, the story next relate,
> Of Keppech, the imperious chit of state;
> Of foreign birth, and undescended too,
> Yet he, like Bentir, mighty feats can do.
> Our ravished honours on his shoulder wears,
> And titles from our ancient rolls he tears (van der Zee, p. 416).

A dandy and a womaniser, he had a number of mistresses and was described by Bishop Burnet as being 'so much given up to his own pleasures, that he could scarce submit to the attendance and drudgery that was necessary to maintain his post' (as above). His life was not given over solely to pleasure, however; he also had ability as a soldier and in the same year in which he was enobled was promoted to major-general in the army. In 1700 he was given the Garter.

He remained William's constant companion until the latter's death in 1702 and was at the king's bedside when he died. It was to him that William entrusted his personal keys with the admonition 'You know what to do with them.' He thereafter returned to Holland and took his seat in the States-General as a member of the nobility. His latter years were spent in military service; he served under Marlborough and fought at Ramilles and Oudenarde. In 1701 he took a Dutch wife, by whom he had a son and daughter.

The original portrait by Kneller was painted in 1700, of which versions exist in the NPG and in the Albemarle collection. The painting shows him as a handsome young man with fine pleasing features, wearing the Garter ribbon and Lesser George.

Sources:     *DNB*; J.G. Simms, *The Williamite Confiscation in Ireland 1690-1703* (London, 1956); D. Piper, *Catalogue of the Seventeenth Century Portraits in the National Portrait Gallery* (Cambridge, 1963); H. and B. van der Zee, *William and Mary* (London, 1973).

**300**
Photo Robin Briault, St Saviour, Jersey

## **300** *Elizabeth Villiers, Countess of Orkney (1657-1733)*

BY SIR PETER LELY (1618-80)
EARL OF JERSEY

Oil on canvas 129 x 105 cms.
Prov:   By descent; sitter was the sister of the first Earl of Jersey.
Exh:   *Glorious Revolution. The World of William and Mary*, Nieuwe Kerk, Amsterdam, June-
September 1988 (149), as by an unknown artist.

Elizabeth Villiers was a childhood companion of the Princesses Mary and Anne
as her mother, Lady Frances Villiers, was governess to the royal children.  On
Mary's marriage to William in November 1677 Elizabeth and her sisters Anne
and Katherine accompanied the royal party to The Hague as maids of honour to
Mary.  Although William apparently seldom looked at other women, he appears
to have embarked upon an affair with Elizabeth in 1679, a situation which Mary
seemingly knew about by the spring of the following year. Elizabeth, though
plain and lacking in physical charms - Swift declared she squinted 'like a
dragon' - was witty and intelligent and indisputably meant a great deal to
William. Whether their relationship was platonic or physical remains uncertain
and a subject for speculation; nevertheless, gossip at the time pointed to a
full-blown affair.

In 1685 the liaison was brought out into the open when members of Mary's
household, possibly encouraged by James II who had begun to meddle in his
daughter's domestic affairs, told Mary of the relationship (she had hidden her
knowledge of it for years).  After a tearful and traumatic confrontation with
William, Mary dismissed her disloyal and meddlesome servants and sent
Elizabeth back to England.  She quickly returned to The Hague, however and
settled with her sister Katherine, much to the disapproval of her brother-in-law
Bentinck (later Earl of Portland) (see no. 169) who was married to her sister
Anne.  In time she went back to court and the affair went on as before.  She
returned to England shortly after the Glorious Revolution and settled near
Kensington, where she continued seeing William on a regular basis. The liaison
lasted until 1695 when William, grief-stricken at Mary's death and (it is said)

286

touched by a letter she had left him begging him to discontinue the relationship, finally ended the affair. (Apparently the Archbishop of Canterbury had also admonished him). William subsequently engineered a marriage between Elizabeth and Lord George Hamilton, afterwards Earl of Orkney, in November 1695.

As with William's other favourites, Elizabeth too received a grant of Irish land, in her case the 'private estate' of James II. An area of 95,649 acres spread over sixteen counties, it had the highest value of all the granted estates and was the most controversial. Its disposal, planned by the king in 1692, was cloaked with mystery: it was initially placed in the care of trustees before being finally granted to Elizabeth in 1695, after Mary's death.

There was considerable discussion at the time as to whether the land was in fact William's to give. Irish law officers in 1695 considered that it was not crown property, nor could it be forfeited as James was not attainted. William, however, judged that he was entitled to take it over from James, as he had taken over the crown. Nonetheless, William's title to the land was not clear, as it was a private estate granted to James under the Act of Settlement; there was some feeling that Princess Anne might have a better claim. Elizabeth, anxious to have her ownership settled beyond dispute, endowed a school on the Co. Cork lands (the present Midleton College) and tried to have the grant confirmed by parliament. This never came about. Its existence caused the commissioners of enquiry considerable unease - should it be excluded from their report, to spare the king embarrassment? It was eventually included and, like William's other grants, was cancelled in 1700.

Lely, a Dutch artist, came to London c. 1647 and from 1650 had the largest portrait practice of any artist in the kingdom. His female portraits, which usually show the sitters posed gracefully in the open air, in loose-fitting gowns, tend to exude an atmosphere of voluptuousness and sensual languor. This portrait is no exception. Elizabeth Villiers, wearing a rich russet gown, is seated amidst a lush landscape, her face (not unattractive as Swift maintained) turned towards the spectator with a knowing expression. The picture was probably painted c. 1679-80, when she was in her early twenties. The portrait is full of sexual symbolism: with her right hand she holds firmly on to a lamb, a symbol of innocence (in her case perhaps virginity); with her left she reaches towards Cupid, who holds a pair of doves, symbols of love and, by extension, lust. The painting seems to pose the question: will she sacrifice herself to William's desires and leave behind her chastity? The fact that her fingers are touching the doves gives an indication of her answer.

Sources:     R.B. Beckett, *Lely* (London, 1951); J.G. Simms, *The Williamite Confiscation in Ireland 1690-1703* (London, 1956); S.B. Baxter, *William III* (London, 1966); H. and B. van der Zee, *William and Mary* (London, 1973).

## 301 *James Corry MP (1633-1718) (1695)*

By Thomas Pooley (1646-1723)
Earl of Belmore and National Trust

Oil on canvas 73.6 x 58.5 cms.
Lit:     The Earl of Belmore, 'Governor Hamilton and Captain Corry,' *Ulster Journal of Archaeology*, 2nd series, vol. II, no. 2, January 1896, p. 110, repr. p. 109.
W.G. Strickland, *A Dictionary of Irish Artists* (Dublin, 1913), vol. II, p. 252.

James Corry of Castle Coole, near Enniskillen, succeeded his father John to estates in counties Fermanagh and Monaghan about 1686 and thereafter continued to acquire land when the opportunity arose. A magistrate for Co. Fermanagh, he was also an army captain, having been commissioned in 1666 to raise a regiment of foot (which appears to have been no longer in existence by 1688). In December 1688, when local Protestants refused to admit two Catholic companies of foot into Enniskillen, he declined to become involved and advocated non-resistance to James II (the Enniskilleners did not declare for William and Mary until 11 March of the following year).

Many of Enniskillen's inhabitants at that stage were of the same opinion as Corry but from less ideological motives: 'Most were for admitting the two companies, alledging the strength of the Irish in that country, they being well armed and provided in ammunition ... we wanting both arms and ammunition, wanting soldiers amongst us ...' However, 'the townsmen, with the gentlemen

**301**

that came out of the barony of Magheraboy stood firm to the resolution of neither submitting themselves to be slaves, nor to assist the making of others so; carpenters were set to work again at the bridge [a drawbridge]; and indeed, though Captain Corry would not at all comply with our resolution, yet when we sent for the chains and irons that had formerly belonged to the bridge, he sent them in to us' (Belmore, *UJA*, vol. II, no. 2, pp. 114-115).

Corry's attitude of non-resistance no doubt stemmed partly from the fact that he was in the king's service as magistrate and army captain; but he may also have felt no sense of impending danger. The inhabitants of Enniskillen assumed their defensive stance initially because they feared a massacre was imminent and their religion threatened. Corry's advice to the townspeople was similar to that given by Mountjoy to the people of Derry: trust in the protection of the king. By January or February 1689, however, he changed his allegiance and came firmly down on the Williamite side. When Enniskillen declared for William and Mary in March, his name and that of his son John were included in an address from the town to the new monarchs. He was present on board the *Deliverance* when Lundy took the oath of allegiance to William on 21 March. Shortly afterwards he went with his wife and three children to England, where he remained throughout the fighting.

After the war Corry claimed compensation for losses incurred during it. His petition to the lords justices on 16 December 1691 stated that he had raised a troop of sixty cavalry and one hundred foot soldiers, had kept and maintained them at his own expense at Castle Coole until they were summoned into Enniskillen to help the garrison, and that on 13 July 1689 the governor of the town had ordered Castle Coole to be burnt, to stop the Duke of Berwick using it as his base. He also claimed that a quantity of his goods (wheat, oats, malt and beef), three hundred head of oxen and cows, timber and boats, to the value of £3,000, were used by the garrison, and that he had not received anything from his estate of £1,000 a year for three years and that he had had to borrow to support his family in England. In July 1692 the lords justices approved his claim.

As part compensation, Corry requested a lease of the forfeited estate of his neighbour, Cuconnaucht Maguire of Tempo (killed at the battle of Aughrim), claiming that by reason of its contiguity it was convenient to him but of no advantage to the Crown. His petition for the estate was referred to the solicitor-general on 21 March 1693. On 3 May of the following year the lord lieutenant recommended the claim to the Secretary of State, describing Corry as 'a person highly deserving our favour, and one who upon all occasions, not only in person but with his fortune, had given undeniable testimonies of his great zeal to our service' (Belmore, 1891, p.35). On 29 November 1694 he received a grant of the Maguire property (the last estate in Fermanagh still in Irish hands).

In 1699 Bryan Maguire, Cuconnaught's son, began litigation against Corry to recover the property, claiming that under marriage articles of 1675 his father had been only tenant for life. He also claimed to be protected against forfeiture under the terms of the treaty of Limerick. Before this suit could be decided Corry was deprived of the estate by the Act of Resumption of 1700, which cancelled nearly all William's grants and vested the forfeited lands in trustees. Maguire proved his claim before the trustees and recovered the estate.

The Act of Resumption was the outcome of investigations by a body of commissioners appointed by the English parliament. In their report, published in 1700, the commissioners made a personal attack on Corry, claiming that 'he gave no Assistance to the Garrison of Iniskilling. That in the Town of Iniskilling he publickly declared, he hoped to see all those Hang'd that took up Arms for the Prince of Orange; and his House was Burnt by the said Garrison.'

In an attempt to clear his name, Corry obtained a certificate from the provost and seven of the burgesses of Enniskillen refuting the commissioners' allegations. The certificate pointed out that 'James Corry was verry Industrouse and Diligent in Raiseing and Arming men for hs late Majesties service, and for ye support and defence of the Protestant Interest of this Kingdom, that he raised a very good troope of horse and foot company, and mounted and arm'd many of them at his own expence ... that by his Incouragement seaverall of his Relations and friends followed his example; that the Garrison of Iniskillin were supplied with considerable quantities of timber, Boards, Lyme, and seaell [several] Boats that belonged to ... the said James Corry ... yt ye said words Aleged to bee spoke by ye said James Corry (vizt.) that he said yt he hoped to see ym all hanged yt tooke up Armes for ye Prince of Orange, were never spoke by him, for yt wee never heard him charged with ye same till by the said Report, nor doe we believe his principales lead him to any such expressions ...' (Belmore *UJA*, vol. II, no. 2, p.124).

From 1692 Corry was MP for Fermanagh, of which county he was appointed governor in 1705, and was commissioned as a colonel of the horse militia. He died at Castle Coole on 1 May 1718.

Thomas Pooley, a lawyer turned portrait painter, established a fashionable practice among the Anglo-Irish in Dublin in the 1680s. He painted portraits of Charles II, William and Mary for Dublin Corporation, and in 1700 executed likenesses of Queen Anne and the Duke of Gloucester for the Royal Hospital, Kilmainham. The lettering on the Corry portrait was obviously added by a later hand.

Sources:     *Report of The Commissioners Appointed by Parliament To Enquire into the Irish Forfeitures* (London, 1700); Earl of Belmore, *History of the Two Ulster Manors of Finagh ... and Coole* (London and Dublin, 1881); Belmore, *History of the Corry Family of Castlecoole* (London and Dublin, 1891); Belmore, 'Governor Hamilton and Captain Corry,' *Ulster Journal of Archaeology*, vol. II, nos. 2 and 3, 1896.

## 302   *James Hamilton of Tollymore (d. 1701) (1686)*

BY AN UNKNOWN ARTIST
PRIVATE COLLECTION

Oil on canvas 73.7 x 99 cms
Inscr: 'James Hamilton of Tollymore Esq. A.D. 1686' t.l.

James Hamilton of Tollymore was the eldest son of William Hamilton, (a nephew of that extraordinarily successful Scottish planter James, first Viscount Claneboye) and Ellen Magennis, daughter of Brian McHugh McAghorley Magennis of Castlewellan. The Tollymore estate was thus one of the few in Ulster to have been transferred from Gaelic to settler ownership by marriage rather than by confiscation. Hamilton married Anne Mordaunt, daughter of John Mordaunt, first Viscount Mordaunt and sister of Charles, Earl of Peterborough and Monmouth. He served as MP for Downpatrick in 1692 and for Co. Down in 1695. His son James, who succeeded him at an early age, became Baron Claneboye in 1719 and Earl of Clanbrassil (of the second creation) in 1756.

**302**

In 1699 he was one of seven commissioners chosen to examine the handling of the Irish forfeitures, the other six being Lord Drogheda, John Trenchard, Francis Annesley, Sir Francis Brewster, Henry Langford and Sir Richard Levinge (see no. 303). All seven had been at odds with the administration at some time or other; it would seem that they were selected by the government opposition in the hope that they would produce a report which would be critical of official management of the Irish forfeitures.

For most of William's reign the king and the Commons were engaged in a contest over his right to dispose of forfeited Irish lands, which in turn was part of a larger struggle - who had political control, king or parliament? The latter repeatedly failed to secure the passage of legislation on the subject, while William continued to award large grants of Irish land to favoured individuals, despite the wishes of the Commons. The bulk of the property granted went to a handful of foreigners, among whom Albemarle, Galway, Ginkel and Portland's son were prominent. These grants in particular served to exacerbate the dislike and resentment which the English landed gentry felt for courtiers.

The seven commisioners of enquiry eventually split into two factions. Annesley, Langford, Trenchard and Hamilton formed the majority group, and were keen to discredit the government's handling of the forfeitures. The minority group, Drogheda, Brewster and Levinge, were determined to obstruct their wishes. As the historian J. Ralph explained in his *History of England* of 1744: '...of these commissioners, which were seven in all and all presumed to be anti-courtiers, four were disposed to put every circumstance to the torture with a view to inflame the report, and three were for the court under the pretence of candour and moderation' (Simms, p. 99).

There was much objection in Ireland to this parliamentary enquiry, partly because it was instigated by the English parliament and partly because much of the land given by the crown to the various grantees had been already sold to buyers in Ireland. The commissioners therefore met with a hostile reception when they reached Ireland to begin their task, for the purchasers (many of whom were leading Protestant gentry) were vehemently hostile to any attack on their interests.

Considerable dissension took place among the commissioners as to the problem of the 'private estate' in Ireland of James II, which had been granted by

William to his mistress Elizabeth Villiers, Countess of Orkney. Should it be included in the commissioners' report, or excluded to spare the king embarrassment? Fearful of William's wrath, Drogheda wished to exclude it, while Trenchard maintained that the report would be meaningless if it were not included. It was eventually decided by the majority group that the grant would be included in the report, on the grounds that some of Lady Orkney's lessees were forfeiting persons. The decision, however, hung in the balance at one stage, with Hamilton having the casting vote. Although Lord Orkney was both a relative and friend, Hamilton finally decided that the commissioners had little option but to include the grant, on the grounds that 'we have made so great a noise about this estate by examining so many people to the value and sending for the rentrolls of it that it is now the public discourse that it will be reported and I know the world must needs say we are bribed and corrupted if we do it not' (Simms, p. l03).

In the event, the report was submitted with only the majority group's signatures attached. The record of the commissioners' investigations, consisting of their report and nine books of statistical material, was presented to the Commons on l5 December 1699. On the same day it was decided to bring in a resumption bill, to cancel all the grants made during William and Mary's reign. To deter the Lords from throwing it out, it was 'tacked' on to a finance bill. This was a direct attack on the king's policy and a challenge to his conception of the royal perogative. The bill finally passed the Lords after Lady Orkney's brother, Lord Jersey, persuaded William to tell his friends to drop their opposition to it; a possible constitutional crisis was thus avoided. William was enraged and mortified at having his prerogative diminished on the issue and wrote to Lord Galway, one of the deprived grantees, 'you may judge what vexation all their extraordinary proceedings gave me and, I assure you, your being deprived of what I gave you with such pleasure was not the least of my griefs ...' (Simms, p. 113). By the Act of Resumption, all grants of the forfeitures and the private estate were declared null and void.

Thirteen trustees were chosen by ballot from the Commons, among whom were the four majority commissioners. Functioning as a parliamentary agency, their task was to hear claims, manage the forfeited estates, collect rents and conduct sales. Each trustee was to be paid £1,500 per year and take an oath not to purchase any of the forfeited estates. Hamilton, however, died in London in l701, shortly after his appointment to the trust.

The portrait, which has considerable merit, shows him as a dignified and urbane man in his fifties. His pose, with the hand tucked inside the waistcoat, was fashionable etiquette.

Sources:    T.K. Lowry, ed., *The Hamilton Manuscripts* (Belfast, l867); G.E.C., *The Complete Peerage* (London, l926); J.G. Simms, *The Williamite Confiscation in Ireland 1690-1703* (London, l956).

## 303  *Sir Richard Levinge (d. 1724)*

BY RALPH HOLLAND (FL. EARLY EIGHTEENTH CENTURY)
ALEC COBBE, NEWBRIDGE

Oil on canvas 125.1 x 99.3 cms.
Prov:    By descent; Levinge's daughter, Dorothea, Lady Rawdon, married Charles Cobbe, archbishop of Dublin, who established the family at Newbridge.
Lit:    A.O. Crookshank and The Knight of Glin, *Irish Portraits 1660-1860*, p. 14.
       J. Cornforth, 'Newbridge, Co. Dublin', *Country Life*, 20 June 1985, p. 1734, repr.

Richard Levinge, second son of Richard Levinge of Parwich, Ashbourne, Derbyshire, entered the Inner Temple as a student in September 1671 and was called to the Bar in November 1678. In 1686 he became recorder of Chester and was MP for the town from 1690 to 1692. He served as solicitor-general for Ireland from 1690 to 1694 and in 1692 received a knighthood. In the same year he was elected MP for both Belfast and Blessington and chose to sit for the latter constituency in the Irish Commons. In October 1692 he was chosen as Speaker of the Commons and stayed in office until parliament was dissolved in 1695. Later in the year he was elected MP for Bangor and Longford and sat for the latter.

**303**

In 1699 he was chosen by the English House of Commons as one of the seven commissioners appointed to examine the handling of the Irish forfeitures. He himself had bought from William III's Dutch favourite Albemarle over 1,500 acres in Westmeath (the forfeited estate of Walter Tuite) and thus had personal reasons for opposing a condemnatory report of the government's administration of the forfeitures. Along with Drogheda and Brewster he formed the minority group of commissioners, who were opposed to discrediting the government and were against including James II's 'private estate' within the commissioners' report. Rancour between the minority and majority commissioners was considerable: on 16 January 1700, following publication of the report, Levinge was sent to the Tower for three months by the English Commons for spreading scandalous gossip about his opponents (who were paid twice as much for their services).

In 1703 he was re-elected MP for Longford and the following year was created a baronet and again appointed solicitor-general for Ireland, in which post he remained until 1709. Two years later he was promoted to attorney-general for Ireland. He was elected MP in the English parliament for Derby in 1710, and in the Irish parliament for Gowran and Kilkenny in 1713 (he sat for the latter). In 1720 he was appointed lord chief justice of the Irish court of common pleas and remained in office till his death on 13 July 1724.

Ralph Holland, an eighteenth century Irish artist about whom little is known, painted the portrait early in 1724; the Cobbe family account books for 8 April in that year record 'To Mr. Holland for my father's picture 6-18-0 to his man for the frame 2-17-6' (*Irish Portraits 1660-1860*, p. 14). The painting, which shows Levinge in his robes as lord chief justice, is competently executed.

Sources: *DNB*; J.G. Simms, *The Williamite Confiscation in Ireland 1690-1703* (London, 1956).

**306**

## 304 *Report of the Commissioners*
*Appointed by Parliament To Enquire into the Irish Forfeitures,*
*Deliver'd to the Honble House of Commons the 15th Of December*
*1699 (London and Dublin, 1700)*

ULSTER MUSEUM, BELFAST

24 pp.

The Report of the seven commissioners was presented to the English House of
Commons by Francis Annesley. On the basis of the commissioners' rather
optimistic calculations as to the amount of Irish land that might be available for
sale, and the price it might fetch, the Commons pushed through the Resumption
Act of 1700 which cancelled all the grants of forfeited land made by William III.

The Report was signed by four of the commissioners, the other three
dissenting from it because the 'private estate' of James II (granted by William to
Elizabeth Villiers) was included.

## 305 *The Act of Resumption, 1700*
*(11 & 12 Will. III, c.2 [Eng.], 11 April 1700)*

TRINITY COLLEGE, DUBLIN
REPRODUCTION OF FIRST PAGE

On the basis of the report of the commission appointed in 1699 to enquire into
the Irish forfeitures, the English House of Commons resolved that - with a few
exceptions - all the grants made by William should be resumed (i.e., taken back)
and that the proceeds from the sale of the lands should go towards paying the
cost of the Irish war (over six million pounds). Because it was 'tacked' to a
supply bill for raising revenue, William was forced to accept this severe rebuff.
Under the Act the forfeited lands were put in the hands of thirteen trustees, who
were to decide on claims and sell the remainder by auction.

Apart from the pleasure of humiliating the king, and depriving his favourites
of their gains, the outcome was very disappointing. Successful claims
considerably reduced the amount of land available, and by the time the sales
began (in late 1702) the bottom had fallen out of the market. In the end a large
amount had to be sold off cheaply to a consortium of speculators.

**307**

## 306 *Deed box, probably c. 1690*

BY ROBERT GIBTON, DUBLIN
NATIONAL MUSEUM OF IRELAND, DUBLIN (3-1989)

Decorated wood, length 35.5 cms.

The wood is covered in pony skin (much of which is missing) bound and decorated with leather straps fastened with iron studs. The lining is wood-block printed paper with floral and foliate design; iron lock. There is a printed label on the inside inscribed: 'Robert Gibton,/Trunk and Plate-Case Maker,/At No. 3, in Pudding-row, near Ormond-Bridge,/Dublin;/Makes and sells all manner of Trunks, Sumpter-Car-Trunks, large and small/ Portmanteaus, with or without Hat-Cases, French Portmanteaus, travelling/ Gun Cases for Gentlemen, in the most compleat Manner, cases for Plate, China and/Glass; likewise cases for musical Instruments of all sorts./ N.B. As said Gibton is a new Beginner, and is determined his work shall be/executed in the neatest and [stron] gest Manner, at the most reasonable Rates, together/with his constant Study to please, he flatters himself to merit the Favour and Recom/-mendation of his Friends and the Public.'

## 307 *Sir Cyril Wyche (1632?-1707)*

BY AN UNKNOWN ARTIST
ROYAL HOSPITAL, KILMAINHAM
REPRODUCTION

Cyril Wyche was born in Constantinople, where his father Sir Peter Wyche was ambassador, and was educated at Oxford, where he obtained the degree of doctor of common law in 1665. Knighted by Charles II at The Hague in 1660, he served as a clerk in chancery between 1662 and 1675 and was called to the Bar in 1670. He was MP for Callington, Cornwall from 1661 to 1678, for East Grinstead in 1681 and for Saltash from 1685 to 1687.

In 1692 he went to Ireland as secretary to Henry Sidney, the newly-appointed lord lieutenant, and was made an Irish privy councillor. The following year he was appointed one of the three lords justices of Ireland who were placed in charge of the government of the country after Sidney's recall to London in 1693. (The other two were Lord Capel of Tewkesbury and William Duncombe). Both he and Duncombe, as lords justices, refused to sign the warrant granting to Elizabeth Villiers the private estate of James II; this was subsequently not effected until Capel became lord deputy. Wyche and Duncombe tried to carry through impartially and fairly the terms of the treaty of Limerick; Capel, on the other hand, supported the cause of the English interest in Ireland to the full.

There was a similar divergence of opinion over the advisibility of calling a parliament. Both Wyche and Duncombe were eventually removed from office and Capel was appointed lord deputy in May 1695 (and summoned a parliament). Wyche went to Turkey as ambassador but returned to England in 1697. In 1700 he was chosen as one of the thirteen trustees appointed to deal with the Irish forfeitures. As the most distinguished member, he acted in effect as their chairman until the trust completed its work in June 1703. He served as MP for Preston from 1702 to 1705 and died on 29 December 1707.

Sources:     *DNB*; J.G. Simms, *The Williamite Confiscation in Ireland 1690-1703* (London, 1956).

## 308 *A List of the Claims*
*As they are Entred with the Trustees at Chichester - House on College - Green, Dublin, On or before the Tenth of August, 1700 (Dublin, 1701)*

ULSTER MUSEUM, BELFAST

folio

This copy has marginal notes on the Trustees' decision in each of the 3,103 claims and also - in addition to the printed alphabetical index of claimants - two manuscript alphabetical indexes to the names of the forfeiting parties and the names of the purchasers.

## 309 *Minutes of the Trustees for the Irish Forfeitures, 1700-03*

PUBLIC RECORD OFFICE OF NORTHERN IRELAND

This is a volume from the records kept by Francis Annesley, who was a member of both the commission of enquiry in 1699 and also of the trust appointed under the Act of Resumption to dispose of the forfeitures. The Annesley manuscripts are an important source for historians of the Williamite land settlement. They contain copies of the proceedings of both bodies, correspondence of the commissioners and minutes of the trustees' proceedings, as well as the text of a number of private acts of parliament not found elsewhere.

Francis Annesley (1663-1750) of Castlewellan, Co. Down and Thorganby, Yorkshire, was the only surviving son of Francis Annesley of Castlewellan, son of the first Viscount Valentia. By profession a lawyer (he was a barrister of the Inner Temple), he was a member of both the English and Irish House of Commons at the turn of the century, sitting in the latter as member for Downpatrick. Following the commissioners' report, which he presented at Westminster, he was censured and expelled by the Irish House of Commons.

Annesley married three times. His sixth son by his first wife was created Baron Annesley and Viscount Glerawly in the peerage of Ireland and was father of the first Earl Annesley.

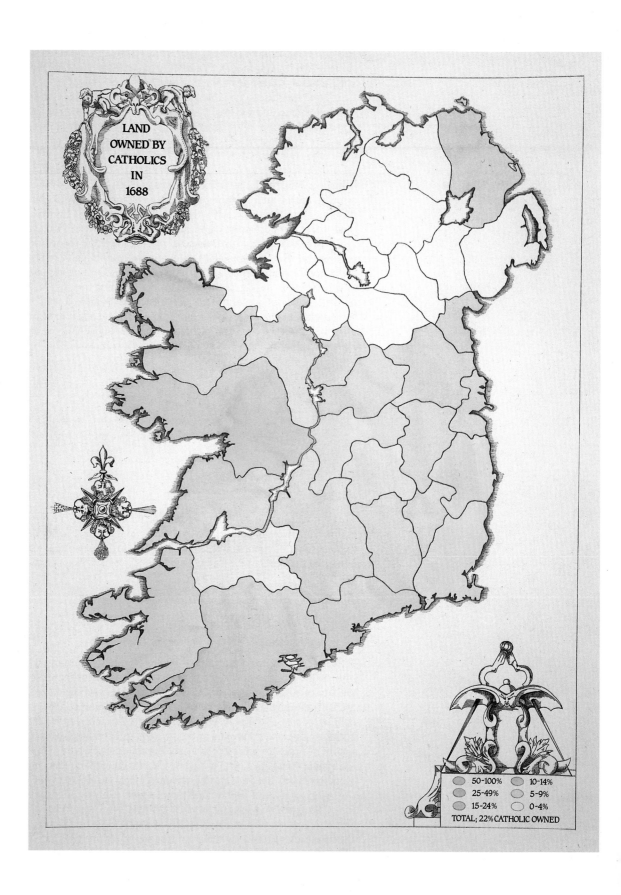

LAND
OWNED BY
CATHOLICS
IN
1688

50-100%    10-14%
25-49%     5-9%
15-24%     0-4%
TOTAL; 22% CATHOLIC OWNED

LAND
OWNED BY
CATHOLICS
IN
1703

25-49%   5-9%
15-24%   0-4%
10-14%
TOTAL; 14% CATHOLIC OWNED

# 12. Religious Consequences

William's victory led to the restoration of the Church of Ireland as the only official church in Ireland, supported by state endowments and by the tithes that everyone, Catholics and Dissenters included, had to pay to its clergy. When James held his parliament in Dublin in 1689 and summoned the Church of Ireland bishops to attend as lords spiritual several of those who had remained in the country did so, prominent among them Dopping, bishop of Meath. By doing so, of course, they acknowledged James and risked offending William. Subsequently, however, they welcomed the Protestant deliverer. Bishop King's book *The State of the Protestants of Ireland*, justifying his and their behaviour, was strongly challenged by the Reverend Charles Leslie, chancellor of Connor, one of the few Irish Protestant Jacobites, who ended his days in France. Most of the clergy of the established church supported William from the first, however; only one bishop declined to swear allegiance to him and was deprived of his see, whereas five of the seven English bishops arrested by James in 1688 felt unable to take the oath.

The Presbyterians, who had done so much to save Ulster for William and who had thrown in their lot with him at an early stage, were very disappointed with the outcome. The Toleration Act in England and the establishment of Presbyterianism as the Church of Scotland raised hopes of similar official recognition and support in Ireland, but their erstwhile allies in the Church of Ireland, who detested them as anti-episcopalians and feared the spread of their influence, prevented such concessions. William did, however, revive and increase the royal bounty (*regium donum*) first paid to approved Presbyterian clergy by Charles II.

For the Catholics the outcome was disastrous. Despite promises made in the treaty of Limerick that they would be free to worship as in the reign of Charles II, and that no oath other than a simple oath of allegiance would be required of them, penal laws were enacted which ran counter to these undertakings. Though William himself was tolerant in matters of religion, his Protestant subjects in England and Ireland were not and had few qualms about breaking the spirit of a treaty that they had always thought to be far too generous in its concessions. Unfortunately for his Catholic subjects, as a result of the Revolution and of his constant need for money to support the war against France, William could not do without parliament as Charles and James had done and so could not save them from the intolerance of the time. Such intolerance existed everywhere, it is true - in France and Spain and the Empire Protestants were persecuted severely - but only in Ireland were the persecuted a majority of the population in the area concerned.

The effects of the penal laws on the organisation and activities of the church and its hierarchy were not so serious as the tone and terms of the acts might lead one to suppose. For one thing, eighteenth century government was not all that efficient. For another, Protestants were not entirely of one mind on the matter: seven Church of Ireland bishops protested against the mutilated form in which the Treaty of Limerick was ratified by the Irish parliament in 1697, and eight of them voted against the law of 1709. More important, the courage and fortitude of many of the Catholic clergy matched that of Protestant pastors persecuted in France and the Habsburg dominions, and kept the vast majority of the people secure in their faith. In any case, despite occasional fits of activity such as the publication of the Prayer Book in Irish in 1712, the established church made no serious attempt to convert the Catholic population.  The motivation behind the penal laws was in fact more political than religious. Until the 1760s the papacy recognised the Stuarts as the rightful rulers of the country and accepted their nominees as Irish bishops. This and the existence of a large force of Irish Catholics in the Continental armies opposed to England was bound to make Irish Protestants apprehensive about the loyalty of the Catholic population. Their response was to deprive Irish Catholics of all political power; and, since political power largely depended upon ownership of land, the main targets and the main victims of the penal laws were Catholic landowners.

**310**

**311**

## 310 *Narcissus Marsh D.D. (1638-1713)*

BY AN UNKNOWN ARTIST
TRINITY COLLEGE, DUBLIN
REPRODUCTION

Marsh was born in Wiltshire and studied at Oxford, where he became a doctor of divinity in 1671. In 1662 he was ordained and served as chaplain to Seth Ward, successively bishop of Exeter and of Salisbury, and later was chaplain to Lord Chancellor Clarendon. He was appointed Provost of Trinity College, Dublin in January 1679 but found the position taxing and unrewarding; the undergraduates were 'both rude and ignorant, and I was quickly weary of 340 young men and boys in this lewd, debauched town' (*DNB*, pp. 216-7). Despite this, he worked diligently and took a particular interest in the teaching of Irish, for which he employed a converted Catholic priest. A keen mathematician, he was a founder member of the Dublin Philosophical Society in 1683.

In that year he resigned the provostship, having been made bishop of Ferns and Leighlin. At the beginning of 1689 he was driven from his see by James's unruly soldiery and fled to England, where he was treated with extreme kindness by his fellow clergy and appointed canon of St Asaph. He returned to Ireland in July 1690, after the battle of the Boyne, and the following year was appointed archbishop of Cashel. In 1694 he became archbishop of Dublin, in 1703 archbishop of Armagh. When archbishop of Dublin he founded a library in St Sepulchre's, close to St Patrick's Cathedral; it still exists, and is the oldest public library in Ireland. He died in Dublin on 2 November 1713 and was buried in St Patrick's Cathedral, near his library.

Sources:     *DNB*; W.G. Strickland, *A Descriptive Catalogue of the Pictures, Busts and Statues in Trinity College, Dublin, and in The Provost's House* (Dublin, 1916).

312

## 311 *Anthony Dopping D.D. (1643-97)*

BY AN UNKNOWN ARTIST
TRINITY COLLEGE, DUBLIN
REPRODUCTION

Anthony Dopping was born in Dublin and studied at Trinity College, where he became a doctor of divinity in 1672. In 1669 he was appointed vicar of St Andrew's, Dublin. Ten years later he was made bishop of Kildare. He was translated to Meath in 1682 and was also appointed to the privy council, on which he remained until its dissolution by James II, shortly after his accession in February 1685.

An ardent champion of the Protestant interest in Ireland, he made repeated attacks on Catholicism from the pulpit, to the extent that James remarked upon it to Clarendon. When Narcissus Marsh, bishop of Ferns and Leighlin, fled to England early in 1689, Dopping became administrator of his spiritualities in his absence. James's Irish parliament, summoned on 7 May 1689, included four Church of Ireland bishops but no Catholic ones, as he did not wish to offend English Protestant opinion. Dopping, the ablest of the four, became in effect leader of the opposition; during the debate on the repeal of the acts of settlement and explanation the four bishops were united against it. (James was pleased at this; he too was opposed to it but had little choice in the end but to agree to repeal).

After the Boyne Dopping led a deputation of clergy to William in his camp outside Dublin and, besides offering congratulations, defended himself and his brethren against the charge of being 'trimmers or favourers of popery' because they had collaborated with James. (Most Irish Anglican clergy supported William from the beginning, but worked with James out of self-preservation and for the sake of their congregations).

In 1690 he was again appointed to the privy council. Like most Williamites, he regarded the treaty of Limerick as being too conciliatory to the Irish and preached a sermon denouncing the folly of relying on their promises of submission. For this he was temporarily removed from the privy council. He died in Dublin on 25 April 1697 and was buried in St Andrew's church.

Sources:     *DNB*; J.G. Simms, *Jacobite Ireland 1685-91* (London, 1969).

## 312 *The Dopping porringer, 1685-6*

BY JOHN PHILLIPS, DUBLIN
ULSTER MUSEUM, BELFAST

Silver, height 24.8 cms; hallmarks on base and lid; the arms of Dopping engraved on the bowl and
Weldon impaling Dopping on the cover.
Purchased, London 1956, with the aid of a grant from the National Art-Collections Fund.

The bowl has cast caryatid handles and bears repoussé decoration of flowers
encircling a lion. The domed cover has similar repoussé work depicting an eagle,
and is surmounted by an opening bud finial.

The porringer is thought to have been the property of the Rev. Anthony
Dopping, D.D., Bishop of Meath. In 1721 Arthur Weldon of Rahinderry,
Queen's County, married as his second wife Mary, daughter of Anthony
Dopping, at which time the arms were probably engraved. The porringer
remained in the possession of the Weldon family until 1956, shortly before it
entered the Museum's collection.

By the seventeenth century, the porringer was a popular piece of domestic
silver and could often, in its different forms, be referred to as a caudle cup,
cupping bowl or posset cup. Porringers were generally lidded and seem to have
been used for any semi-liquid food. Two popular cures for minor ailments which
would have been served in a porringer were spiced caudle, (a fine oatmeal gruel
served with the addition of ale or wine) and posset (a hot milk drink also served
sweet and curdled with ale or wine). Some porringers had matching salvers,
indicating that they were intended for ornamental rather than domestic use.

Throughout most of the seventeenth century porringers tended to have
robust, almost pear-shaped bodies which were richly decorated in the lower part.
The most popular decorative motifs were tulip-like flowers, leaf repoussé work
and real or imaginary animals such as unicorns, stags or, as on the Dopping
Porringer, a lion. The two side handles were usually the elegant cast caryatid type
or else scroll-shaped. During the latter part of Charles II's reign the full, robust
porringer shape gave way to a taller and more straight-sided vessel with finer
and less extravagant decoration.

## 313 *Charles Leslie (1650-1722)*

BY AN UNKNOWN ARTIST, ENGLISH SCHOOL, AFTER ALEXIS-SIMON BELLE
(1674-1734)
NATIONAL GALLERY OF IRELAND, DUBLIN

Line engraving 13.5 x 7.6 cms (plate cut).
Lit:    Adrian Le Harivel, ed., *National Gallery of Ireland Illustrated Summary Catalogue of
        Prints and Sculpture* (Dublin, 1988),p.26, repr.

Charles Leslie, an Irish Anglican Jacobite and controversialist, was born in
Dublin and educated at Trinity College, where he studied law before taking holy
orders in 1680. Thereafter he went to live at the family seat at Glaslough, Co.
Monaghan. In July 1686 he was appointed chancellor of the diocese of Connor
through Clarendon's influence, and held the position until the Revolution of
1688, when he was removed from office for refusing to swear allegiance to
William III. A staunch supporter of James II, he was one of the few nonjurors in
the Church of Ireland and a highly articulate spokesman for the Jacobite cause.

In 1691 he wrote his first and most influential work, *An answer to a book,
intituled The State of the Protestants in Ireland under the late King James's
Government* (see no. 316). On its publication the following year, the government
declared it libellous and sought to bring Leslie to justice but were unable to track
him down; proceedings against him were accordingly dropped. In 1693 he
visited James at St Germains and received from him the *conge d'elire* [royal
authority to elect] for the nonjuring bishops. Shortly afterwards he published an
attack on William III, accusing him of complicity in the assassination of the anti-
Orange Dutch statesman Johan de Witt in 1672 (a long-established rumour). He
also attacked, through numerous publications, Whig divines such as Burnet and
Tillotson, who replaced Sancroft as archbishop of Canterbury. Quakers and Jews
also fell victim to his polemics, as did mixed marriages. In 1704 he founded a
periodical entitled *The Rehearsal*, through which he expounded his views on
theology and politics. In July 1710 a warrant was issued for his arrest after he had

**313**

implied, in *The Good Old Cause, or Lying in Truth,* that Queen Anne was a usurper. He went into hiding until April 1711, when he escaped to St Germains and presented a memorial to the Prince of Wales (the Old Pretender) concerning the prospects of the Jacobite cause in England.

He subsequently returned to England under a false name ('Mr White') and continued to publish articles on political topics. In August 1713 he went to France again by invitation of the Pretender and joined his household. From there he issued two manifestoes to Bishop Burnet and the Anglican clergy, lauding the Pretender and his promises to make concessions to the Anglican church in the event of his restoration. After the Jacobite rising of 1715 he accompanied the Pretender to Avignon and Rome, which became the seat of the Stuart court in 1719. From there he continued to write on matters relating to the Church of England. He returned to Ireland in the autumn of 1721 and died at Glaslough on 13 April 1722.

Source:       *DNB*; J.G. Simms, *Jacobite Ireland 1685-91* (London, 1969).

**314**

Photo Pieterse-Davison International, Dublin

### 314 *Oak altar table, 1686*

By James Tabary
Royal Hospital, Kilmainham

A talented Frenchman who worked in Dublin in the 1680s, Tabary executed some notable wood carving for the chapel of the Royal Hospital in 1686, at a cost of £250. The altar table has a fluted frieze and acanthus decorations on the legs. The table and details of the carving in the chapel are illustrated in *Irish Furniture*, by The Knight of Glin (Eason's Irish Heritage Series, no. 16, Dublin 1978).

### 315 *King,William (1650-1729)*

*The state of the Protestants of Ireland Under the Late King James's Government : In which Their Carriage towards him is justified and the absolute Necessity of their endeavouring to be freed from his Government, and of submitting to Their present Majesties is demonstrated (London, 1692, 4th edition)*

Ulster Museum, Belfast

octavo: 432 pp.

The author of this influential work, the purpose of which is clearly described in its sub-title, was William King, who at the time of its first publication in 1691 was bishop of Derry. In his early days King had been an ardent advocate of the doctrine of passive resistance to an anointed king, but his experiences in Dublin under the Catholic government of Tyrconnell and James changed his mind and made him an ardent supporter of William of Orange (he was twice imprisoned on suspicion of treason to James).

The partial nature of the book is reflected in the Whig bishop Burnet's praise of it as 'not only the best book that hath been written for the service of the government, but without any figure it is worth all the rest put together, and will do more than all our scribblings for settling the minds of the nation' (*DNB* entry

305

on King). It was effectively answered in 1692, anonymously, by the nonjuror Charles Leslie (see no. 313).

The numerous appendices in this edition include the text of the Act of Attainder passed by James's Dublin parliament in 1689.

As bishop of Derry King was hostile to the Presbyterians, who were very numerous in the diocese and whom he described as 'mighty insolent'. This led to a pamphlet war with the Dublin minister Joseph Boyse. In 1703 King was translated to the archbishopric of Dublin, where he spent the rest of his career.

## 316 *Leslie, Charles (1650-1722)*
*An answer to a book, intituled, The state of the Protestants in Ireland under the late King James's government... London, printed... 1692*

THE QUEEN'S UNIVERSITY, BELFAST

quarto:   [22], 195 [ie., 197], 77, [6] pp., folding table.
Lit:       Wing L1120.

The book defends James against attacks made upon him by archbishop William King and criticises rebellion. Leslie (see no. 313) was one of the most effective Jacobite controversialists anywhere in the British Isles. Many scholars felt that he had the better of the argument with King.

## 317 *An act for Relief of the Protestant Irish clergy*
*(1WILL. III & MARY, 20 August 1689)*

ULSTER MUSEUM, BELFAST

quarto:  3 pp.

This act protected the rights of clergy of the Church of Ireland, who had fled to England 'for fear of the Irish Rebels' and had accepted cures in England, in their Irish benefices - provided they returned to Ireland within three months 'after the Courts of Justice in Ireland shall be open and furnished with Protestant Judges' and resigned their English appointments.

## 318 *The Book of Common Prayer*
*Leabhar Na Nornaightheadh Ccomhchoitchionn (London, 1712)*

J.A. GAMBLE

octavo:  text in English and Irish.

Following the Williamite victory, the Church of Ireland was restored as the established religion of the country, though the vast majority of the inhabitants were Catholics and many of the rest Presbyterians. Only occasionally, and then only in a half-hearted manner, was any attempt made to convert the Catholic population by preaching and teaching. One such period of activity, in the years after 1709, led to the publication of parallel texts in English and Irish of the prayer book and the catechism; 6,000 of each were printed and distributed, along with a similar number of Lewis's *Exposition of the Church Catechism*, and a professorship of Irish was established at Trinity College. The printing of the Prayer Book was due in part to the efforts of Jonathan Swift.

Even when the clergy showed some enthusiasm for the task of conversion, however, no party or leading politician in parliament was prepared to promote it or provide funds for it. Indeed, to have made all the Catholics into Protestants would have deprived the ruling Irish elite of its distinctive position. As the archbishop of Dublin, William King, remarked a dozen years later: 'It is plain to me by the methods that have been taken since the Reformation, and which are yet pursued by both the civil and ecclesiastical powers, that there never was nor is any design that all should be Protestants.'

Sources:       R. Mant, *History of the Church of Ireland* (London, 1840); W.A. Phillips, ed., *History of the Church of Ireland* (Oxford, 1933).

319

320

### 319 *Chalice, 1679*

BY EDWARD SWAN, DUBLIN
ULSTER MUSEUM, BELFAST

Silver, height 23.6 cms; hallmarks beneath the rim.
Bequeathed by R.Greeves Esq., Belfast 1966.

The chalice has a bucket-shaped bowl with flared lip and is engraved IHS, incorporating a cross above the bar of the H and a heart beneath. The biconical curved stem has a central ring knop.

### 320 *Paten salver, c. 1695*

BY ROBERT GOBLE, CORK
NATIONAL MUSEUM OF IRELAND, DUBLIN (15-1927)

Silver, diameter (of platform) 23.5 cms.

Circular platform with raised gadrooned rim and chased border of flowers, scrolls, imbrication and architectural motifs in six panels, inscribed underneath with the letters 1.1; trumpet-shaped foot with gadrooned torus. Stamped on the platform with the maker's mark RG (Robert Goble) and with a ship between two castles, a town mark of Cork.

**321**

### 321 *Letters patent from William III, 28 September 1699, renewing the Regium Donum*

UNION THEOLOGICAL COLLEGE, BELFAST

Parchment (2 membranes), 40 x 60 cms, with engraved portrait of the king; seals missing.

The *regium donum* or royal bounty, paid to support the stipends of approved Presbyterian ministers in Ireland, was first granted by Charles II in 1672, when the amount was £600. It was discontinued under James II. At Hillsborough, Co. Down on 19 June 1690 William III received a deputation of ministers, who saluted him as a fellow-Calvinist, pointed out that they formed the majority of Ulster Protestants, and drew attention to the part played by Presbyterians in the siege of Derry (Walker, bishop-designate of that city, contradicted them indignantly but out of the King's hearing). William thereupon restored the grant and increased it to £1,200 (persuaded by his Scottish general Douglas to go beyond the £800 he had first intended); this gave each minister £15. An order was issued to Christopher Carleton, collector of customs at Belfast, authorising him to pay £1,200 annually out of the customs revenue. This grant was regularised, and made payable out of the Irish exchequer, by letters patent issued by Mary II in September 1691.

With the death of the original trustees named in the grant it became necessary to issue these new letters patent. Following the death of William, Queen Anne renewed the grant by her letters patent of 11 March 1703. Payment of the bounty was suspended for a time in 1714, but it was restored and raised to £2,000 a year by George I. It was paid in increasing amounts until the disestablishment of the Church of Ireland in 1869, at which time the payments made to the Presbyterian and Catholic churches also ceased.

### 322 *James Kirkpatrick (d. 1744)*

BY AN UNKNOWN ARTIST
FIRST PRESBYTERIAN CONGREGATION, BELFAST

Watercolour 16.8 x 14.5 cms.

The career of James Kirkpatrick illustrates several important points about the Presbyterians in the north of Ireland during this period. One was their Scottish origin, and the close ties that they maintained with their co-religionists in

322

Scotland. Kirkpatrick was the son of a Scottish Presbyterian, Hugh Kirkpatrick, who became minister of the congregation at Ballymoney, Co. Antrim. Kirkpatrick himself was probably born in Scotland before his father settled in Ireland. He studied divinity at Glasgow University, as most Ulster ministers did then and throughout the eighteenth century, before being licensed by the Route presbytery in Co. Antrim and being ordained at Templepatrick in 1699. Like other Presbyterians he welcomed the Revolution. A sermon on the death of William III in 1702, which he published, contains a eulogy of that monarch.

In 1706 Kirkpatrick moved to Belfast as assistant to the Rev. John McBride, minister of the First Presbyterian Congregation in Rosemary Lane. The congregation needed an assistant minister because McBride had been obliged to flee to Scotland after refusing to swear the oath abjuring the Pretender (he was one of only four Presbyterian nonjurors who scrupled to swear that the Pretender was not the true son of James II). When a second congregation was established in 1708 Kirkpatrick was appointed its minister.

Like McBride, Kirkpatrick was involved in pamphlet warfare with the clergy of the Church of Ireland. In 1713 he published, anonymously, *An Historical Essay upon the Loyalty of Presbyterians in Great Britain and Ireland, from the Reformation to the present year, 1713*, a defence of Presbyterianism which stressed that, while members of the church might have seemed like rebels on occasion, they were firm supporters of constitutional government and monarchy. This ponderous work (according to Witherow the style was 'so prolix and heavy that at no time could it have had very many readers') was a direct reply to a blast from the vicar of Belfast, Tisdal, alleging that Presbyterians were disloyal and constituted a state within the state. Tisdal, the embittered champion of the established church in a town dominated by Presbyterians, had been reponsible for the denunciation of McBride as a Jacobite.

Though Kirkpatrick, unlike McBride, had no difficulty with the oath of abjuration, he baulked at having to subscribe the Westminster Confession as a test of Presbyterian orthodoxy. This led to a permanent schism in the 1720s, when the Synod of Ulster put all the non-subscribing ministers into one presbytery and refused to hold communion with them.

Kirkpatrick was a doctor both of divinity and of medicine and successfully combined pastoral duties and a medical practice. He died in Dublin in 1744.

Sources: J.S. Reid and W.D. Killen, *History of the Presbyterian Church in Ireland* (London, 1853); T.Witherow, *Historical and Literary Memorials of Presbyterianism in Ireland (1623-1721)*, (Belfast, 1879); A. Gordon and G.K. Smith, *Historic Memorials of the First Presbyterian Church of Belfast* (Belfast, 1887); *A History of Congregations in the Presbyterian Church in Ireland 1610-1982* (Belfast, 1982); R.F. Holmes, *Our Irish Presbyterian Heritage* (Belfast, 1985).

## 323 *The Psalms of David In Meeter*
### *(Patrick Neill, Belfast, 1700) (Ms. inscr. on flyleaf: 'David Smith's Gift to Belfast Meeting House 1705')*

FIRST PRESBYTERIAN CONGREGATION, BELFAST

This little (32 mo) book, one of the earliest surviving productions of Belfast's first printer, has a later tortoiseshell cover with silver clasps.

By the end of the seventeenth century Presbyterianism was strongly established in Belfast and growing rapidly as more settlers arrived from Scotland; a second congregation and meeting house date from 1708. Most of the leading citizens of the town were Presbyterians, as were most of the members of the corporation that ran its affairs, until they were excluded from office by the operation of the Test Act of 1704. This made it compulsory for all holders of public office to take the sacrament in the established church.

## 324-325 *Two Presbyterian Communion cups, 1690s*

FIRST PRESBYTERIAN CONGREGATION, BELFAST

Silver
No.324 inscr: 'The Gift of James Stewart to the Meeting-house of Belfast 1693'.
No. 325 inscr: 'Donum Tho. Craford Coetiu Presbyter de Belfast 1698'.

## 326 *(St) Oliver Plunkett, Archbishop of Armagh (1629-81)*

BY JAN VANDERVAART, AFTER GARRET MORPHEY (FL. 1680-1716)
NATIONAL GALLERY OF IRELAND, DUBLIN

Mezzotint 32.8 x 24.8 cms (plate cut), published 1681.
Lit: Adrian Le Harivel, ed., *National Gallery of Ireland Illustrated Summary Catalogue of Prints and Sculpture* (Dublin, 1988), p.376, repr.

Oliver Plunkett was born on 1 November 1629 at Loughcrew, Co. Meath into a well-known Old English family whose members included the earls of Fingall and Louth. He was educated by Lord Fingall's brother, Patrick Plunkett, titular abbot of St Mary's, Dublin and in 1645 went to Rome to study at the Irish College. After ordination in 1654 he was appointed professor of theology at the Propaganda College and taught there until 1669. In July of that year he was nominated archbishop of Armagh, and was consecrated in Ghent in November. He returned to Ireland in March 1670 and accepted the hospitality of Lord Louth, whose residence was in the centre of his mission. His return to Ireland coincided with the appointment of Lord Berkeley of Stratton as viceroy, 'a moderate and prudent man' in Plunkett's opinion, whose attitude to the Catholic church was benevolent by the standards of the time. Berkeley encouraged Plunkett to set up schools and gave him financial assistance towards that end.

Plunkett's early months in Ireland were busy and fruitful. By June 1670 he had held two synods and two ordinations and had confirmed over ten thousand people. His labours on behalf of the church, and for the many landed Catholic families who had lost their properties under the Act of Settlement, greatly impressed his fellow clergy; in October 1670 his bishops wrote to the Holy See

**326**

expressing gratitude for his appointment as their primate and lauded his efforts on their behalf.

Under the Earl of Essex, who succeeded Berkeley in the viceroyalty, conditions for Catholics became harsher and more repressive as the effects of the Test Act of 1673 (which virtually excluded Catholics from office under the crown) reverberated throughout Ireland. Many priests and bishops fled to the Continent. Plunkett and a companion went into hiding and endured severe deprivation during the winter of 1673, often without food and with only scanty shelter to protect them from the elements. Nevertheless, despite such hardships and the general repression under which the Catholic church was labouring, Plunkett could report that by December of that year he had confirmed 48,655 people. His missionary zeal was not confined to the cure of souls: he introduced regularity and discipline into the houses of religious orders and applied himself to eradicating the problem of drunkenness among the clergy (and became a total abstainer himself, to set an example).

Between 1674 and 1679 Plunkett made numerous visitations throughout his province, preaching and ministering to his flock in both English and Irish. The extreme poverty which he was experiencing convinced him that it would be foolhardy for the Holy See to add new bishops to the existing hierarchy. Writing to the papal internunzio in September 1677, he reported that there were two bishoprics vacant in the province of Cashel and that 'The richer of these does not annually yield 80 scudi; now you yourself will judge, how can a Bishop (why do I say Bishop, how could his servant) support and clothe himself with 80 scudi a year? No Bishop in Ireland has two servants, and it is one and the same that acts as his servant and stable-boy, and it is the stable-boy that serves the Bishop's mass. Moreover, none of them have their own house: to procure food they go to-day to the house of one gentleman, and to-morrow to the house of another, not without their shame; and indeed the gentry are now tired of these visits ... I have three servants, but my friends support them, and give hay and oats to my horses: however, were it not for their charity, the stable-boy would also be the server of my mass ...' (Moran, pp. 186-7). During his subsequent imprisonment for high treason, fears that new bishops would be appointed still weighed heavily upon him; to increase their number in the tense atmosphere of the aftermath of the Popish Plot would, he believed, bring about greater persecution for those of his faith.

During 1678 persecution of the Catholic church increased considerably, as the Popish Plot hysteria swept across England. Oates's 'plot' - the basic details of which were that Charles II and his government were going to be overthrown by the Jesuits, Protestants were going to be massacred in their thousands, Ireland was going to be invaded by the French and the Duke of York was going to become king and rule under the direction of the Jesuits - swelled to enormous proportions; even the queen was implicated. Although the king knew the plot to be a fabrication, the fears it aroused suited those who were opposed to the Duke of York as his successor, particularly the virulently anti-Catholic Earl of Shaftesbury.

In Ireland an order was given that bishops, Jesuits and regular priests should leave the country by 20 November 1678. This was subsequently extended to include the secular clergy. Convents, seminaries and schools were suppressed and the saying of mass was forbidden. Although there was no evidence of a conspiracy in Ireland, nor that the French were planning to invade, Shaftesbury was determined to establish the existence of a plot and took steps to find witnesses to swear to the event. This proved to be none too difficult; Irish informers who travelled to England to give evidence 'with bad English and worse clothes, and returned well-bred gentlemen, well-caronated, periwigged and clothed' (Ogg, p. 596) were plentiful. The first victim of the persecution was archbishop Talbot, brother of Richard Talbot, later Earl of Tyrconnell, who was arrested and imprisoned in Dublin Castle in October 1678 for an alleged part in a plot to murder the viceroy Ormonde. By May 1679 the situation for Catholics in Ireland was extreme. Bishops and priests were being hunted down by soldiers and spies, and rewards were being offered as an inducement to informers - £10 the going rate for the arrest of a bishop or Jesuit, £5 for a friar or vicar-general.

Plunkett came out of hiding in November 1679 to visit a dying relative, the bishop of Meath, and was subsequently arrested in Dublin on 6 December and placed in solitary confinement for six weeks. The only crime of which he was then accused was that of remaining in Ireland and performing his prelatical duties, in contravention of the edict of expulsion. For six months this was the only charge against him. By the summer of 1680, however, the accusations had changed. On the evidence of an apostate priest whom he had punished for various crimes, John MacMoyer, together with that of other false witnesses, he was charged with the following: that he had plotted to establish the Catholic religion in Ireland and to murder all Protestants; that he had invited Louis XIV to take possession of Ireland; that he had enrolled 70,000 soldiers to join with the French on their arrival; that he had taken money from the clergy to pay the French; that he had visited and explored all the seaport towns and fortresses in Ireland, looking for a secure port for the projected French invasion; that he had held many synods to collect money for the French.

Plunkett's trial was held in Dundalk on 23 and 24 July, before an all-Protestant jury. MacMoyer, his chief accuser, failed to appear and the proceedings were postponed. In October he was brought to London, where he languished in Newgate for several months, until his arraignment on 3 May 1681 for high treason. He was subsequently given thirty-five days to procure witnesses for his defence, not an easy task as he was short of money to pay their expenses, a number of them were afraid to travel to London and he was unable to obtain proof of the guilty characters of his accusers, especially MacMoyer. (He was never able to procure copies of Irish court records which would have proved the criminal characters of his accusers).

Plunkett's speech at his trial in June was reasoned and dignified. After pointing out that his accusers had absented themselves from his Irish trial because they feared he would be able to clear his name, they had contrived to have him brought to London 'where I could not have a jury that knew the qualities of my adversaries, or who knew me, or the circumstances of the places, times, or persons ... I have been accused principally and chiefly for surveying the ports, for fixing upon Carlingford for the landing of the French, for the having of 70,000 men ready to join the French, for collecting money for the agents in this matter, for assisting the French, and enlisting this great Utopian army. A jury in Ireland, consisting of men that lived in that country, would immediately under-stand the folly of such charges, and any man in the world that hath but seen Ireland in a map, would easily see there was no probability that Carlingford should be a place fit for the French to land in ... for the raising of the 70,000 men, and the monies that are collected of the clergy in Ireland, they cannot be true, for they are a poor clergy, that have no revenue or land - there is not a priest in all Ireland that hath, from certain or uncertain sources, above three score pounds a-year, and that I should collect from them sums sufficient for the raising of an army, or for the landing of the French at Carlingford, if it had been brought before a jury in Ireland would have been thought a mere romance' (Moran, pp. 342-4). Plunkett totally denied the charges against him and maintained that all he had done was to carry on with his duties as an archbishop; that was *praemunire* but not treason.

Despite perjured witnesses and lack of evidence, Plunkett was convicted and was hung, drawn and quartered at Tyburn on 1 July 1681. It is now generally accepted that his trial was a travesty of justice and that he was a victim of political intrigue. His relics are in Downshire Abbey and his head in St Peter's church, Drogheda, Co. Louth. In 1920 he was beatified as a martyr for his faith; canonisation followed on 12 October 1975.

The mezzotint is after an oil portrait by the Irish artist Garret Morphey of c. 1681, of which there is a copy in the NPG. Morphey, a Catholic, may have gone over to England in 1681 to paint the archbishop; a mezzotint by T. Laurie, from a crayon drawing by Morphey, records that Morphey made the drawing in Newgate during Plunkett's confinement there.

Sources:    P. Moran, *Life of the Most Rev. Oliver Plunkett* (Dublin, 1870); *DNB*; D. Ogg, *England in the Reign of Charles II* (Oxford, 1934); D. Piper, *Catalogue of the Seventeenth Century Portraits in the National Portrait Gallery 1625-1714* (Cambridge, 1963); J. G. Simms, *Jacobite Ireland 1685-91* (London, 1969); T.W. Moody, F.X. Martin, F.J. Byrne, eds., *A New History of Ireland III 1534-1691* (Oxford, 1976).

### 327  *The Articles of Limerick, 1691*
*First page of the Articles as officially published in A Diary of the Seige & Surrender of Lymerick: with the Articles At Large, both Civil & Military (London, 1692)*

THE QUEEN'S UNIVERSITY, BELFAST
REPRODUCTION (SEE NO. 236 FOR ORIGINAL)

During the negotiations leading to the surrender of Limerick the benefit of the Articles was extended - at Sarsfield's insistence - to include not only all soldiers of the Irish army in Limerick, Clare, Kerry, Cork, Sligo and Mayo but also 'all those under their protection in the said counties'. These words were inadvertently omitted from the copy that was signed and sent to London. William restored the 'missing clause' and it was included, as here, in the official printed version. The Protestant parliament in Dublin, when it eventually ratified the Articles in 1697, deliberately left out the clause again. Its omission at that stage seems to have made little difference, however, since most of the Catholics who might have been affected had already recovered their estates and property.

Much more serious for Irish Catholics was parliament's refusal to observe the first of the Civil Articles, whereby they were promised 'such privileges in the exercise of their religion as are consistent with the laws of Ireland; or as they did enjoy in the reign of King Charles the II'. Whatever meaning may have been intended by this rather vague formula, and however long it may have been intended to last, the penal laws enacted by the Irish parliament in the reigns of William and Anne certainly contravened it.

**328**

## 328 *Henri de Massue de Ruvigny, first Earl of Galway (1648-1720)*

BY JOHN SIMON, AFTER PHILIP DE GRAVES (SEVENTEENTH CENTURY)
NATIONAL GALLERY OF IRELAND, DUBLIN

Mezzotint 37.3 x 26.6 cms (plate 34.8 x 25.2), published c. 1704.
Lit:    Adrian Le Harivel, ed., *National Gallery of Ireland Illustrated Summary Catalogue of Prints and Sculpture* (Dublin, 1988), p. 104, repr.

Historians over the years have labelled Galway (see no. 223) as the virtual perpetrator of the penal laws, the persecuted Huguenot who turned persecutor with a vengeance, the architect of the 1697 act under which Catholic bishops and regular clergy were banished from Ireland. Yet the act did not originate with Galway, but stemmed back to October 1695. Furthermore, the initiative for it did not come from the government in London but from the Protestant colonists in Ireland, the group which had been excluded from the negotiations at Limerick. Why then did Galway carry the banishment act through, thereby violating the terms of the treaty of Limerick, which had stipulated that Catholics were to 'enjoy such privileges in the exercise of their religion' as they had under Charles II? And why was the leglislation against the practice of Catholicism coupled with measures against the status of Catholics as landowners, professionals and citizens?

    The answer to the first question seems to be that, in Galway's view, if the bishops and monks were banished the Catholic church would be more amenable to government control. Influence might then be brought to bear on the secular clergy allowed to remain. However, if a proclamation were issued which stated how many secular priests were allowed to stay, this might mean that such priests were exempted by the law. This, in Galway's opinion, would establish a liberty of conscience which would greatly exceed toleration. Galway seems not to have been overly concerned with the violation of the treaty, despite questions about the king's honour.

One of the reasons why he became the target of abuse and vilification was that he had offended Louis XIV (who had accorded him and his father special treatment) by changing sides. Efforts by the Catholic church to blacken his name began in Brussels in November 1697, six weeks after the passing of the banishment act, when the papal internuncio, Orazio Spada, tried to influence William's Catholic allies and have them put pressure on the king to prevent anti-Catholic leglislation. Spada spoke of Galway as wanting 'nothing but the destruction of the Catholic religion ... by doing so he hopes to take vengeance for the expulsion of the French Huguenots ...' (Kelly, pp. 245-6). From this and similar sentiments at the time, it became apparent that Irish Catholics were preparing a propaganda campaign abroad to counter the threatened leglislation against them. Furthermore, Galway was their target: they wished to discredit him with William's Catholic allies and make his position in Ireland an embarrassment to the king.

There was, however, a more sinister aspect to the campaign to blacken Galway's name. French attempts to damage him appear to have been allied with their disinclination to return his French estates to him, which would have been permitted under the terms of the treaty of Rijswick of 1697. By vilifying Galway to William's Catholic allies such as the Elector of Bavaria (who was personally well disposed to Galway), the refusal to return the estates was made more respectable. Louis had a further motive for discrediting his erstwhile subject. It seems likely that when in Savoy as William's envoy Galway had learnt about Louis's part in the Jacobite plans to assassinate William in February 1696 - a complicity which Louis always hotly denied. Galway subsequently also discovered that Louis had actually hired an Italian assassin to come to England to do the deed in the spring of 1696. Louis hastened by black propaganda to discredit Galway before Galway could discredit him. When the question arose of restoring Galway's French estates in May 1698, Louis could refuse without fear that the Catholic powers would intervene.

Philip de Graves was an obsure seventeenth century English portrait painter, evidently of French origin, about whom almost nothing is known.

Source:    P. Kelly, 'Lord Galway and the Penal Laws,' C.E.J. Caldicott, H. Gough, J.-P. Pittion, eds., *The Huguenots and Ireland* (Dun Laoghaire, 1988).

## 329 *The Irish House of Lords, c.1708*

## 330 *The Irish House of Commons, c.1708*

BOTH BY NICHOLAS GUEUDEVILLE (C.1654-1721)
ULSTER MUSEUM, BELFAST
REPRODUCTIONS

Coloured engravings illustrating CARTE DU GOUVERNEMENT CIVIL ET MILITAIRE ... DU ROYAUME D'IRLANDE, from *Atlas Historique* (Amsterdam, 1708).

During the seventeenth century and the first three decades of the eighteenth, the Irish parliament sat in Chichester House, Dublin, which occupied the site later used for the new Parliament House, now the Bank of Ireland. No illustration survives of the exterior of Chichester House during the period when parliament met there. These two engravings are the earliest pictures of the Irish parliament in session. An entirely Protestant body after 1690, it met much more frequently than before the Glorious Revolution and was thus able to frustrate any tolerant intentions William III and his successors may have had towards their Irish Catholic subjects.

Gueudeville was born at Rouen but worked in Holland for most of his life. He died at The Hague in 1721.

**329**

**330**

## 331 *Penal laws, 1695-1709*

*Titles or first pages of Acts of the Irish parliament during the reigns of William III and Anne restricting the organisation of the Catholic church and discriminating against its adherents*

ULSTER MUSEUM AND LINEN HALL LIBRARY, BELFAST; TRINITY COLLEGE, DUBLIN.

Photographs

During the reigns of William and Anne the Irish parliament, an entirely Protestant body, enacted a number of laws which restricted Catholic worship, excluded conscientious Catholics from all positions of public influence and profit, and severely penalised Catholic landowners. It was an act of the English parliament, however, that in 1691 excluded Catholics from parliament itself; and English governments, especially in Anne's reign, did nothing to discourage anti-Catholic laws, though they had the power to do so under Poynings' Law.

The worst of the early penal laws were passed in reaction to the threat of Jacobite invasion - a persistent worry for Irish Protestants after their miraculous deliverance from James II and Tyrconnell. The motive behind most of the laws, even those aimed directly at the Catholic clergy, was therefore a political one. The Catholic authorities were actively committed to a Jacobite restoration. The papacy recognised as rightful king not only James himself but after him his son and grandson, and accepted their nominations of Irish bishops until 1766. In these circumstances no conscientious Catholic could take an oath denying the legitimacy of the Jacobite claim; without such an oath no Catholic was regarded as a loyal subject. No real attempt was made to convert the mass of the people, but the laws affecting landowners were rigorously (and successfully) enforced. The essential purpose of the penal laws, as Professor Beckett puts it, was 'not to destroy Roman Catholicism, but to make sure that its adherents were kept in a position of social, economic, and political inferiority' (J.C. Beckett, *The Making of Modern Ireland 1603-1923*, London, 1966, p. 159). See also M. Wall, *The Penal Laws, 1691-1760* (Dundalk, 1976).

*(a)*   An Act to restrain foreign education (7 Will. III, c.4)
This Act prohibited the sending abroad of Catholic children to be 'trained up in any Priory, Abby, Nunnery, Popish University, Colledge or School, or House of Jesuits.' Since Trinity College was closed to them, Catholics would have been cut off from all higher education if this act had not been widely evaded. The prohibition on any Catholic teacher opening a school in Ireland was also impossible to enforce strictly.

*(b)*   An Act for better securing the Government by disarming Papists (7 Will. III, c.5)
This Act required Papists to 'discover and deliver up to some Justice or Justices of the Peace ... all their arms, armour and ammunition' by 1 March 1695. The only exceptions were those who could claim the protection of the articles of Limerick.

The same act forbade any Catholic to have a horse worth £5 or more (an exception was later made for stud horses). The purpose of this was to prevent Catholics from being able again to raise troops of cavalry. For similar reasons, Catholics were prevented from joining the army and gunsmiths were forbidden to have Catholic apprentices.

*(c)*   'An Act for banishing all Papists exercising any ecclesiastical jurisdiction, and all regulars of the popish clergy out of the kingdom' (9 Will. III, c.1)
Since the Catholic authorities were actively committed to a Jacobite restoration, the Irish Protestant government sought to prevent political subversion by expelling bishops, friars, Jesuits and others who had direct links with the Continent.

The Banishment Act had severe consequences for the authority and discipline of the Catholic church in Ireland. At one stage only four bishops remained in the country, all in hiding or passing themselves off as parish priests.

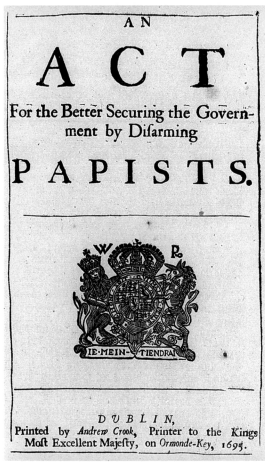

**331(b)**

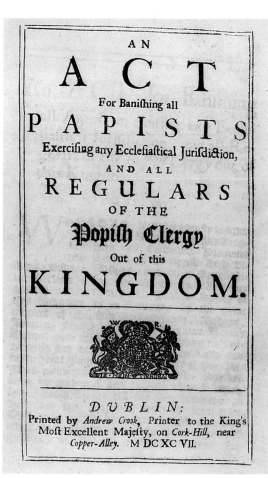

**331(c)**

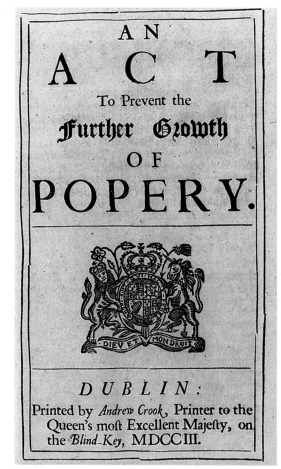

**331(h)**

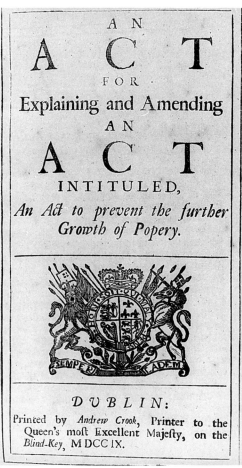

**331(j)**

**(d)** An Act for the Confirmation of the Articles Made at the Surrender of the City of Limerick (9 Will. III, c.2)
Many Irish Protestants felt that the terms of the Treaty of Limerick were far too generous to a defeated enemy. Only in 1697 did the government manage to get it ratified by the Irish parliament and, when it was, the first article (by which Catholics were to have the freedom of worship they had had in the reign of Charles II) was omitted entirely. In the House of Lords, seven Church of Ireland bishops voted against this breach of faith and the bill passed by only one vote.

**(e)** 'An Act to prevent Papists being sollicitors' (10 Will. III, c.13)
The only exceptions to this prohibition were those who could claim the benefit of the articles of Limerick, by definition a diminishing number.

**(f)** An Act To Prevent Popish Priests from coming into this Kingdom (2 Anne, c.3)
Alarmed at the number of Catholic priests remaining in Ireland (nearly 900 by a census of 1697), the Irish parliament passed this act, by which 'every clergyman of the popish religion' coming into the country after 1 January 1704 would be subject to the same penalties as those imposed on bishops and regulars by the Banishment Act. The operation of the act was restricted at first to fourteen years, but it was made perpetual in 1709.

**(g)** An Act for Registring the Popish Clergy (2 Anne, c.7)
Under this act every popish priest was required - under pain of banishment - to register his name, address, parish and details of his ordination. He had to give securities for his good behaviour and was not to leave the county in which he was registered. No priest was to have a curate. The 1,089 priests who registered were free to say mass and carry out all the functions of a parish priest; in effect they were given recognised legal status. In theory, the banishment of bishops should have prevented further ordinations of priests and Catholicism would eventually have died out, but in practice the laws could not be fully enforced.

**(h)** An Act to prevent the Further Growth of Popery (2 Anne, c.7)
By far the most important provisions of this major act of discrimination were those dealing with real property. In order to prevent any increase in the amount of land held by Catholic landowners, no Catholic could buy land or get a lease of more than thirty-one years in land, or acquire land from a Protestant by inheritance or marriage. Furthermore, a Catholic landowner could not leave his land by will; on his death it was to be divided among all his sons, unless the eldest became a Protestant, in which case he inherited all.

The Act also reinforced existing restrictions and added some new ones. Catholics were forbidden to act as guardians for minors; before voting at parliamentary elections they had to take not only the oath of allegiance but also an oath abjuring the Pretender; and a sacramental test closed any remote possibility of public employment. The Test was also to be applied to Protestant dissenters and in fact affected the Presbyterians far more than the Catholics. Since 1691 all civil and military employments had been open to them; after 1704 they were excluded, notably from the corporations of Belfast and Londonderry which they had controlled.

**(i)** An Act to explain and amend an Act intituled 'An Act for Registring the Popish Clergy', (4 Anne, c.2)
By an oversight, the Registration Act of 1704 had applied only to priests who were in the country at the time and did not cover those ordained subsequently. This act closed that loophole.

**(j)** An Act to explain and amend an Act intituled 'An Act to prevent the Further Growth of Popery' (8 Anne, c.3)
The Popery Act of 1709 was a direct result of the Jacobite scare of the previous year, when a French fleet with the Pretender on board planned to invade England. In Ireland priests were seized and imprisoned as a precaution, and it was decided to plug the loopholes in the act of 1704.

The Act of 1709 further restricted the property rights of Catholics. So far as their clergy were concerned, large rewards were offered for discovering regulars and persons exercising ecclesiastical jurisdiction. In

**332**

order to hunt down unregistered priests, magistrates were given wide powers to summon and examine any Catholic over the age of sixteen. Worse, the act decreed that all registered priests should be compelled to take, in open court, the oath abjuring the Pretender, on pain of banishment. The concerted refusal of the clergy to do so (only thirty-three are known to have sworn, out of 1,089) made this part of the act a dead letter, however.

### 332 *Christopher Butler (1673-1757), Archbishop of Cashel*

By James Latham (1693-1747)
Kilkenny Castle
Reproduction

Christopher Butler, brother of Colonel Thomas Butler of Kilcash (see no. 174) was born at Garryricken on 18 January 1673. He was educated in France for the Catholic priesthood, being unable to study in Ireland under the penal laws, and received a doctorate in divinity and canon law from the Sorbonne. He was ordained a priest for Ossory but does not appear to have ever discharged any missionary duties in the diocese. On 9 August 1711 he was nominated for the archbishopric of Cashel and was consecrated in Rome in October 1712. He subsequently returned to Ireland and despite the difficulties of his position under the law, administered his diocese with reasonable freedom from persecution. (The fact that his family was well connected and popular made persecution less likely).

Without any fixed abode, he stayed with family and friends at Kilcash, Garryricken and Westcourt House, Callan, home of his cousin Colonel Richard Butler, periodically on the move when political pressures forced him to be. (He eventually settled at Westcourt). He published a number of pastoral instructions to his priests, on such topics as faith, fasting, penance and marriage, and a *Psalter of Cashel*. Active until the end of his life, he died at Westcourt on 6 September 1757 and was buried in the family vault at Kilcash.

The portrait shows him in clerical robes, holding an episcopal cross in his left hand. A mitre and candlesticks are on an altar to his left. The Rock of Cashel can be seen in the right background. There are two other versions of the portrait, both in the archbishop's palace at Thurles. One may be by Latham, while the other is after him and is a reversed image of the painting.

Sources:     Rev. W. Carrigan, *The History and Antiquities of the Diocese of Ossory* (Dublin, 1905; Kilkenny, 1981); W.P Burke, *The Irish Priests in the Penal Times (1660-1760)* (Waterford, 1914); Anne Crookshank,' James Latham 1696-1747,' *The GPA Irish Arts Review Yearbook,* 1988; additional information from Jane Fenlon.

**334**

### 333 *Chalice and paten*

> MAKER'S INITIALS A S ON CHALICE (POSSIBLY ANTONY STANLEY) AND M W
> ON PATEN (POSSIBLY MATTHEW WEST)
> POSSIBLY DUBLIN, LATE SEVENTEENTH CENTURY
> ULSTER MUSEUM, BELFAST

Silver, gilded inside bowl; height 21 cms.
Inscr:   'This chalice belonged to Fa: Thomas Archbold, renewd by Robt. Archbold 1716.'
Purchased Belfast 1965.

The chalice has a bell-shaped bowl and double-domed foot and is engraved with
a crucifix. The baluster stem has an ovoid knop with two collars above and
below. The paten is engraved IHS.

### 334 *The William Shee chalice, c.1689*

> PROBABLY MADE IN DUBLIN
> NATIONAL MUSEUM OF IRELAND, DUBLIN (313-1909)

Silver, with bowl gilt on the inside; height 19 cms.

The knop and base are decorated with applied cast winged cherub heads. The
foot is engraved with the crucifixion and inscribed 'Me Fieri Fecit Hunc Calicem
Fr Guillelm 'Shee Comissar' G Lis ords Carmelitarum Calceatarum AD vsum
Provinciae Lageniae 30 Nov l689' (Brother William Shee Commissary General
of the Order of Calced Carmelites caused me, this Chalice, to be made for the
use of the Leinster Province 30 Nov 1689).

# 13. Survivors

The cost of the Jacobite war in Ireland, in both blood and treasure, was a heavy one. In terms of money the amount was more than six million pounds in the currency of the day. In terms of men the cost was also heavy, as much by disease as by death in action or from wounds: Schomberg lost more men by sickness in his 1689 campaign than the Jacobites did at Aughrim, the greatest battle of the war.

Many soldiers on both sides who survived the Irish campaign fought each other elsewhere, in the Continental battles of the war between William and Louis and later during the War of the Spanish Succession. Some made great names for themselves. Sarsfield died too soon, at the battle of Landen in 1693, but Berwick (who married his widow) became a marshal of France. Owen Wynne, who fought for William at the Boyne, ended his career as commander of the army in Ireland in the 1730s. His contemporary Michael Rothe reached similar eminence in the army of France. The careers of these two were not uncommon, if more successful than most. The second duke of Ormonde, on the other hand, is a unique example of a leading Williamite who later chose the Pretender in preference to George I and ended his days as a Jacobite exile.

The lives and lineages of people, at least prominent people, are sometimes known, but the beasts which bore them into battle are seldom remembered except by association with an Alexander the Great or a Robert E. Lee. The Byerley Turk is an exception, a survivor of the Boyne who became famous in his own right.

**335**

### 335 *James Butler, second Duke of Ormonde (1665-1745)*
### *(1713)*

BY SIR GODFREY KNELLER (1646-1723)
NATIONAL GALLERY OF IRELAND, DUBLIN

Oil on canvas 125 x 102 cms.

Lit:     David Piper, *Catalogue of the Seventeenth Century Portraits in the National Portrait Gallery 1625-17l4* (Cambridge, 1963), p.260.
        *National Gallery of Ireland Illustrated Summary Catalogue of Paintings* (Dublin, 1981), p.89, no. 485.

James Butler, son of Thomas, Earl of Ossory, a close friend of the Prince of Orange, was born in Dublin Castle on 29 April l665. Educated in France and at Oxford, he returned to Ireland in l680 on the death of his father and lived with his grandfather, the first Duke of Ormonde. He succeeded to the title in July l688 and pursued an independent course during the last few months of James's reign. Together with Prince George of Denmark. he dined with James at Andover on the night of 24 November but then, shortly after the king had retired, defected with the Prince to join William.

He acquiesced readily in the Revolution and acted as lord high constable at William and Mary's coronation. In return for his loyalty he was given the Garter, together with the office of gentleman of the bedchamber and the colonelcy of the second troop of Life Guards. In May l689 he was attainted by the Dublin parliament of James II and his vast estates declared forfeit. (His name, together with the archbishop of Dublin's, headed the list of some 2,400 persons attainted). He accompanied William to Ireland in June l690 and fought at the Boyne. James did not readily overlook his defection: in his declaration of

20 April 1692, which promised various benefits to his subjects if they would but resume their allegiance to him, Ormonde's name was at the head of those excluded from pardon.

In January 1691 he accompanied William to The Hague and during the next two years served in the campaigns on the Continent, being captured by the French at Namur and exchanged for the Duke of Berwick. In the later years of William's reign he became increasingly identified with those who resented the king's obvious preference for his fellow countrymen. When Albemarle, William's Dutch favourite, was promoted over his head in March 1689 to be first commander of the Guards, he resigned his command of the second troop in protest. Fifty MPs thereupon expressed their support of him in this and there was talk of introducing a bill to exclude all foreigners from official employment. The matter, however, ended in a compromise and Ormonde withdrew his resignation. Despite this setback he remained on good terms with William and was among those present at his deathbed on 8 March 1702 (OS).

In August 1702 he commanded the English and Dutch troops which accompanied Sir George Rooke's fleet on the expedition against Cadiz and took part in the capture of the Franco-Spanish treasure fleet at Vigo in the following October. On his return to England he was welcomed with considerable acclaim. Shortly thereafter he was made a privy councillor and, in 1703, lord lieutenant of Ireland. He held this position for three years and was reappointed in 1710. This time, he was called away from Ireland in less than two years and replaced Marlborough as captain-general of the army. He served in Flanders between April 1712 and the spring of 1713 and was rewarded for his services with the wardenship and admiralty of the Cinque Ports and the constableship of Dover Castle.

Towards the end of Queen Anne's reign his allegiance veered towards the Jacobite cause and he entered into a correspondence with the Duke of Berwick. Shortly after the accession of George I (in 1714), he was deprived of his command in the army and dismissed from all his posts because of his Jacobite leanings. (As a Tory, he was included in the political proscription of the party which took place under George I and II. Whig propaganda, which described the Tories as crypto-Jacobites, had considerable weight with the first two Georges). In the summer of 1715 he was impeached because of his Jacobitism and fled to France. His estates were accordingly declared forfeit. In September of that year he landed at Plymouth, to lead a Jacobite rising he had already planned in the west. Realising the futility of this venture, however, he abandoned it and returned to France. He never saw England again.

He continued to work for the Jacobite cause abroad and in 1719 was placed in command of an expedition to England. However, his invasion fleet after leaving Cadiz foundered in heavy seas off Cape Finistere and only two frigates eventually reached British shores.

He lived for a number of years in Madrid, where he received a pension from the Spanish government, and spent the latter part of his life in Avignon. He died on 16 November 1745 and was subsequently buried in the family vault in Westminster Abbey. The family titles became extinct on the death of his brother Charles, Earl of Arran in 1758.

Ormonde sat to Kneller several times and was also painted by Wissing and Dahl. Portraits by the latter are at Badminton and in the NPG.

Sources:     *DNB*; Piper, as above; J.G.Simms, *Jacobite Ireland 1685-91* (London, 1969); F.McLynn, *The Jacobites* (London, 1985).

## 336 *Lieutenant-general Michael Rothe (1661-1741)*

By Nicolas de Largillière (1656-1746)
Private collection

Oil on canvas 127 x 94.5 cms (sight).

Exh:     *Paintings from Irish Collections*, Hugh Lane Municipal Gallery of Modern Art, Dublin 1957 (67).

Michael Rothe, a native of Kilkenny, was commissioned as a lieutenant in the royal Irish regiment of footguards in 1686 and accompanied James to France in 1688, at which time he was promoted to captain. In January 1689 James sent him to Dublin with a letter for Tyrconnell, giving an account of his flight to France

**336**

**337**

and his reception there. Rothe's travelling companion to Ireland was Pointis
(see no. 84), a French military expert charged with preparing a report on the
situation in Ireland prior to the French decision to intervene. Rothe subsequently
became an alderman of Kilkenny. He fought at the Boyne in the king's own
Guards, under the command of lieutenant-colonel William Dorrington, and saw
service throughout the rest of the Irish campaign.

After the treaty of Limerick, he and his regiment elected to go to France and
accordingly left Ireland in the winter of 1691. As a result of his adherence to the
Jacobite cause he was attainted and his Kilkenny estate forfeited. His regiment was
incorporated with the Irish brigade in French service and he spent the rest of his
military career fighting for his adopted country. In 1698 James's Guards became
Dorrington's regiment, of which Rothe was made lieutenant-colonel. In 1701 he
was promoted to colonel and five years later was appointed to the rank of
brigadier. In 1710 he was made major-general and so distinguished himself in the
defence of Bethune against Marlborough that Louis XIV nominated him for the
commandership of the order of St Louis (which he received in April 1712). On
Dorrington's death on 11 December 1718 he was given command of the regiment,
which thereafter became known as Rothe's regiment. He fought in Spain under
Berwick in 1719 and was appointed lieutenant-general on 13 March 1720. He
remained in command of his regiment until May 1733, when he resigned in favour
of his son, Charles Edward. He died in Paris on 2 May 1741.

The portrait, which is very finely executed, shows him wearing a jewelled
badge of a Spanish order, probably the Royal Military Order of Calatrava. This
makes it likely that the portrait was painted c.1720. Largillière was born in Paris
but studied in Antwerp, where he became a Master of the guild in 1672. He
worked in London from 1674 to 1680, probably with Lely, and settled in Paris in
1682, where he established a substantial reputation as a painter of the wealthy
bourgeoisie. He also painted commemorative portrait-groups for the City of Paris
(a kind of Baroque version of the Dutch corporation group), and religious pictures.
He and his contemporary Rigaud are regarded as the most brilliant portrait painters
of eighteenth century France.

Sources:     *DNB*;  D.C. Boulger, *The Battle of the Boyne* (London,1911).

**338**

## 337 *Lieutenant-general Owen Wynne (c. 1665-1737)*

<small>BY JAMES LATHAM (1696-1747)
PRIVATE COLLECTION</small>

Oil on canvas 76 x 62.5 cms.
Lit:    Anne Crookshank, 'James Latham 1696-1747,' *The GPA Irish Arts Review Yearbook*, 1988,
        p. 71, no. 69.

Lieutenant-general Owen Wynne of Hazlewood, Co. Sligo had a distinguished
military career. Born c. 1665, the son of Colonel Owen Wynne of Lurganboy,
Co. Leitrim and Catherine, daughter of James Hamilton, second Baron Strabane,
he was educated at Trinity College, Dublin and studied for the bar. In 1689 he
served as captain in the Earl of Roscommon's regiment of foot, and the
following year fought with the Williamite forces at the Boyne. He saw service in
Colonel Charles Ross's Regiment of Dragoons in 1695, fought at Blenheim in
1704, and was promoted to colonel in 1705. In 1727 he was appointed lieutenant-
general and from 1732 was commander-in-chief of the army in Ireland.

   In addition to his military career he was active in politics, in the Whig
interest, as MP for Carrick 1692-3 and 1695-9; for Ballyshannon 1713-14 and
1715-27, and for Co. Sligo 1727-37. He served as a privy councillor 1726-7.

   The portrait was painted during the 1730s. The format, bust length without
hands in a painted oval, is a favourite of Latham's.

<small>Source:        History of the Irish Parliament Research Project (PRONI).</small>

## 338 *The Byerley Turk*

BY AN UNKNOWN ARTIST, POSSIBLY JOHN WOOTTON (C.1682-1764)
PRIVATE COLLECTION
REPRODUCTION

The Byerley Turk, foaled about 1680 and supposedly captured from the Turks during the emperor Leopold's campaign in Hungary in 1686-7, was ridden by Captain (later Colonel) Robert Byerley at the battle of the Boyne. The horse was put to stud at Byerley's place in Yorkshire and became (through his great-grandson King Herod, 1758) the progenitor of a large part of the thoroughbred stock in the world.

Wootton, a pupil of Jan Wyck, painted battle pieces, hunting and racing scenes and also portraits of horses and dogs (in which genre he created a new and distinctly English form). He is known to have executed an engraving (whereabouts unknown) of the Byerley Turk. This painting is perhaps the original upon which the engraving was based.

## Selected Index
(Numbers refer to catalogue entries)